D1237065

Uncertainty and Structure as Psychological Concepts

Uncertainty
and
Structure
as
Psychological
Concepts

Wendell R. Garner

Professor of Psychology

The Johns Hopkins University

John Wiley and Sons, Inc., New York • London

Library of Congress Catalog Card Number: 62-10919
Printed in the United States of America

To Barbara

Preface

This book deals with some selected psychological topics, and with some concepts which I think are useful in dealing with these topics. The primary concepts with which I am concerned are those of *uncertainty* and *structure,* as the title suggests. These concepts have for me a quite specific meaning, however, and that meaning comes from a mathematical basis for defining them. This mathematical basis allows us to see some relations within these problem areas which do, might, or should exist.

The mathematical basis comes from what has been called information theory, although I am not too happy with that term. At any rate, this is not intended to be a book on information theory, or even information theory as applied to psychology. Rather, I have used a mathematical basis which comes from information theory to develop ideas about and an understanding of some psychological problems. To me the information measure is so valuable not because it is the basis of a theory of communication, but rather because it provides a very general type of mathematics. It requires no underlying assumptions about the metrics of variables, but at the same time allows a multivariate type of analysis. Thus the mathematical measure of information, or uncertainty, provides great generality while at the same time allowing an analytic approach.

I would have preferred to develop first the concepts of the different kinds of structure which are introduced in Chapter Five, but I have compromised my approach by introducing psychological material where it is relevant to the mathematical concepts which are first discussed. Nevertheless, my intention to provide primarily a means of problem analysis, rather than a simple statistical tool, has led to the almost complete omission of some material which is ordinarily considered part of information measurement in psychology. In particular, I discuss none of the problems of sampling, the biases which exist, and ways of estimating information measures when the sample size is too small for accurate direct calculation. Thus, the reader interested in these topics will not be able to find much help here. My purpose has been to discuss the nature of the psychological problems, and I have kept to that purpose as much as possible.

For this reason, the great majority of my references come from the psychological literature. Most of these references listed at the end of the book are specifically cited in the main text, and the author index will indicate the places of citation. However, this list includes perhaps a dozen references for which there are no specific citations in the text. These are the articles or books which have influenced my thinking, but to which I have made no specific reference in the text. My listing of them with the references is my way of acknowledging this contribution.

The thanks which an author owes are many, and mere mention in a Preface seems a woefully inadequate means of expressing this gratitude. I hope that all will recognize my very real appreciation. The first draft of the book was written during a year's leave from my normal university duties. My own university gave me one term of leave, and a second term was made possible by Research Grant M-3558 from the National Institutes of Health. Over many years my research activities have been supported by a contract between The Johns Hopkins University and the Office of Naval Research, and this book constitutes Report No. 19 under the present Contract Nonr-248(55).

In a less financial vein, James E. Deese of Johns Hopkins acted as a sounding board for me to try out several of these ideas. Professors Ward Edwards of the University of Michigan and William J. McGill of Columbia University read the original manuscript in detail and offered many valuable comments and criticisms. So also did several members of a seminar which I held in the fall of 1960. There were too many students to mention all by name, but their contributions were, nevertheless, real and valued. Last, and most important, is my gratitude to Mrs. Dolores Pubanz, who typed and retyped the entire manuscript, catching many of my errors in the process. Her pride in the work and her attention to detail made my job much more pleasant.

Baltimore, Maryland   WENDELL R. GARNER
January, 1962

Contents

CHAPTER ONE

Information and Uncertainty: An Introduction

OVER THE YEARS, PSYCHOLOGISTS have generally been eclectic in their attempts to solve the particular problems in the field of psychology. They have taken from other disciplines that which is useful, modifying techniques if necessary and, occasionally, borrowing wholesale. Throughout this process, however, the problems on which psychologists work have remained basically psychological.

In this book we shall be trying to gain some further understanding and insight into some psychological problems, using a particular mathematical tool as a means of analyzing in detail the nature of some of these problems. The tool we shall use comes from communication theory and is concerned with the measurement of information as a quantifiable commodity. Our use of it will primarily be as a method of logical analysis, in particular as a method of logical multivariate analysis. While our primary concern will be with the psychological problems, we must also comprehend the particular properties and concepts which define the nature of the tool.

The concept of information itself has been implicit in many areas of science for centuries, both as a substantive concept important in its own right and as a consonant concept which is ancillary to the entire process of science. In the former sense, information is the fundamental commodity with which the communication scientist must deal, whether he be concerned with a physical communication system or whether he be concerned with communication as a social

1

phenomenon. What is communicated is information, and the nature of the communication process cannot be properly understood until the fundamental commodity of communication is quantified.

In the second sense, science itself is a process in which we, as scientists, take observations, do experiments, and make measurements, all in order to be better informed about some aspect of the universe. In other words, the scientific process is the acquisition of information. It is clear that to be able to evaluate the efficiency of the process—to know when we have acquired a little or a lot of information—would be most valuable, but to do so requires that we be able to measure the amount of information which any scientific act gives us.

When we consider the importance of the concept of information to science, it is remarkable that its quantitative measurement is of such late origin. However, the rapid growth in recent years of fields and subfields of science concerned with the measurement of information leads to the inescapable feeling that the scientific world was waiting for the developments which began just before the middle of the present century.

THE FUNDAMENTAL NATURE OF INFORMATION

Before looking further at the historical background of the measurement of information, we would probably find value in discussing the basic nature of information in a preliminary way. These ideas are now commonly accepted among communication scientists, and they form the backbone of the entire system of information measurement.

As so often happens when a concept in general use becomes an accepted part of a scientific system, the word "information" has acquired a somewhat technical, even esoteric meaning. Fortunately, this technical meaning is not seriously at variance with ordinary lay ideas about the nature of information. Information is something we get when some person or machine tells us something we didn't know before. We may read a book, have a question answered, or simply observe or listen to the world. By these various acts we acquire knowledge or information about the world—at least in most cases. Now in its technical sense, the amount of information we get by any communicative act has no relevance to whether the information is correct or incorrect, useful or useless. When we measure the amount of information, we are only concerned with how much information has been obtained, not with the value of the obtained information. We could be concerned about such problems quite legitimately, but it is important that we not confuse the *amount* with the *value of the received amount.*

To be slightly more exact, any communicative act provides information only insofar as it reduces a condition of ignorance or uncertainty about the state of things under consideration. If, for example, I am told that today is Thursday, and I already know that today is Thursday, then that statement gives me no information because I had no uncertainty about that particular fact beforehand. Thus information exists in a message or communication only if there is an a priori uncertainty about what the message will be. If I throw a two-headed coin in the air, I have no uncertainty about whether it will come down a head or a tail; thus, I get no information when I observe how it does come down. If the coin has both a head and a tail, however, then I have some a priori uncertainty and get some information when the coin comes down.

Thus information occurs only if there exists some a priori uncertainty, and the *amount* of information is determined by the *amount* of the uncertainty—or, more exactly, it is determined by the amount by which the uncertainty has been reduced. Information and uncertainty are closely related concepts, and if we can measure uncertainty we can measure information as the decrease of uncertainty. These opposing concepts—uncertainty as a state of ignorance, and information as the opposed reduction of uncertainty—are quantitatively the same thing.[1]

The uncertainty about the outcome of any act is quantitatively related to the number of possible outcomes that exist. Tossing a normal coin has two possible outcomes, but throwing a die has six possible outcomes. Therefore, there is less uncertainty about the coin-tossing outcome than about the die-throwing outcome. Similarly, after the outcome is known, we have obtained less information about the coin toss than we did about the die throw. Since in each act the outcome is definite and unique, then all the uncertainty has been reduced, and we have obtained exactly as much information as there was originally uncertainty.

As a first approximation, then, we could simply take the number

---

[1] In order to specify the amount of information which any act gives us, we must be able to specify the amount of uncertainty which existed prior to the act. Ordinarily, it is of little use to us to say that we have an a priori complete ignorance, since complete ignorance amounts to infinite uncertainty. Actually, of course, we never really have complete ignorance, but only an unspecified ignorance, or an indeterminate uncertainty. But if the uncertainty is indeterminate, then so is the information, and we must have more precise statements of both in order for the concepts and the measurements to be useful.

of possible outcomes of an event as the amount of uncertainty in the event, and thus also as the amount of information obtained at the conclusion of the event. There is, however, another consideration which suggests that such a simple measure of quantity of uncertainty or information is not entirely adequate.

Consider, for example, that we toss two coins, or throw two dice. Two coin tosses have four possible outcomes (HH, HT, TH, and TT), and two dice throws have thirty-six possible outcomes. Likewise, three coin tosses in succession have eight possible outcomes. If one coin toss gives us 2 units of information (because there are two possible outcomes), then each successive coin toss should give us that much more information. However, while two successive tosses do give us twice as much information as one toss, three tosses appear to give us four times as much information. And two throws of the dice appear to give us six times as much information as one throw. Thus it seems intuitively obvious that we cannot use simply the number of possible outcomes of an event as our measure of uncertainty and information, but must find some measure which satisfies the two conditions that (a) it is monotonically related to the number of possible outcomes and, (b) each successive event adds the same amount of uncertainty and thus makes available the same amount of information.

The measure which satisfies these conditions is a logarithmic one, of the form

$$U = c \log k, \qquad (1.1)$$

where U is the required measure of uncertainty, k is the number of categories or possible outcomes, and c is a proportionality constant whose only function is to establish the particular unit of measurement. It has become accepted practice to use logarithms to the base 2 for this measure, and to define the unit of measurement in this logarithmic system so that the proportionality constant becomes 1. Thus common practice today defines uncertainty as

$$U = \log_2 k. \qquad (1.2)$$

When this definition is used, the unit of uncertainty and information is called the *bit*, where 1 bit is the uncertainty involved in an event with two possible (and equally likely) outcomes. The term itself is a contraction of the words *binary digit*, because 1 unit of information is that necessary to make a binary choice. While now in accepted usage, and defined by an IRE Standards Committee in 1958, the term *bit* is not without its faults. In many ways it was an unfortunate choice, because of its possible confusion with the commonly used

word meaning a small amount. Goldman (1953), because of this confusion, suggests the term *binit*, which would be much better. Unfortunately, however, the term bit is now probably too widely used for
us to be able to change it, and we shall use the bit as the basic unit
of amount of information—even with its faults.

Occasionally the use of the binary system, and its concomitant
logarithms to the base 2, has produced some confusion about the
measure, because it is at times assumed that there is something inherently necessary about the binary system. It should be clear that
the choice of the binary system is entirely arbitrary, and that any
logarithmic system would have served the purpose just as well. In
fact, all measurements of uncertainty and information can be made
in the common system of logarithms to the base 10, and by simply
multiplying by the appropriate constant (see Eq. 1.1), we can change
the numbers into the bit system. The IRE Committee gives a standard name to the unit of information if the base-10 system of logarithms is used—the *Hartley*. The reason for this name will become
clear later.

While the use of the binary system is indeed quite arbitrary, it
does have certain intuitive and natural advantages which the decimal
system does not have. One bit of uncertainty is that involved in a
doubling of the number of categories on a variable, or the number
of possible outcomes of an event. If there are sixteen possible outcomes, then the uncertainty is 4 bits; and if there are thirty-two
possible outcomes, the uncertainty is 5 bits. Likewise, eight possible
outcomes give an uncertainty of 3 bits. Thus any doubling of number
of possible outcomes increases uncertainty by 1 bit, and any halving
decreases it by 1 bit. Also, in obtaining information, any decrease of
the uncertainty by 1 bit leads to halving the remaining number of
possible outcomes.

If we have an existing uncertainty specified in bits, then it is possible for us to ask a series of questions which can be answered
dichotomously (yes or no), and each question can reduce the uncertainty by 1 bit, if the question is properly asked. In turn, each binary
answer gives us 1 bit of information. For example, the old parlor
game of "Twenty Questions" is played in exactly this manner: One
person thinks of an object, or a number, or whatever is agreed upon
ahead of time as appropriate, and then another person or persons
ask a series of questions which must be answered "yes" or "no."

Suppose, for example, you are thinking of a number from 1 through
16 (as agreed on ahead of time). Now this situation has 4 bits of
uncertainty, a fact which means that four binary answers can deter-

mine the number for me. If I ask you first whether the number is above 8, the answer narrows down the remaining possibilities to half as many as before. The answer to my next question can narrow down the answers by a factor of 2 again, until, with four answers to four questions, I know the number you are thinking of. Note that the questions must be asked in a sensible form in order for me to get 1 bit with each answer. If my first question is, "Is the number you are thinking of 14?", the answer may give me a lot of information if I am right, but most likely will give me very little information, since if I guess wrong, there are still fifteen possible outcomes. Clearly a game played efficiently with the full twenty questions can give a very large amount of information. Twenty well-phrased questions can provide 20 bits of information, which is the potential information or uncertainty involved in over one million possible outcomes.

It should be clear that the use of the bit as the unit of information in no way requires that the questions in such a situation be binary. I could, in our game, ask you directly what the number is, and if you tell me, then I have asked a 4-bit question and received a 4-bit answer, since both the question and the answer are based on 16 possible alternatives. On the other hand, I might ask you whether the number is 1 to 4, 5 to 8, 9 to 12, or 13 to 16. Your answer would in this case give me 2 bits of information, since it would reduce the remaining uncertainty from 4 bits to 2 bits. A second 2-bit answer would reduce all of the uncertainty. Thus the use of the bit does not necessarily imply anything about the form in which information is received, or the amount of information which any communicative act transmits. The number of bits of information simply states the number of equivalent binary reductions of uncertainty.

Regardless of the logarithmic base used, the logarithmic measure clearly satisfies the condition that amounts of uncertainty and information should be additive. For example, the fact that each question in the twenty-questions game can elicit the same amount of information is due to the logarithmic nature of the measure, in which equal ratios lead to equal amounts of information. This is the basic property of logarithmic measures: Where multiplication is appropriate in the original number system, addition is appropriate in the logarithmic system.

This condition is a very necessary one, since many uncertainties are compounded of separate uncertainties in such a way that the total number of possible outcomes is computed as the product of the number of separate possible outcomes. We have already discussed briefly the successive tossing of coins or throwing of dice, where the total number of possible outcomes increases exponentially with the number of successive tosses or throws. However, we have other situations, not necessarily involving successive events of the same kind, where the logarithmic property is required. For example, suppose we want to present a subject in an experiment with tones which can have four possible pitches, and also four possible loudnesses. In such a case, the total number of possible tones is determined by mutiplication of the four pitches by the four loudnesses, assuming all possible combinations to be equally probable (that is, there is no correlation between pitch and loudness in the specified situation). There are, therefore, sixteen possible tones, but the uncertainty with regard to pitch is 2 bits, and with regard to loudness it is also 2 bits, so that together they provide 4 bits. If the two variables are independent, then the information which we can obtain from both should be the sum of the information which we can obtain from each, and this condition is satisfied only with the logarithmic measure.

In brief summary, information is obtained by a reduction of uncertainty. Thus uncertainty is potential information, and the measurement of the amount of information is the same as the measurement of the amount of uncertainty. The ideal measure of amount of uncertainty is one based on the logarithm of the number of possible outcomes of an event. Since information and uncertainty, although opposite in meaning, are so interrelated, in many cases they become used almost interchangeably. What now constitutes uncertainty is always potential information, and, in a moment, may be information; and what is information for you may be uncertainty for me. Thus we have a single system of measurement of what is in reality a single commodity, but this same commodity can be interpreted in different ways depending on the particular situation.

One aspect of information measurement is worth stressing. Information cannot be obtained unless there exists uncertainty about the outcome of an event prior to the event, and the amount of information which can be obtained is solely determined by the amount of uncertainty which exists. The amount of uncertainty itself is a function of the number of outcomes which could happen and is entirely unaffected by which of the outcomes actually occurs. Thus, also—and this is the important point—the amount of information obtained from any event or act of communication is not a function of what does happen; rather it is a function of what could have happened but didn't. This fundamental emphasis on the number of things which did not occur, but could have, is critical in the use of information concepts in psychology.

A LITTLE HISTORY

In 1948, C. E. Shannon published a two-part paper entitled "A Mathematical Theory of Communication." Within a very short period of time the number of papers published on this general topic had mushroomed to the point that separate sections of journals were devoted to the topic; finally, special journals were founded to take care of the large number of papers published annually. Just barely more than a year after the publication of Shannon's article, the concepts presented in it were introduced into the psychological literature by Miller and Frick (1949), and the general ideas in this mathematical theory were rapidly, almost avidly, accepted, used, elaborated, and occasionally discarded by psychologists. In the spring of 1951, less than 3 years after Shannon's paper, a special conference on the psychological use of information theory was held at Harvard University, and it was well attended. Another 3 years later, a conference held at the University of Illinois resulted in a full volume of articles and reports written primarily by psychologists (Quastler, 1955).

It would seem worthwhile to look into the background of this development, and to attempt to get some understanding of the factors involved in its present status in psychology.

Communication engineering

There are two major backgrounds involved in information measurement, one from communication engineering, and the other from statistics and experimental design. Of these two, it is communication engineering that has had the more direct impact on psychology and on the development of information concepts in general.

The demands of a real world cannot always await scientific developments, and, in matters having to do with information, the demands of the real world, while great, have been met to a surprising degree. The design of languages, special codes, and other communication devices has been accomplished in ways which are not too deviant from what modern communication theory shows are ideal. Cherry (1952 and 1957a) has written a brief but very interesting historical review of the development of communication theory, and he points out, for example, that Samuel Morse, in devising his dot-dash telegraphic code, made quite effective use of the general statistics of language in assigning short codes to frequently used letters, and the longer codes to the less-frequently used letters. This is an accepted principle of communication theory.

To come to more modern times, however, the real beginnings of modern information measurement came in 1924 when Nyquist, working at the Bell Telephone Laboratories, published a paper on factors affecting telegraph speed. In this paper, Nyquist discussed the efficiency of the transmission of "intelligence," and noted that the efficiency is related to the logarithm of the number of possible current levels. Cherry points out that in the same year Küpfmüller, working in Germany, noted the interrelation between time and frequency as had Nyquist—an interrelation equivalent to the relation between number of alternatives per event and the number of successive events.

Four years later, in 1928, Hartley (also from the Bell Telephone Laboratories) published a paper which stated explicitly the need for a logarithmic measure of the number of alternative possible sequences as a measure of information. Interestingly enough, Hartley also remarked that this measure has no relation to information in the psychological sense, but only in the physical sense. This problem, which we will discuss later, has created a certain amount of ambiguity in some psychological applications.

There followed a silent period, lasting nearly 20 years. Then in 1946, Gabor in England published an article entitled "Theory of Communication," in which he introduced the idea of a *logon,* an elementary quantum of information. Then in 1948, Wiener, in his book, *Cybernetics,* discussed the possibilities of quantifying information. In the same year, Shannon published his paper, and it is clear that whatever the background material available, Shannon added something which took the topic to a technical level opening many new possibilities. As Shannon pointed out, both Nyquist and Hartley had seen the necessity of a measure of information which was based on the number of alternative possibilities and which was also logarithmic. Shannon made two critical contributions to these ideas. The first was to treat the problem in a more general statistical sense, so that we no longer have just number of categories or possible messages, but we have each category or message with a stated probability of occurrence. The second was to provide a method for dealing with the effects of noise in a communication system. In other words, it became possible to deal with the uncertainty of a message itself and also with the uncertainty or variability of other sources of signals which are irrelevant to the message system. These were important additions.

Statistical theory

The other important development in the measurement of information came from statistical theory, and primarily from R. A. Fisher, who in his constant search for efficient statistics and experimental designs inevitably had to deal with the problem of amount of information. As early as 1922, Fisher defined the *efficiency* of a statistic in terms of the available relevant information, and the *sufficiency* of a statistic in terms of whether any other statistic can provide more information about a sample. Then in 1934, he talked about the possibility of measuring the quantity of information in such a way that the property of additivity will hold.

In retrospect we can see how closely Fisher's concepts parallel those of modern information measurement, and the fundamental nature of Fisher's measures is quite similar to that of measures developed from communication theory. In a sense it is unfortunate that these two trends did not merge earlier—perhaps both would have been materially advanced. As important as these concepts are, however, they did not as directly lead to the current use of information measurement in psychology as did those deriving from communication engineering.

MacKay, in 1950, attempted to bring these two developments a little closer together. He distinguished between two kinds of information: *logon* content (using Gabor's term) and *metron* content. The logon content is the a priori information due to the logical structure of a set of observations or of an experiment. It may be the number of independent observations, or variables, which the structure of the experiment makes possible. It is closely related to the concept of degrees of freedom. The metron content, on the other hand, is the information which is obtained from the numerical measurements we take. It is related to the precision of the experiment, not to the number of observations or logical structure of the experiment, and as such is identifiable with information measurement according to Fisher's concept of information measurement.

To illustrate this distinction between logon and metron content, suppose we decide to measure reaction time as a function of the modality of the stimulus. We decide to use three different stimuli, one visual, one auditory, and one tactual. This decision to use three different stimuli has already determined to some extent the amount of information we can get from the experiment, since we can get less information if we use fewer stimuli, and more information if we use more stimuli. This aspect of the problem provides logon content. We then measure reaction time for each of these stimuli. This measurement also provides information, but its amount is limited by the precision of measurement; and we ordinarily determine several such reaction times in order to obtain some estimate of the precision of the measurement. This aspect of the problem provides metron content.

Now to make the arithmetic simpler, if we had used two stimuli, we had a possibility of 1 bit of information from our measurements, since we arranged the experiment to provide for a binary distinction. Whether we actually get this much information, however, depends on the metron content, since if the two mean reaction times are very close together compared to the dispersion of the measures, we cannot make with perfect assurance an accurate binary statement concerning these two stimuli. Thus, in this case, our obtainable information would be limited by the lack of metron content. But it need not be. If, for example, the measurements are much more precise (that is, stable), then we could obtain more information by including more stimuli in the experiment; and our failure to do so means that we are limited by the logon content.

This distinction between logon content and metron content which MacKay makes has considerable importance to psychology. In many physical communication systems it should not and does not make any difference what kind of information is being transmitted—in fact, the entire emphasis in communication theory was to find a single measurement. In behavioral work, however, the distinction between structural or logical information and metric information is very meaningful, since living organisms do not use both types equally effectively. For example, questions which we will examine later, such as a comparison of the effectiveness of many categories on a single variable as opposed to few categories but many variables, are essentially questions concerning whether logon or metron information is more effective for human processing.

THE IMPACT ON PSYCHOLOGY

This brief look at the history of information measurement makes it clear that the basic developments did not take place within the field of psychology. And yet many problems of psychology are truly problems relating to the concept of amount of information. What has been the impact of these developments from communication theory and statistics on psychology?

The mathematical *Zeitgeist* in psychology

One question which has intrigued many people is why psychology so quickly accepted and used information concepts after Shannon's developments, and yet had not done so previously. As pointed out above, both Nyquist and Hartley had realized 20 years earlier that a measure of amount of information must be a logarithmic measure of the number of alternative possibilities. Much of the experimental use of information measurement in psychology has in fact required no more than these two basic ideas, and sometimes the only critical factor has been the recognition of the role of number of alternatives in behavior. Yet these ideas were available many years ago.

The answer seems to lie in the fact that the *Zeitgeist* in psychology was not yet appropriate for the ideas. But by 1948 psychology had already shown a strong tendency toward more mathematical concepts, and particularly mathematical concepts of the general statistical variety. Learning theories were becoming statistical, and decision and game theory was becoming popular. So when Shannon made information measurement far more statistical in nature than had the earlier writers, psychologists found it much to their liking. Perhaps the real crux of the problem lies in the term used by Miller and Frick when they introduced information measurement to psychologists—they spoke of *statistical behavioristics,* a term which correctly characterized the interest of psychologists in these developments.

Thus psychologists were already interested in this type of mathematics. Shannon made information measurement statistical in nature, and psychologists felt quite at home with such measurement. In addition, Shannon showed how to handle the problem of unwanted signals, or noise, and this emphasis also struck a happy note with psychologists, who had long ago learned to live with the inherent variability of human behavior. Some psychologists, of course, had felt that to live with this variability was to compromise their honor among scientists. Many others, however, had made a virtue of necessity, and had learned to use behavioral variability as the cornerstone of their science.

For both of these groups information measurement in a statistical sense provided something valuable. For the former group, honor was reestablished by the aura of respectability which a more mathematical treatment of variability provided. For the latter group, the acceptance of these new concepts provided an elaboration of ways of working they had been using all along.

The value of information measurement in psychology

Psychologists have undergone the inevitable appraisals of the role and value of information concepts to their field. When any new development occurs in science, there is a tendency for its use to become so great, and occasionally so indiscriminate, that we cannot help but call the process a fad. After the excitement of the fad has worn off, it is possible to evaluate a little more dispassionately the true role of the developments, and to see exactly what has and what hasn't led us to anything useful for solving psychological problems. And, of course, our ultimate evaluation must be in these terms, since as psychologists we have accepted the solution of psychological problems as our long range goal.

After a fad, as after an adolescent romance, many people tend to lean in the opposite direction and to deny any value of a particular development. This reaction is the inevitable result of having expected too much in the first place, so that when the full expectation is not realized, a public repudiation is called for. However, if one expects less, as in a mature romance, perhaps one finds more.

A symposium was held at the International Congress of Psychology in Brussels in 1957 on the topic of information measurement in psychology. Several points of view were expressed there, and these points of view varied widely as to the value of these concepts in psychology. Faverge, for example, felt that only another statistic had been provided—a useful one, to be sure, but still just a statistic. Information measurement would, he felt, take its place along with other statistical tools, and in time would provide just another section in a statistics text. McGill (1957a) has expressed similar feelings, although with perhaps more enthusiasm for the importance of the statistics.

At the same symposium, Broadbent expressed quite an opposite point of view. He felt strongly that the information concepts from communication theory have really contributed to psychology as a theory. Here is a direct quotation from his talk:

S-R theorists have used as their central variable the occurrence of stimuli, past and present. Gestaltists have considered the pattern of stimuli present at any one time. But neither of them have talked about the effect at any moment of the stimuli which might have occurred but did not.

Broadbent considers the emphasis of information concepts on what might have happened but did not to be of major importance to psychology. Certainly we shall see plenty of evidence here that Broadbent is right, and that probably the ultimate value of these concepts to psychology is even greater than he suggested.

Orientation of this book

I was also a speaker at the Brussels symposium, but I did not make a specific statement pro or con the value of information concepts to psychology. Rather, I talked about a particular problem which I thought information concepts were helpful in solving. This very lack of expression of a definite point of view is by its nature truly a point of view, and it will provide the orientation of this book.

Readers may now be aware of the fact that I have not used the term "information theory" in this introductory chapter. There is partisan malice in that omission, since it has been by deliberate intent. It is difficult to avoid using a term which has become so common, and which in many ways has genuine legitimacy; and yet it seems to me necessary to avoid some erroneous implications of the term.

It is never possible to define words precisely enough, even in science, to avoid ambiguities and misunderstandings. The term *theory*, in particular, has so many almost contradictory connotations that I have felt it best to try to avoid using the term. The major difficulty is simply this: When we use a term like information theory, it is difficult if not impossible to avoid assuming that we must talk about *the* theory, and that its role in our psychological and experimental work is to provide an exact model for behavior. If our experiments show that the model correctly predicts behavior, then we accept the model; and if the model does not predict correctly, then we reject the model.

In the physical communication sciences, there is such a thing as communication theory, and even, possibly, information theory. An ideal system can be described mathematically, and many physical systems can be found which closely approximate the performance of the ideal system. The natural tendency has been to take these models which are appropriate for physical systems and to test them against behavior. However, behavioral systems and physical systems (in the engineering sense) are not the same thing, and we should not be too surprised when behavior fails to conform to the requirements of an ideal communication system in which information measurement may be important. Thus I have tried, and will continue to try, to avoid using the term information theory, in order to avoid the implication that in this book we are testing a well-defined mathematical model.

On the other hand, from these developments have come many concepts which have proved to be very useful in psychological research. The basic concept of a quantity of information has been extremely useful; so also have been concepts of redundancy, information transmission, and occasionally channel capacity. A concept may, however, be useful in providing an adequate method of specifying the conditions of an experiment, or in providing a more meaningful measurement of a dependent variable. It does not need to be a total theory.

Such is my intended use of information concepts in this book.

Wherever general ideas, specific predictions, or just plain better description has improved our understanding of, or ability to solve, psychological problems, I shall discuss the role of information. At no time, however, will I attempt to set up a general theoretical model which is to be accepted or rejected. Our task is simply to try to understand some psychological problems better. As psychologists, we are certainly free to use the concepts in any manner which helps us, and we may even develop them to suit our particular purposes better. We refuse, in other words, to be concerned about a comment Cherry (1957b) once made in discussing the role of communication theory in experimental psychology. He stated that a particular use of information concepts went beyond *established* communication theory. He was undoubtedly correct in that statement, but, as psychologists, we are not particularly concerned with this. If going beyond or even distorting established usage helps solve our behavioral problems, then we should feel free to do so.

It is clearly impossible in a book of this sort to try to draw a sharp line between theory and pure empiricism; nor will I attempt to do so. There are times when it is meaningful to use some concepts from information measurement as specific hypotheses for test, and when such a procedure seems reasonable, I shall not hesitate to do so. The outlook here is entirely pragmatic: What works I shall use. If pure description works, or if the information measure is only useful as a statistic, then I will demand no more. On the other hand, if particular predictions about behavior can be made from information concepts and mathematics, then I will not hesitate to make them. And as we shall see, there are a few situations where specific predictions can be made with such authority that the experiments become primarily demonstrational.

Perhaps my use of information concepts in this manner will not appeal to some psychologists, since there is a general tendency in psychology to require that mathematics be used in only two ways: Mathematics may be used to provide an exact model for behavior, and in this use mathematics is simply providing a particular medium in which a theory is expressed; or, if mathematics is not used as a model, then it must be used as a purely statistical tool for analyzing data.

Mathematics may, however, be used as a tool, sometimes a powerful tool, to examine theoretical problems without itself being a theory, nor yet becoming simply a technique for data processing. Mathematics may help us ask questions without presuming answers. I may be concerned about the orthogonality (a mathematical concept) of stimulus dimensions as a factor in perceptual discrimination, but to use, measure, and specify orthogonality in mathematical terms is not to deduce the experimental answer.

Thus I shall be concerned about psychological problems, and I shall be using information concepts to help provide an understanding of these problems, and even occasionally to provide some theorizing about these problems, but I am not offering a general, unified theory of behavior based on information measures. This is, therefore, not a book on information theory; rather, it is a book on a variety of psychological problems which I feel can be better understood and solved with the use of information concepts.

ORGANIZATION OF THE BOOK

The organization of this book has been heavily determined by the conviction that one general mathematical approach from information measurement has been most effective. That approach is the multivariate analysis of uncertainty or information. McGill (1954) first introduced these ideas, and they were later elaborated by McGill and myself in various publications. This approach perhaps has a special appeal to the psychologist, because, as Garner and McGill (1956) showed, the mathematical terms which can be elaborated from the multivariate uncertainty analysis are quite analogous to terms obtained in an analysis of variance—a technique which is almost second nature to most experimental psychologists.

The organization of the book is based on an increasing complexity of the multivariate analysis. Starting with the single variable measurement, the book progresses through bivariate and multivariate distributions, and then into a form of this analysis which goes beyond what is possible with analysis of variance. I have endeavored to fit the psychological material into a framework based on the multivariate analysis. Most of the time this procedure has not been too difficult, but occasionally it has been necessary to presume a slight knowledge of material occurring later in the book in order to keep the psychological material reasonably compact and coherent. Sometimes I have handled this problem by the use of small simplifying assumptions.

More specifically, in Chapter Two I discuss the general univariate measure of average information, and present evidence that this concept is a meaningful factor in learning, discrimination, and reaction times. In Chapter Three, I progress to the bivariate information measures, with the addition of the concept of a contingent uncertainty. Here the widest application has been the use of the contingent uncertainty as a measure of information transmission in perceptual tasks, where it is interpreted as a measure of amount of discrimination. The concept of channel capacity is shown to be valid for unidimensional stimuli. In Chapter Four, I discuss the multivariate analysis in which one variable is predicted from two or more other variables. In this type of analysis the concept of an interaction uncertainty becomes necessary. Here the role of multiple dimensions in stimulus discrimination work is the primary subject matter, and we learn how vastly better multidimensional discrimination is compared to unidimensional discrimination, with some examination of the reasons.

In Chapter Five, I introduce some new concepts which are used throughout the rest of the book. In particular, I show that we can consider a quantity of total structure or constraint (identifiable as a form of meaning) to be composed of internal plus external constraint, and that these two types of constraint are interchangeable. Furthermore, if internal constraint is greater than zero, then the form of both the internal and the external constraint can be varied by appropriate selection of categories. These variables and concepts should be meaningfully related to behavior, but in different ways depending on the particular behavior involved. Thus the same informational variables should affect psychological performance in different ways depending on the particular performance.

In the last five chapters I discuss in turn the relation of these concepts to pattern perception, language (including a chapter on the measurement of redundancy of language), other types of sequential behavior, and lastly, concept formation problems. In these several areas I feel that a correct understanding of the role of internal constraint and the form of the redundancy produced by it leads to considerable clarification of the nature of the psychological problems. In addition, it indicates directions in which research could profitably go. Whether the use of these concepts and this approach are truly meaningful must now be left to the opinion of the reader.

OTHER SOURCE MATERIAL

Since my primary purpose in writing this book is to examine psychological problems with the specific aid of some information concepts, my major concern in developing the information concepts themselves will be to explain the concepts I use, and to provide meaning for them within the specific context of the book. In no sense can this book be considered a general treatise on the mathematics of information theory. Rarely will I, in developing a particular set of relations, attempt to provide general mathematical proof. Rather, I shall be showing interrelations between various mathematical terms, to a large extent considering the original justification for the use of the terms as given.

Thus the reader interested in more mathematical detail concerning the information measurement per se will need to do considerably more reading than is provided here. Of substantial use in this connection will be Attneave's book, *Applications of Information Theory to Psychology*. Attneave pays somewhat more attention to general formulas, methods of calculations, and problems of sample estimates than I do. So also does Luce in his 1960 book. Then Quastler's edited book, *Information Theory in Psychology*, while a compilation of several different articles, contains several good articles on the mathematics of information measurement. Goldman's book, *Information Theory*, is a good general reference for the mathematics of information theory from an engineering point of view. And, of course, to read the original Shannon articles on information theory is a most rewarding experience.

CHAPTER TWO

Univariate Uncertainty
and Perceptual Discrimination

In this chapter we shall consider the simplest information statistic —the uncertainty or potential information in a univariate distribution. We shall then also discuss some applications of information measurement in psychology, with the intent of showing not only that the information measure can be profitably used, but that its application has led to some important conclusions about the nature of behavior.

THE UNIVARIATE UNCERTAINTY STATISTIC

We have already seen that the uncertainty of an event is the logarithm of the number of possible outcomes which the event can have, and that the information obtained when the event occurs is identical if the event reduces the uncertainty to zero. This elementary definition of information assumes that all of the outcomes are equally likely. Yet in most situations, the various possible outcomes are not equally likely. All letters of the alphabet do not occur equally often, nor do all words. And the number of times aircraft are at different stated altitudes or positions is not the same for all altitudes or positions. If the information measure is to have general applicability, it must be able to deal with these situations as well as the simpler cases where all outcomes, or categories of a variable, are equally likely to occur. Shannon's work provided this much needed general definition of quantity of information by means of the concept of average information.

Average uncertainty

Suppose we have a single variable, x, which can take any value x_i, where $i = 1$ to k. Now if each value of x has an equal chance of occurrence, we have already seen that[1]

$$U(x) = \log k. \qquad (2.1)$$

If we consider that $p(x_i)$, the probability of occurrence of any one category of x, is the reciprocal of the number of different things which can occur, then we can just as easily write[2]

$$\begin{aligned} U(x) &= \log [1/p(x)] \\ &= -\log p(x). \end{aligned} \qquad (2.2)$$

$U(x)$, when all categories of x are equally likely, is both the uncertainty of any given outcome and the average uncertainty of all of the outcomes. Since all probabilities are equal, it is quite unnecessary to distinguish between the average uncertainty and the particular uncertainty. When, however, the different categories of x have different probabilities, it is necessary to distinguish between the uncertainty of any given outcome and the average uncertainty of the entire distribution.

When we have a discrete probability distribution with respect to x which is not rectangular (that is, all categories do not have equal probability), the average uncertainty is computed by determining the uncertainty associated with each of the values of x separately, and then obtaining a weighted average of these various uncertainties. This process is illustrated in Table 2.1, where we have four different categories, A, B, C, D, with associated probabilities respectively of .500, .250, .125, and .125. Now the uncertainty associated with each of these outcomes separately is determined by the equivalent value of $-\log p$,

---

[1] It has become standard in information measures to use logarithms to the base 2, and I shall use them; but since they will be used throughout this book, I shall omit the subscript denoting the base of the logarithms.

[2] It is difficult to maintain both a very precise notation as well as an efficient one. While it is more correct to write $p(x_i)$, I shall simply use $p(x)$ to mean the probability of occurrence of any particular category or value of x. Thus I am using x to refer both to the general variable as well as to the specific value, but this shorthand will rarely, if ever, lead to confusion. An alternative notation, frequently used, is $p(i)$, but this notation becomes confusing later when we have several different variables, and it becomes necessary to remember which subscript originally went with which variable.

and these values are shown in the third column of Table 2.1. For example, when category A actually occurs, the information is 1 bit, since A has an a priori probability of occurrence of ½. But when C or D occur, the associated information is 3 bits, since on the average each of these categories will happen just ⅛ of the time, with an a priori uncertainty of 3 bits.

Table 2.1

An illustration of the average uncertainty of a
distribution when the probabilities of the
various outcomes are unequal.

Outcome category	p	$-\log p$	$-p \log p$
A	.500	1.00	.500
B	.250	2.00	.500
C	.125	3.00	.375
D	.125	3.00	.375

$$-\Sigma p \log p = 1.75 \text{ bits}$$

In the long run, then, we have a series of events occurring in which the various outcomes or categories happen with the relative frequencies indicated by these associated probabilities. Each time a particular category actually occurs, we know the information associated with it. If we want to know what the long-term average information is, we simply average all these uncertainties, weighting each of them with the actual probability of occurrence. In other words, we obtain a weighted average of the various uncertainties. In equation form, then, the average uncertainty associated with a discrete probability distribution is given by

$$U(x) = -\Sigma p(x) \log p(x). \tag{2.3}$$

This is the Shannon measure of average information, and its application to our distribution of Table 2.1 gives an average uncertainty of 1.75 bits.[3]

This procedure for obtaining a weighted average uncertainty is

[3] The equations I shall use in the main body of this book will use the symbol p as a general symbol for probability. In a strict sense I should differentiate between a true probability which is known a priori and a proportion which is obtained from a sample. Since I will primarily be dealing with general mathematical derivations, and will be more concerned with the nature of terms than with the exact arithmetic of them, the distinction is not of great importance.

identical with that of obtaining a weighted average of any other statistic. Since the equation is written in terms of probabilities, however, no division step (to obtain a mean) is necessary, since the total number of cases is 1 by definition. Thus the equation is written only with the summation, but this fact should not obscure the nature of the statistic—it is truly an average.

Rationally, in obtaining the weighted average, we use the procedure shown in Table 2.1. However, since we always have a summation of a series of terms involving $-p \log p$, it is not necessary to go through the step of first obtaining the actual uncertainty associated with each category, and computational tables are available directly in the $-p \log p$ form. The general relation between p and $-p \log p$ is shown in Fig. 2.1. Note that while simple uncertainty is inversely related to probability, the maximum contribution to average uncertainty occurs with a probability of about .37. This fact does not mean that maximum uncertainty occurs when $p = .37$, but only that the product of p times its logarithm is at a maximum.

Another point about the nature of this statistic worth noting is that

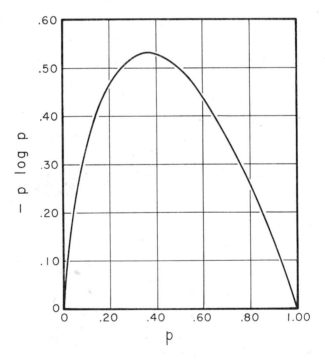

Fig. 2.1. Values of $-p \log p$ as a function of p.

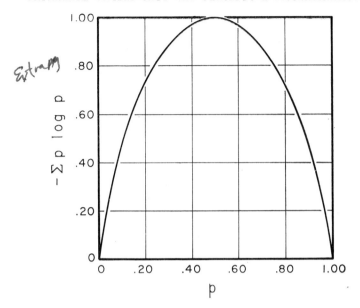

FIG. 2.2. Uncertainty of dichotomous distributions with probabilities p and $(1 - p)$.

the maximum uncertainty for any distribution with a given number of categories occurs when all categories have equal probabilities. Notice, for example, our illustration in Table 2.1. With four categories, the average uncertainty would be 2.0 bits if all categories occurred equally often, but our computed uncertainty is only 1.75 bits. This discrepancy is the loss (and in a sense the inefficiency) due to the lack of equal probabilities. The extent of this loss due to unequal probabilities is shown in Fig. 2.2 for dichotomous distributions. The average uncertainty when the two categories have probabilities of .50 is, of course, 1 bit, and distributions with probabilities as discrepant as 60–40 show some loss. But the loss becomes more extreme as one of the probabilities goes toward 0 (or 1).

It will at times be necessary to distinguish between the actual uncertainty of a distribution and the uncertainty which would occur if all categories occurred equally often. Whenever the distinction is necessary, we will refer to the actual average uncertainty of the distribution simply as the uncertainty, and we will call the uncertainty which would have been obtained if all probabilities were equal the *nominal uncertainty*. Thus the nominal uncertainty for any two-category distribution is 1 bit, and for any four-category distribution it is 2 bits, etc.

We use the designation nominal in the same sense that we use the term nominal value, the face value which does not exist in actual fact, but in name only.

Uncertainty as probability

The uncertainty associated with any particular outcome of an event is inversely related to the probability of that particular outcome; and thus the information obtained when the particular outcome occurs can be directly interpreted in terms of the probability of occurrence. Following this line of thinking, the uncertainty of a particular outcome can also be interpreted as the probability of correctly guessing that particular outcome, on the assumption that the probability of guessing the particular outcome is the same as the probability of the outcome. To illustrate, suppose that in a series of guesses about the four possible outcomes of Table 2.1, we guess that category D will occur on $\frac{1}{8}$ of our guesses. Now since category D actually occurs $\frac{1}{8}$ of the time, then every time we guess category D, our probability of being correct is in fact $\frac{1}{8}$, which is the antilogarithm of the uncertainty associated with this possible outcome.

The average uncertainty can be interpreted in a similar, although somewhat more complicated, manner. Suppose that a finite series of events occurs with alternative outcomes whose probabilities are known a priori. To illustrate, we can continue to use the four categories of Table 2.1. Suppose further that a series of 200 independent events is generated. Now if we were trying to guess the outcomes of this series of events, and knew the probabilities, we could generate a series of events which exactly matched the probabilities. In other words, we would generate a guessing series which had exactly 100 A's, 50 B's, 25 C's and 25 D's.

The actual probability that any particular series such as this would in fact have been randomly generated is determined by multiplying all of the probabilities together, since these are independent events. Thus the probability of occurrence of any series having exactly this number of A's, B's, C's, and D's is $.500^{100} \times .250^{50} \times .125^{25} \times .125^{25}$, which is a very small number indeed. In general form, we can write this probability as

$$P = \Pi p(x)^{p(x)n} \tag{2.4}$$

where P is the probability of occurrence of any finite series which exactly matches the a priori probabilities, and n is the number of events in the series. If we take logarithms of both sides of Eq. 2.4,

$$\log P = n\Sigma p(x) \log p(x). \tag{2.5}$$

The negative of the right-hand quantity, divided by n, is the Shannon measure of average information. Dividing by n gives us an average figure, and this average figure is associated with the probability of being correct on every one of a finite series of guesses, *if our series of guesses exactly matches the probabilities of the outcomes.*

It should be clear that the measure of average uncertainty cannot be interpreted as the average probability of being correct on a given trial. When we divided by n just above, we were taking an average, but an average of the logarithmic measure, not an average of the probability measure. In effect, we were taking the geometric mean of the actual probabilities, not the arithmetic mean. The average probability of being correct on a single trial is simply $\Sigma [p(x)]^2$, which reduces to the equivalent of the average uncertainty only when all outcomes have equal probabilities.

Thus the Shannon measure of average uncertainty is related to the probability of being entirely correct in a sequence of guesses, but does not provide a direct calculation of that probability. Furthermore, it is an average of uncertainties, not an average of probabilities; and while the uncertainty for a particular outcome is directly related to the probability of correctly guessing that outcome, the average uncertainty is only indirectly related to the average probability of correctly guessing a sequence of outcomes.

Binary coding of information

As pointed out earlier, the measure of information in bits is a statement of the number of equally likely binary decisions which must be made, or questions which must be asked, to determine exactly which of several possible outcomes actually occurs. This principle is easy to understand when we are concerned with only a fixed number of outcomes or categories, but needs a little more explanation when we are dealing with distributions with unequal probabilities. Once again, we must deal with the binary questions or decisions on an average basis.

For purposes of illustration let us refer to the distribution of probabilities of Table 2.2. Here we have eight categories, with probabilities ranging from .50 to .0156. Except for rounding error, the uncertainty of this distribution is 2.0 bits. Now this value says that *on the average* we should be able to determine which of the eight possibilities occurs on a given event with two binary questions; or that the information can be transmitted with two binary statements. While it is quite true that two binary statements can designate one out of these eight possibilities on the average, we must use a coding system (or question system) which some of the time re-

Table 2.2

An illustration of the use of efficient coding to represent
the categories of a distribution when the probabilities
are unequal. (n is the number of binary digits
required to code each category.)

Outcome category	p	Efficient binary code	pn
A	.5000	1	.5000
B	.2500	01	.5000
C	.1250	001	.3750
D	.0625	0001	.2500
E	.0156	000011	.0937
F	.0156	000010	.0937
G	.0156	000001	.0937
H	.0156	000000	.0937

$$\Sigma = 1.9998$$

quires many more than two binary statements in order to realize the
computed average of 2.

The binary code shown in the third column of Table 2.2 is a
means of realizing the expected coding efficiency of two binary statements. The principle involved in the code is really very simple: Each
binary statement must reduce the uncertainty by exactly 1 bit.
Using 0's and 1's for our code, we assign the code such that the first
statement divides the total probabilities in half. We accomplish this
by giving category A a coded value of 1 for the first binary statement, and all others a value of 0. Since A occurs half of the time,
and the others occur the other half of the time, this binary statement
satisfies our requirements. Now if A is the correct category (and
the code "1" is used), then no further binary statements are needed.
However, if the first code is 0, then we need to give a second code
which also divides the remaining categories in half. We accomplish
this again by assigning a 1 in the second position to category B,
since B constitutes half of the remaining probability, and assigning
a 0 to all the others. No further code is then needed for B. Then for
the third code position, a 1 is assigned to category C, since that category now contains half of the remaining probability. Likewise for
the next coded position we assign the 1 to category D. Finally, for
the last four categories, we assign the four possible codes in the
last two positions.

If we had assigned a binary code in the more usual manner for eight categories, we would have used the eight possible codes involving three binary steps (000, 001, 010, 011, 100, 101, 110, and 111). With this code we would always be sure that after three binary statements we would have the category completely determined. Similarly, we would always require the full three binary steps to designate one out of the eight, even for category A, which occurs half of the time.

The efficient binary code of Table 2.2 sacrifices the guarantee of correct designation after three binary steps in exchange for the long-run advantage of quickly designating the most probable categories. Thus even though four of the categories require six binary steps (instead of the guaranteed three with the simple code), these categories occur infrequently enough that the average cost is not great. And in exchange for this small cost, the exact category is designated half of the time with just one binary step, and another quarter of the time with just two binary steps.

The long-run average length of message is determined in the last column of Table 2.2. Here n is the number of binary digits required to code that particular category, and p is the probability of occurrence of the category. The summed product of these two gives the average number of binary steps required to designate one out of these eight categories, with the stated probability distribution. Note that the average is in fact 2 bits, exactly what the uncertainty of the distribution says it should be.

One fact which is not immediately apparent is that for each category the value of pn is exactly the $-p \log p$ value appropriate for that category. What we are doing, in effect, is to code by exactly the same principle as that involved in the determination of the average uncertainty. For each category we use as many binary steps as the probability for that category indicates would be necessary if that were one of a distribution involving equal probabilities. For example, the last four categories have probabilities of $\frac{1}{64}$, and a six-unit code is needed to designate one of sixty-four equally probable categories. But the A category has a probability of $\frac{1}{2}$, and thus one binary step is used for it.

For any probability distribution it can be shown that there is such an ideal binary code which will require on the average as many binary units for the code as there are bits of uncertainty in the distribution. In many cases, however, the code must be somewhat more complex than we have illustrated here. If there are very many categories in the distribution, it will usually be possible at least to approximate an ideal code by an appropriate grouping of categories. In other cases, however, it may be necessary to accomplish the coding by grouping successive events to form a larger number of categories. For example, if we have four categories per event, there are sixty-four categories of triple events, and these sixty-four categories can be grouped to provide an efficient code more easily than can just the four categories.

LEARNING

Is uncertainty or information a meaningful concept in dealing with psychological problems? Certainly the concept has been widely used. Occasionally the application is a quite straightforward test of the human's ability to use information processes effectively, as in Bendig's (1953) experiment on the use of binary questions in the twenty-questions game. He found that the earlier questions used were effective, that is, reduced uncertainty by 1 bit each, but that the later ones were not. Thus, to a degree, humans are able to use information efficiently.

If information concepts are meaningful in human behavior, then the number of categories in any choice situation should have important consequences on behavior. On the other hand, for differences in uncertainty or information to be meaningful, we must be able to know rather accurately just how many categories of choice or behavior there are (as well as the probabilities of each category); the information concept becomes meaningless when we have an indefinite or unknown set of possible alternatives. In psychological tests, for example, when a multiple choice question is used we can specify exactly the amount of potential information in the answer, but when open questions are used, we are unable to specify the amount of information obtained by an answer since we do not know how much uncertainty existed prior to the answer. Cane and Horn (1951) compared accuracy and time scores on tests containing both types of items, and came to the conclusion that subjects respond quite differently to these two types of question. They suggest from their results that the behavior of subjects is of an essentially different kind when responding in a limited-response situation and when responding in the unlimited-response situation. Their conclusions are based primarily on the fact that the relation between time and accuracy scores is different for these two types of question.

The concept of uncertainty implies the idea of choice or discrimination, and we would be most apt to expect the quantitative measurement of uncertainty to be important in those behavior situations which involve discrimination and choice. Much of learning, of course, quite directly involves such a process, although the exact amount of choice is not always specified in the experiment. When the amount of choice is specified, however, the data leave little doubt that the uncertainty prior to the response is an important variable.

This relation has been demonstrated in a very direct manner by Riley (1952). He ran a paired-associates learning problem, in which eight different nonsense syllables served as the stimuli, and the subjects were required to learn another nonsense syllable as a response to each stimulus by the method of anticipation. For one group, if the response was not correctly anticipated, the single correct response was exposed. For another group, two possible responses were exposed; and for a third group, four possible responses were exposed. The greater response uncertainty for these two groups led, as expected, to considerably slower learning, such that with four alternative responses learning (mean trials to criterion) took approximately twice as long as it did with just the single response.

Analogous experiments were carried out by Brogden and Schmidt (1954a,b), except that their experiments were of the verbal maze variety. Such experiments are basically the same as the paired associates learning task except for the greater emphasis on the sequence of choices. In their experiment, they varied the number of choices at each choice point in the maze from two to twelve and found that both total time to criterion and total errors to criterion were approximately linearly related to the number of choices per unit of the maze. Over this range of choices, both time and errors varied by a factor of 4, a value which makes it clear that we are not dealing with an effect which is significant but trivial. Number of choices is an important variable in learning experiments.

In learning lists of nonsense syllables or words, it has been known for a long time that the rate of learning is a function of the length of the list, that is, the total number of items to be learned. This relation is in itself no evidence for the importance of amount of information as a variable, since the number of different items to be learned is completely confounded with the total amount of learning to be accomplished. Adelson, Muckler, and Williams (1955) have, however, shown that response uncertainty is an important variable in this type of learning over and above the factor of total length of list. In their experiment, they had subjects learn lists of alphabetic letters which were always fifteen items long, but a different number of alternative letters was used for each list.

These authors, whose results are shown in Fig. 2.3, used three basically different ways of generating the lists of letters to be learned. In the simplest condition, the fifteen-item lists consisted of two, four,

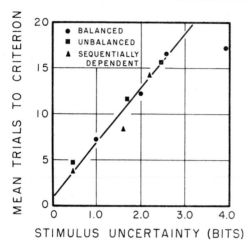

Fig. 2.3. Learning of lists of letters as a function of the uncertainty of the stimulus list. All lists were 15 letters long, and consisted of two, four, six, or fifteen different letters. The letters occurred equally often for the balanced lists, in unequal proportion for the unbalanced lists, and equally often but in controlled order for the sequentially dependent lists. (Data from Adelson, Muckler, and Williams, 1955.)

six, or fifteen different letters, chosen at random with equal a priori probabilities, except that the last list contained all fifteen letters. As shown in Fig. 2.3, the increased uncertainty of the symbols required a greater number of trials to reach criterion, and the relation between uncertainty and trials is essentially linear except that the fifteen different letters required less time to learn than would be expected from the other results. This particular case is somewhat different from the others, however, since when all fifteen letters must be different, the uncertainty decreases the farther down the list one goes. Thus the average uncertainty is considerably less than log 15. The median uncertainty, that is, the uncertainty of the middle item in the list, is 3 bits, since after seven letters, there remain eight possibilities. If this point were plotted with a stimulus uncertainty of 3 bits, it would be nearly in line with the general function.

In a second condition, lists with two, four, and six different letters were used, but these letters were used with unequal probabilities. For example, in the four-letter list, the letter "b" had an a priori probability of .50, and the other three letters had lower probabilities. As pointed out earlier, average uncertainty is decreased whenever probabilities are not equal, so that such lists have less uncertainty than lists with the same number of different letters occurring with equal probability. Nevertheless, when these data are plotted in terms of stimulus uncertainty, they fall on the same function as do the earlier data. Thus it would appear that not only is the number of alternatives an important parameter, but also the relative probability of occurrence of each alternative is important. In other words, the measure of average information is psychologically meaningful.

In a third condition a slightly more complicated scheme was used. For this condition, the probability of each letter's occurrence was equal to the probabilities of all other letters in the set, but the probability of a letter following another was altered; that is, the sequential probabilities were altered. This procedure also has the effect of lowering the stimulus uncertainty, since the probabilities of the letters are not equal once the first letter has been known. Once again the learning data fit the same function as do the data for the other conditions, and we have reasonable evidence that average stimulus uncertainty is an important parameter in learning, regardless of the manner in which changes in stimulus uncertainty are produced.

There is, incidentally, no good reason why the function in Fig. 2.3 should be linear, nor should we take too seriously the fact that it is. Another measure of learning would not necessarily show a linear relation, and there is no sensible rationale for using one measure rather than another. In addition, the points actually plotted in this figure are plotted with regard to the a priori uncertainties with which the lists were constructed, rather than with the proportions which the subject actually observed from the finite length lists. Particularly with the sequentially dependent lists, a list fifteen items long is too small for these probabilities to be even approximately represented with accuracy. Thus the main conclusion to be drawn from this and related studies must be simply that uncertainty is an operative factor, and we need not be overly concerned about the exact shape of the function, or how exactly various methods of reducing uncertainty produce the same results.

Learning and recognition

Ordinarily we think of perceptual discrimination and recognition as processes distinct from learning, even though a recognition type test may be used either as a measure of learning or as a measure of perceptual discrimination. In actual fact the line distinguishing learning from perception is often so thin as to be invisible, and the same experiment may be designed to investigate both learning and perception. Recognition may be poor because of the failure of the subject to know what he is to recognize (failure of learning) or because of the failure of the subject to discriminate pertinent aspects of the stimuli (failure of perception). Regardless of whether failure of recognition is due to faulty learning or to faulty perception, the evidence is clear that the accuracy of recognition is a function of the number of alternatives used in the experimental situation.

Postman (1950) reported an experiment in which he used a recognition scoring criterion for a verbal serial learning task. The subjects were required to learn a list of thirty-six nonsense syllables, and learning was measured by their ability to select correct items in a multiple-choice test. The thirty-six items were divided into four equal groups, and each group had its items imbedded in two-, four-, seven-, or ten-item multiple-choice groups for the recognition test. After the recognition score was corrected for chance guessing, the recognition score was 4.9 items for the two-alternatives test, and 3.1 items for the ten-alternatives test. Thus here again learning performance is related to the uncertainty in this test situation.

A recognition experiment in which both learning and perceptual variables were incorporated was carried out by Bruner, Miller, and Zimmerman (1955). These authors had their subjects learn lists of monosyllables either eight, sixteen, thirty-two, or sixty-four words long. Their basic scoring method was free recall, but interspersed in the course of learning were some recognition tests in which the words being learned were presented in a masking noise for auditory recognition. They found, as expected, that learning was a function of the length of list, and that the recognition performance improved along with the recall performance, even though the recognition test was under adverse perceptual circumstances. In addition, the recognition performance was a function of the number of alternatives on the list.

To some extent this result would be expected on the basis of the fact that the longer lists would be less well learned, and thus that recognition would be poorer since it is a measure of amount of learning. However, the critical finding of this experiment, for our purposes, was that when the various learning conditions were equated for percent recall, there was still a difference in recognition performance attributable to the difference in number of alternatives, and this difference was maximum at asymptotic levels of learning. In other words, stimulus uncertainty was affecting perceptual discrimination as evidenced in the recognition test after the lists of words were thoroughly learned. It is at this point that we should no longer speak of the effects of uncertainty on learning, but rather of the effects of uncertainty on perception.

PERCEPTUAL RECOGNITION

The fact that perceptual recognition performance is a function of the number of alternatives is now so thoroughly established that only a few experiments need be mentioned at this time. Furthermore, this relation is implicit in so many other experiments which are concerned with some other facet of behavior that in a sense its demonstration will be rampant in the rest of this book.

Miller, Heise, and Lichten (1951) first demonstrated the importance of number of alternatives within the general framework of information measurement with an experiment on auditory recognition of spoken words heard in different levels of masking noise. The test vocabularies consisted of sets of 2, 4, 8, 16, 32, or 256 monosyllables, corresponding to an a priori uncertainty of 1, 2, 3, 4, 5, or 8 bits. One word was read at a time, and the subject always knew ahead of time which list the word was coming from. Furthermore, to ensure that this would be an experiment in perceptual recognition, rather than in memory, the words were always available to each subject, and he checked off from a printed list which word he thought he had heard.

Some of the results obtained by these authors are presented in Fig. 2.4. Here the percent words correctly recognized are plotted as a function of the uncertainty of the test vocabulary, for two of the several signal-to-noise ratios they used. There is little doubt that the size of test vocabulary has a striking effect on perceptual recognition accuracy. While these data have not been corrected for

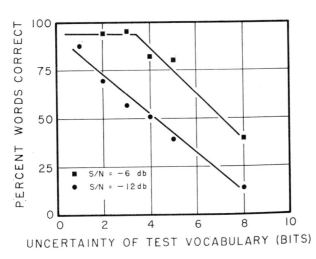

FIG. 2.4. Accuracy of auditory recognition of monosyllables in noise as a function of the size of the test vocabulary. Each set of points is for a different signal-to-noise (S/N) ratio as indicated. (Data from Miller, Heise, and Lichten, 1951.)

chance guessing, the effect is far greater than such a correction would account for.

One fact should be noted about these curves, a fact which is perhaps logically obvious, but needs to be emphasized to keep the role of information measurement in perspective. The upper curve shown is for a higher signal-to-noise condition (that is, less noise) and this curve shows much less of the effect of test uncertainty than does the lower curve. In fact, for low uncertainties, there is no difference in recognition due to uncertainty. In extrapolation, if the lists of words were presented with no noise, we would expect little or no effect of test uncertainty over a very wide range because recognition accuracy is too good. In other words, if perception is very good, the uncertainty variable is of little consequence when performance is measured in terms of recognition accuracy.

In terms of material to be discussed later, we can argue that, if there is far more stimulus discriminability possible than is needed, we have redundancy, and if redundancy is great enough for any sized list we use, then we will have essentially perfect accuracy regardless of the stated experimental uncertainty. In a similar vein, we would not expect there to be performance differences in the learning experiments after the learning has been completely accomplished, and certainly not after a considerable amount of overlearning has taken place. The overlearning is quite analogous to an oversupply of stimulus differentiating cues. In brief, then, when there is enough overlearning or enough stimulus redundancy to overcome the effects of differences in stimulus uncertainty, we not only will get very good performance but also no differences due to stimulus uncertainty.

Another experiment has confirmed the finding of Miller, Heise, and Lichten with nonsense dissyllables as the stimulus words. Once again the recognition tests were auditory perception in noise, but this experiment (I. Miller, 1957) differed in two important respects from the previous one. First, the subjects learned the list of possible words prior to the recognition test, rather than being given a list of the words. Second, the uncertainty of the test was not controlled by changing the size of the vocabulary for a particular test, but rather was controlled by predetermined sequencing of the words as in the Adelson, Muckler, and Williams experiment. As was pointed out before, such a procedure is equally effective in reducing the test uncertainty.

With this experimental procedure, I. Miller obtained results which substantiate the main findings of the previous experiment, namely that test uncertainty affects recognition accuracy and that the amount

of the effect depends on the difficulty of perceptual discrimination—
that is, on the amount of noise.

We have now seen two methods by which a recognition experiment
is made to be an experiment on perceptual discrimination rather than
one on learning: The list of possible stimuli is directly presented to
the subject, or the subject is required to learn the list thoroughly
before the recognition test, so that it can be assumed that any differential effects are not due to familiarity with the stimuli, but rather
are due to discrimination difficulties. There is a third method also,
which is to use materials with which subjects are already thoroughly
familiar before coming to the experiment, or are sufficiently familiar
that only a trifling amount of learning is required. Hyman and Hake
(1954) have essentially used this method in determining tachistoscopic time thresholds for two, three, or four familiar forms. Once
again, discrimination is better for the smaller numbers of alternatives, even after correction for chance guessing, and in this case
discrimination was not determined as percent correct responses, but
rather as that duration at which 50 percent correct responses occur.

Stimulus uncertainty or response uncertainty?

In all of the experiments we have mentioned, there is an a priori
set of possible stimuli. The subject knows what this set of possible
stimuli is, and clearly he must know the set for the experiment to
be meaningful. There is little point in the experimenter's changing
the possible set without the knowledge of the subject, for if information is an important variable in human behavior it must be a variable
which is operative for the subject.

Since the subject knows the set of alternatives, he knows something
which is pertinent to his behavior in two respects. First, he knows
the possibilities that can be presented to him, and second, he knows
what are his possible or permissible responses. We have seen that
with this knowledge, the subject's performance is a function of the
uncertainty of the set of stimuli, as the experimenter sees this uncertainty. It is possible, however, that the critical factor in the subject's performance is not in the restriction in the stimuli, but rather
in the concomitant restriction in his responses.

It is not only logically possible, but experimentally quite feasible,
to determine which of these two alternative explanations is the correct one. Lawrence and Coles (1954) first attacked this problem
experimentally in the following fashion: Subjects were presented
tachistoscopically with one of four possible black-and-white pictures
of familiar objects on a given trial, from a total set of fifty such

pictures. There were two groups of subjects; one of these was informed of the four alternatives before the exposure, and the other was not informed of the four alternatives until after the exposure. Thus the first group was run in the usual fashion, but the second group did not have a priori knowledge of the set of stimuli, but only a posteriori knowledge of the possible responses. The results showed quite unequivocally that these two experimental conditions give the same results in terms of accuracy. Thus it would appear that knowledge of the set of possible stimuli is not a critical factor, but rather that the critical factor has to do with limitations on the possible responses. Such a result eliminates the need for assuming some sort of neural set or selective system which prepares the sensorium for some objects but not for others. More probably we are dealing with a sort of matching-from-sample process in which a larger set of possible responses requires more matches (and eliminations) than does the smaller set.

In a related experiment, Hake and Eriksen (1956) gave subjects prior practice in using some irrelevant labeling responses before later being required to associate these responses to a set of unfamiliar nonsense forms. They found that this prior practice with the responses facilitated the later paired-associates learning, but also found that when the same stimulus forms were imbedded in a group of forms and recognition was required, there was no facilitation due to the prior practice. Thus the practice with the responses had an effect only when the responses were in fact used, giving us additional support for the idea that there can be factors in learning or perception which are unique to the responses, and which are irrelevant to perception per se.

The most thorough set of experiments related to the question of the locus of the uncertainty effect in perceptual recognition has been done by Pollack (1959a). Using auditory recognition of spondees in noise as his experimental situation, Pollack's first experiment varied the stimulus set (as told to the subject) and the response set independently. For example, the subject might expect one out of eight possibilities before the word was presented, and then after it was presented be given two possible responses. Thus his response uncertainty was always equal to or less than his stimulus uncertainty. With these conditions, the results were clear that by far the largest effect was due to response uncertainty, not to stimulus uncertainty.

A second experiment simply required the subject to determine whether the presented word was a preset "monitored" word or not, and the presented word was the monitored one 50 percent of the time, but the non-monitored word could be from a set of one to seven possibilities. Thus the response uncertainty was always 1 bit, but the stimulus uncertainty varied from one condition to another. This experiment showed no effect of stimulus uncertainty.

In a third experiment, there were two to sixty-four possible messages sent, but the subject was simply required to state whether the word heard was in one or another of two sets of words; that is, one set contained half of the possible words and the other set contained the other half. In this experiment the size of the message set produced a large effect, so the critical factor is not the number of responses actually used (which was still just two), but rather the number of response differentiations required of the subject.

The results of Pollack's next experiment are shown in Fig. 2.5. For this experiment, the subject made two responses. The first was with the full message set; he had been told which stimuli or messages would be sent, and he had to respond with a word from this set. The lower curve shows accuracy as a function of message uncertainty when the response uncertainty is the same as the stimulus uncertainty, and the expected drop in accuracy is obtained. The second response made by the subject was delayed until after his first response was recorded, and then he was given just two possible re-

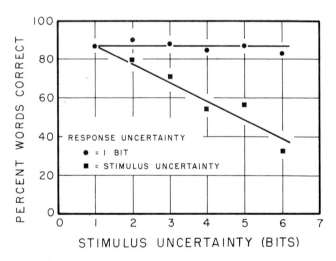

Fig. 3.6. Information transmission for monosyllables heard in noise as a function db) as a function of size of stimulus set. For the top curve, responses were chosen from two categories; for the lower curve, the number of response categories equalled the number of stimulus categories. (After Pollack, 1959a.)

sponses and had to choose between these. The accuracy for this second response is that shown by the top curve of Fig. 2.5. It seems quite clear that response uncertainty is indeed the critical factor.

Pollack's last experiment was designed to determine the nature of the response process. He systematically delayed (up to 16 seconds) giving the subject the set of possible responses, and found that there was a slight but definite decrease in accuracy with increased delay. From this, Pollack argues that the effect is not caused by an encoding process in which the subject categorizes or encodes the heard stimulus and then simply waits for the response categories, since such a process should not be affected by memory losses, at least over such short times. Rather, he feels that the process is one of representation, in which the entire stimulus complex is retained and then matched against the possible responses.

Whether this distinction is entirely necessary is equivocal. But one thing does seem very certain, and that is that some sort of a matching operation goes on, and that the larger the number of categories to be matched against, the greater the possibility for error or apparently faulty perception. We can say that the perceptual confusions among the set of possible responses increase as we increase the number of such responses, and that these confusions contribute to errors of recognition. We are, in other words, not dealing with relations between stimuli which are present and those which are not— rather we are dealing with relations between responses all of which are present and must be chosen from. Response discrimination and choice is a critical factor in any perceptual experiment.

It is not unambiguously clear that restriction of the set of possible stimuli is effective only because it restricts the possible responses. In a series of experiments in 1960 (Reid, Henneman, and Long; Long, Henneman, and Garvey; Long, Reid, and Henneman), it was shown that under some circumstances the restriction of the set of possible alternatives both before and after the stimulus presentation is better than just restriction after the presentation. These authors used, variously, defocused letters and words presented visually, and spoken words. Under some circumstances, primarily with small sets, performance was better with prior restriction of set, and these authors conclude that restriction of set improves performance in three different ways: 1. It allows discrimination of potentially relevant elements or dimensions in the stimulus. 2. It reduces the number of possible responses. 3. It makes the residual elements in the degraded stimulus more interpretable, thus eliminating possible competing responses.

PERCEPTUAL REACTION TIME

As we have seen, differences in perceptual recognition accuracy can occur with changes in stimulus uncertainty only if there is some ambiguity due to lack of familiarity with the stimuli (and, we should now add, responses) or due to poor discrimination in the perceptual situation. When sets of stimuli and responses are thoroughly learned, and when the stimuli are clearly discriminable, measures of accuracy cannot indicate any effect of either stimulus or response uncertainty. Under such circumstances, it is necessary to use a more sensitive indicator of perceptual differences, and for this purpose, reaction times have long been recognized as one of the most accurate and sensitive indicators of perceptual differences available.

In the latter half of the nineteenth century, many reaction-time studies were undertaken with the general purpose of determining times required for various psychological processes. These can be found in any textbook of experimental psychology. These studies usually showed an increase in reaction time as the number of alternative stimuli was increased. Hick (1952) first made use of some of these early data, as well as data of his own, to demonstrate that reaction time was linearly related to the logarithm of the number of stimuli. In other words, reaction time was a linear function of stimulus uncertainty. Hick's own data were obtained in an experimental situation in which a display of lights served as the stimuli, and finger pressings of various telegraph keys were the responses. His stimuli were also presented in a random order, with each stimulus having an equal probability of occurrence.

A year later, Hyman (1953) presented the results of a similar but more elaborate experiment, which was concerned not only with stimulus uncertainty as related to number of stimuli, but also to uncertainty as related to unequal probabilities of occurrence. Hyman also used a display of lights as the stimuli, but he used a voice-reaction timer to measure the reaction time for a vocal identifying response to each of the different stimuli. Three different experimental conditions were used: In one of them, stimuli ranging in number from one through eight were presented in a random order, each stimulus with an equal probability of occurrence. This condition was essentially that of Hick. In a second condition, the stimuli again ranged in number from one through eight, but different probabilities of occurrence were used for the various stimuli. For example, in one set of eight stimuli, two of the stimuli occurred $\frac{1}{4}$ of the time, two of them $\frac{1}{8}$ of the time, and four of them $\frac{1}{16}$ of the time. Thus with this distribution, the stimulus uncertainty was 2.75 bits instead of the 3.0 bits which would have been so if all stimuli occurred equally often. In a third condition, each stimulus occurred equally often, but with unequal probabilities of one stimulus following another. For example, in one stimulus sequence involving three different lights, the light was never allowed to repeat itself; in effect there were just two equally likely alternatives on each trial.

Hyman's results, for one subject, are plotted in Fig. 2.6. These data indicate not only that there is a linear relation between stimulus uncertainty and reaction time, but also that within wide limits it makes little difference how a given stimulus uncertainty is obtained, whether by restriction of total number of stimuli, restriction of probabilities of stimuli, or by restriction of sequences of stimuli.

The effect of stimulus uncertainty on reaction time has been confirmed by other experimenters. Frick (1954) cites an experiment in which subjects were required to read a visually presented word as fast as possible after its presentation. Before each observation, the subject was informed as to which words were possible, and the number of possibilities varied from time to time. Recognition time in

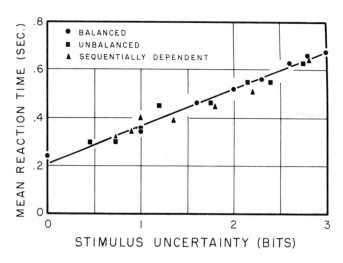

Fig. 2.6. Choice reaction time as a function of stimulus uncertainty. All stimuli occurred equally often for the balanced condition, in unequal proportions for the unbalanced condition, and in equal proportions but in controlled order for the sequentially dependent condition. Data from one subject only. (After Hyman, 1953.)

this task increased as the number of alternatives increased, such that reaction time was linearly related to stimulus uncertainty up to 10 bits of uncertainty. Poulton (1956) required his subject to move a pen either right or left in response to a bell which he heard on his right or left side. In one condition either bell could occur, and in the other only one could occur. Poulton found, in agreement with the earlier studies, that reaction time was faster for the one-bell condition than for the two-bell condition. In addition, he found that the reactions were more precise with the lower stimulus uncertainty—precise in terms of accurate movement of the pen a predetermined distance.

The fact that reaction time to several alternative stimuli is affected by the distribution of the several stimuli in the set has also been confirmed. Crossman (1953), working independently, found, as did Hyman, that unbalanced frequencies lower the average reaction time. Crossman used a card-sorting task, making use of ordinary playing cards, and required his subjects to sort them into different categories. For example, in one case they were required to sort red and black into two piles, but in another to sort pictures and plain cards into separate piles. In both of these cases, there are just two response categories, but in the former case each category occurs equally often, while in the latter case they do not.

Still later, Leonard (1958) found, as an incidental part of another experimental intent, that reaction times are lower with unbalanced distributions than with balanced distributions. In his experiment, each response was not discrete (in this respect somewhat like Crossman's experiment); rather, there was a continued series of responses—telegraph keys were used to respond to a panel of lights. There were five different lights, but when one of the lights occurred much more frequently than did the others, the average number of seconds per response was lower.

Stimulus uncertainty in a reaction time experiment was varied in quite a novel way by Klemmer (1957a), who used a simple reaction-time procedure (one stimulus and one response) but made the time elapsing after a warning stimulus variable. Thus he was dealing with time uncertainty of the stimulus; the subject knew what the stimulus would be, but he wasn't sure when it would be. Klemmer found that reaction time increased with the amount of time uncertainty. Making use of the relation between uncertainty and variance of a distribution,[4] Klemmer related reaction time to time uncertainty in bits, and

---

[4] See Garner and McGill (1956), or Attneave (1959).

found a linear relation, although with a much smaller slope than shown in Fig. 2.6.

Reaction time and probability of particular stimuli

To return for a moment to Hyman's study, while average reaction time to a set of stimuli with unequal probabilities of occurrence is the same as it would be if the same stimulus uncertainty had been obtained by restricting the total number of possibilities, the reaction time to the individual stimulus is not proportionate to the uncertainty associated with the particular probability of occurrence of that stimulus.

In one example which Hyman cites, for the subject whose data are plotted in Fig. 2.6, the average stimulus uncertainty is 0.99 bit, which is obtained by having four stimuli, one occurring $13/16$ of the time, and each of the three others occurring $1/16$ of the time. The uncertainty of the frequently occurring stimulus is 0.30 bit, and for each of the others it is 4.00 bits. From the relation drawn in Fig. 2.6 we would expect a reaction time of 0.258 sec for the frequent stimulus, and 0.824 sec for the other three. These values, when weighted according to the frequencies of occurrence, give an average of 0.363 sec. The observed mean reaction time for the frequent stimulus was 0.306 sec, and for the other three it was 0.585 sec, each of these being closer to the average value than expected. The weighted average of these observed values is 0.361 sec, almost exactly the expected value. Thus we can talk about reaction time being responsive to stimulus uncertainty in a linear fashion, but only when talking about average reaction times to an entire set of stimuli. When dealing with the individual stimuli, we cannot talk so precisely.

In an attempt to investigate this particular phenomenon further, Newbrough (1958) used a perceptual recognition task involving tachistoscopic presentation of words. He used five different series of words involving two, four, five, four, and seven different words per series, and with different probabilities of occurrence of the words. In four of the different series the word "mean" occurred, always with a probability of $1/4$ (and therefore an uncertainty of 2 bits). Newbrough found that the number of errors of recognition increased with increased total stimulus uncertainty, but the number of recognition errors to the word "mean" also increased with the average stimulus uncertainty of the set of words within which the critical word was imbedded. Since the uncertainty for the critical word itself was always constant, errors to that particular word should not have increased if recognition accuracy is a function of the uncertainty of the *particular* stimulus. This result shows, in line with Hyman's results for reaction times, that human performance is quite successfully predicted in terms of stimulus uncertainty, but only for average performance with respect to average stimulus uncertainty. When attempts are made to use uncertainty measures to predict performance to an individual stimulus within a set, the expected relations are not upheld to any great extent.

Reaction times as successive decisions

We have seen that the uncertainty of a set of stimuli can be specified in terms of the average number of binary decisions (or codes) required to completely specify one out of the several alternatives. Since reaction time increases with the total number of alternatives (as well as with uncertainty varied in other ways), it seems logical to question whether the human, in reacting, is essentially performing a similar kind of successive decision or coding process. In a very simple case, for example, is the reaction time to one of four stimuli greater than the reaction time to one of two because in the former case the human effectively makes two successive binary decisions? The linear function relating uncertainty to reaction time suggests this possibility, since if we subtract out the intercept constant of the function as representing a fixed motor reaction time (the time required to carry out the reaction when there is no choice or decision), then reaction time doubles for a doubled uncertainty.

Leonard (1958a) made a direct test of this hypothesis by the use of three different experimental conditions. In one condition, three stimulus lights were used. All three lights came on as the warning signal and shortly later one of them went off as the specific stimulus and the subject was required to push a corresponding switch. In a second condition, six lights went on, followed by one going off, and a response to this light was required. These two conditions simply produced a direct test of the relation between uncertainty and reaction time. The third, and critical, condition consisted of six alternative reactions again, but the indication of the correct light was divided into two distinct phases, separated by various time intervals. First three of the lights (out of the six possible) came on; after a delay one of the three went off, and a response to this one was required. Thus the designation of the correct light was accomplished in two separate steps, the first one providing 1 bit of information, and the second providing the remaining 1.58 bits. Leonard's results show that for very short delays between the two information steps the reaction time for this critical condition is the same as that for the six-choice condition, but that, with delays on the order of 0.30 sec, the reaction time for this critical condition is the same as that to the three-choice condition. Reaction time to a six-choice condition can be reduced to that of a three-choice condition by presenting the six-choice condition in two separate information steps.

However, the somewhat long delay required for reaction time to be reduced to that of the three-choice condition makes it clear that the process is not a simple one in which the stimulus delay required simply corresponds to the time that would have been used if the entire decision making had occurred internally in the subject. To illustrate, the actual reaction time for the three-choice stimulus was, after long training, 0.249 sec, and for the six-choice stimulus it was 0.294 sec, a difference of only 0.045 sec. This difference would suggest that an equivalent delay in the two information steps would reduce the reaction time, but substantially longer time is required. In fact, the actual delay required for maximum reduction of reaction time is more on the order of the total reaction time, rather than in the difference. In other words, the 0.30-sec delay is more like the full reaction time to the two-choice stimulus.

It is clear that while we have evidence for a linear relation between stimulus uncertainty and reaction time, a simple interpretation of that relation is not possible. The temptation is very great—and has not always been avoided—to assume that the intercept constant in the linear equation represents motor movement time, and that the increased time required for reaction with greater stimulus uncertainty represents decision time per unit of information. As we shall see, we can use the fact that reaction time increases as a function of stimulus uncertainty as evidence that stimulus uncertainty is a meaningful variable, but it is quite impossible to assume that the relation is in any sense invariant, or that any given form of the relation allows us to conclude that humans are ideal information processors—ideal in the sense of following exactly the requirements of a mathematical model.

It is not at all clear that the reaction-time effect is due to a successive decision process which corresponds to the logarithmic relation. It may be so in some cases, but there are other situations where it quite obviously is not so. Solley and Snyder (1958), for example, attempted to extrapolate these relations to a determination of the time required to solve jigsaw puzzles as a function of the total number of pieces. While they were able to use simple relations to obtain accurate estimates of more complex relations, they found that the simple relation between discrimination time and number of pieces to be discriminated was linear; that is, discrimination time was linearly related to the number of pieces, not to the logarithm of number of pieces. This relation seems intuitively reasonable for that situation. The subject had one piece and then had to select from a number of other pieces the one that fitted the piece he already had. This problem can hardly be solved in any way other than to try successively the various pieces. However, such a procedure will surely lead to the linear relation found, not the semilogarithmic relation expected from information concepts. Perhaps for some simple selective processes, the psychological process is similar to the successive binary decision process, but there is little reason to expect it in general.

Stimulus uncertainty or response uncertainty?

Just as in the case of perceptual recognition experiments, we can ask whether the observed relation between reaction time and stimulus uncertainty is really due to the degree of restriction in the stimulus, or to the usual concomitant restriction in the available responses. And once again the answer seems to be that the effect is due primarily to the relative restriction in the responses. We do not have as clear-cut data in this situation as we had previously, but the suggestion is certainly strong.

In discussing Crossman's (1953) experiment, we noted that he used for all of his conditions the same total set of stimuli—a full deck of fifty-two playing cards. He created different degrees of uncertainty only by the sorting rule he required of the subject. In effect, then, Crossman was using an experimental situation in which the stimulus uncertainty was the same for every condition he used (all fifty-two stimuli were different each time), but the response uncertainty changed. And yet he obtained a clear-cut relation between reaction time and uncertainty.

In a similar situation, Bricker (1955a) had subjects identify various visual patterns. In all cases he used eight different patterns, but he varied the number of responses required from two to eight. His obtained relation between response latency and response uncertainty had almost exactly the same slope as did Hyman's relation between stimulus uncertainty and reaction time.

Bevan and Dukes (1953) also measured reaction time to tachistoscopically presented geometric figures, sometimes telling the subject beforehand what the figure would be, and sometimes not. These two conditions gave differences in reaction times, but the differences were reduced nearly to zero when the only response the subject had to make under either condition was "Recognize." Now in this latter condition, there was a difference in stimulus uncertainty between the known and unknown stimulus conditions, but no difference in response uncertainty. While there was still a slight difference in reaction time due only to stimulus uncertainty, the difference was very small (0.42 versus 0.44 sec).

There is, then, a clear implication that the expected number of response discriminations is the more critical factor, rather than the number of stimulus alternatives. Nevertheless, just as the Bevan and Dukes experiment leaves the possibility that there is also a stimulus effect, so does an experiment by Brush (1956). In his experiment, subjects were required to determine, initially on a trial-and-error basis, the correct response to a stimulus, when there were one, two, three, or four possible stimuli and four, six, or eight possible responses. Each number of stimuli was paired with each number of responses (that is, the two experimental variables were orthogonal), so that he was able to determine that response latency was more affected by stimulus uncertainty than by response uncertainty. This experimental situation is sufficiently complicated, by contrast with the usual reaction time experiment, that its implications are not unambiguous. Nevertheless we must retain some doubt that the only critical factor is response uncertainty, even though the weight of evidence is in that direction.

Discriminability effects

It is at times alluring to subsume all of a given class of phenomena under a single meaningful variable, such as uncertainty. We would like to say that reaction time is a sole function of stimulus (or perhaps response) uncertainty, and to define uncertainty unambiguously in terms of number of alternatives, or relative frequency of occurrence of alternatives. Reaction time, however, is not simply a function of uncertainty, and Crossman (1955) has stressed the importance of the perceptual discriminability of the stimuli as an important factor in reaction time. He derived a measure of discriminability for his stimuli which he shows is highly related to reaction time, and that number of stimulus alternatives had at most a trivial effect on reaction time over and above the effect due to discriminability. In his experimental situation, number of stimulus categories was confounded with discriminability, and he points out that such is often the case. It is possible, however, that stimulus discriminability could be kept relatively independent of number of categories if the stimuli varied on many different dimensions. Perhaps, then, as Crossman suggests, the simple relation between reaction time and uncertainty would be obtained in a limiting case, where number of alternatives is not confounded with discriminability.

It is questionable that we can ever satisfactorily untangle these two variables. We may indeed be able to produce a reasonably large set of stimuli all of which are highly discriminable from each other; but we may not be able to produce an equally large set of responses all of which are highly discriminable. As we have seen, the degree and nature of the choice of responses is probably more important than the nature of the stimuli. Berlyne (1957a,b,c) has carried this sort of argument even further in identifying information measures with degree of conflict, and he argues, with experimental justification, that choice time is primarily related to degree of conflict (that is, the extent to which it is not clear, for whatever reason, which response should be used on a given occasion). It does seem possible that the reaction time effect can be due primarily to degree of conflict per se, and that number of alternatives has such an important effect only because the degree of response conflict increases in direct proportion to the response uncertainty.

Response conflict

If it is true, as Berlyne suggests, that degree of conflict is the critical factor in reaction time, then we should remember that degree of conflict is not simply a question of the discriminability between the responses or between the stimuli, but is also (and often most importantly) a question of the extent to which a given stimulus inevitably leads to a given response. In other words, poor discriminability can lead to conflict, although conflict can often exist without poor discriminability, but only with poor association between stimuli and responses. A set of stimulus words can be highly discriminable, and a set of response words can be equally discriminable, but unless the subject has thoroughly learned which response goes with which stimulus, he will have conflict—and reaction times or latencies can measure the degree of this conflict. Perhaps there is good reason why latency of response has been such a popular measure of learning in recent years.

Lack of response conflict can be produced in a number of ways. It can, for example, be innate. While the direct experiment has probably not been done, it is doubtful that any of us would expect the latency to a tap on the patella to be larger if such taps were alternated on a random basis with a scratch of the abdomen, or a puff of air to the eye. All of these stimuli lead to reflexes, and we assume that there is no real choice in the reflex response. Thus we would intuitively not expect such reaction times to be a function of stimulus or response uncertainty.

Experimental situations analogous to the reflex response can be found in other ways. One means is to use a set of responses which are highly compatible with the stimuli for which they are responses. Pointing responses are usually of this type. For example, if we have a visual display consisting of a set of lights spaced closely together, and the subject simply puts his finger on a light as it appears, there probably would be at most a small effect of number of lights. In an analogous experiment, Leonard (1959) showed that reaction time is very nearly invariant as a function of number of stimulus categories. He had small vibrators attached to each of several fingers, and the stimulus was the activation of one of the vibrators, while the response was simple depression of the finger so stimulated. In this experiment, the results of which are shown in Fig. 2.7, Leonard found that reaction time was greater for two stimuli than for one, but that no further increase in the number of stimuli produced an increase in reaction time. With this type of stimulus-response relation, it seems reasonable to say that there is at most a small degree of conflict about which response to make to any stimulus.

Stimulus-response compatibility, with its resultant lack of response conflict, need not be innate or even due to the naturalness of a situation. It can be learned, as in fact most of our responses are. And Mowbray and Rhoades (1959) have shown that with a great deal of learning, the relation between reaction time and stimulus uncertainty is flattened out. They used stimulus lights and response buttons activated by the fingers, and found that, after 5 months of practice

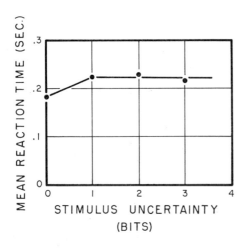

Fig. 2.7. Reaction time as a function of stimulus uncertainty, with a "highly compatible" type of response. (Data from Leonard, 1959.)

and several thousand reaction times, the difference between a four-choice reaction and a two-choice reaction disappeared. This result confirmed and extended the result which Leonard (1958) had previously found as an incidental aspect of his experiment on successive choices. Leonard's results had not shown an ultimately zero effect of stimulus uncertainty, but they had definitely indicated a decrease in the effect with continued practice.

Quastler and Brabb (1956) had discovered a similar effect in having highly skilled typists type random sequences of letters with different sizes of alphabet. They found a difference between one- and two-letter alphabets (in agreement with the Leonard result), but no further effect of the size of alphabet. Thus here again the highly overlearned response—where there is little response conflict—does not show an uncertainty effect.

Another experiment indirectly tends to confirm this finding. Garvey (1957) used a panel of 10 x 10 lights with an equivalent panel of 10 x 10 push buttons for responses. He used an unequal distribution of stimuli, and showed that if the fast responses were assigned to the high-frequency signals, mean reaction time was at a minimum. In other words, he was demonstrating that efficient coding of signals was effective. The incidental result of interest to us here, however, was that the differences due to coding disappeared after many days of practice, by which time the responses had become effectively automatic.

COMMENTARY

At this level of analysis, what can we say about the value of the information concept in psychology? Has it provided truly new insights, or clarified existing psychological concepts? Or has it raised new questions to be answered? At this point it is difficult to assess accurately and fairly the impact of information concepts on psychology, and this difficulty must force us to reserve a certain amount of judgment.

Perhaps the reader has felt a vague uneasiness in reading this chapter, and if he has, I can assure him that it is thoroughly shared by the author. I myself have felt an uneasiness, but knew no good solution for the problems which created the uneasiness. The main problem is that I am not really very happy about much of the research I have reported, and I have had to express caution in interpretation on several occasions. I have nevertheless reported the material in this chapter because these experiments have used only the univariate average information concepts and thus are appropriate at this point. Furthermore, most of these experiments have been done with the intent of using only this information concept.

It would have been nice if such a simple concept had led to great improvements in psychology, but such has not been the case. The basic concept of average uncertainty has been shown to be relevant to psychological problems, but it has rarely allowed a real solution of these problems. It is not that the experiments which have been done are in any true sense wrong, or were incorrectly carried out. Thus I do not feel free to say unambiguously that little or nothing has been accomplished, or that psychologists have failed to find a panacea, so we should all drop the topic. Rather, my feeling is that we simply haven't gone far enough, and that when we do many of these problems certainly will look different, and possibly will be clearer.

Thus I have been in the position of discussing topics with which we can get some degree of understanding at the present level, but which I feel can be handled far better with a deeper level of analysis. For example, I have discussed the effect of stimulus uncertainty on accuracy of perceptual discrimination, and we have the general conclusion that accuracy becomes better with a restricted set of stimulus alternatives. However, we shall see in Chapter Three that this problem looks quite different when we use information measures, rather than accuracy scores, as our performance criterion. The question concerning whether the effect is primarily due to stimulus restriction or to response restriction changes considerably in Chapter Three—to the point where the question almost, but not quite, disappears.

On this question, it is my feeling that the effect is due primarily, and in most cases, to restriction of the responses, except when the nature of the restriction is such that the subject can selectively attend to dimensions of the stimulus. This problem will come up in our discussion of multidimensional stimuli in Chapter Four. The experiments by Long et al. were not carried out as a deliberate test of this idea, but their conclusions carry the suggestion.

Lawrence and LaBerge (1956) and more recently Brown (1960) have also shown that psychological sets to attend to particular aspects of the stimulus can be established, and that such sets can operate prior to the stimulus presentation. However, to really find out about the nature of this perceptual effect, we will have to do experiments which intentionally control the *nature* of the restriction, not just the amount.

Perhaps the strongest positive concept to be derived from the research reported so far is that measures of accuracy or of time of performance will be related to amount of uncertainty as long as there exists some degree of response conflict. Probably we can go a step further and say that the amount of the uncertainty effect is directly related to the amount of response conflict (response uncertainty), but in the sense that the subject is not sure which response should be used on a given occasion.

Such response conflict can exist for a variety of reasons. It may be that the stimuli themselves are not discriminable enough, so that the subject is unsure of the correct response. Such failure of perceptual discrimination will produce response conflict, and this response conflict may produce the relation between perceptual accuracy and uncertainty which has been found.

Another reason for response conflict can be that the responses themselves are not clearly discriminable. We might, for example, have a set of quite discriminable stimuli, but if the responses are not equally discriminable, there will exist some degree of conflict. As an illustration, suppose a subject is required to respond to eight different lights by making pen movements of eight different lengths, graduated in $\frac{1}{8}$ inch. Such a task would almost certainly produce response conflict, and we would expect both errors and reaction times to be a function of the number of stimulus and response alternatives.

A third cause of response conflict is a lack of clear relation between the stimuli and the appropriate responses. Such clear stimulus-response relations can be obtained by making use of innate relations, as with reflex responses, by making use of highly compatible relations, or by thorough training in a particular task.

My emphasis on response conflict should not be interpreted as a lack of appreciation of other factors in both learning and perception. The critical point here is simply that response conflict is the important variable which makes possible the effect of stimulus (or response) uncertainty. Lack of perceptual discrimination itself can cause or make possible an effect of uncertainty on performance, but it does so because of the response conflict it produces, not because of some factor inherent in the perceptual process per se.

SUMMARY

In a univariate distribution we can specify several different uncertainties. The uncertainty of each individual category can be specified as the logarithm of the reciprocal of its probability of occurrence. In addition, we can specify uncertainties for the entire distribution:

Nominal uncertainty is the uncertainty based on a presumed equal probability for all categories, and is simply the logarithm of the number of categories.

Average uncertainty is the weighted average of the uncertainties of all of the individual categories. It is as large as nominal uncertainty only when all categories have equal probability.

In psychological research, the univariate uncertainty measure has been used in a variety of ways to demonstrate that it is a meaningful variable. Learning, for example, is more difficult if either response uncertainty or stimulus uncertainty is increased.

Perceptual discrimination, measured by number of errors of identification, becomes better if stimulus uncertainty is reduced by restriction of the set of possible alternatives. Further research has shown that usually this restriction is just as effective if made after the stimulus presentation as it is if made before the stimulus presentation. Thus it is concluded that the effect is primarily due to response restriction, rather than to stimulus restriction. This result is not unambiguous, however, and is probably related to the nature of the restriction.

Reaction times show, generally, linear increases with increased stimulus uncertainty. This result, however, holds only for average uncertainty of the entire set of stimuli, and not for the uncertainty of the particular stimulus within a set. Furthermore, there is considerable evidence that this effect of stimulus uncertainty on reaction time is also due to the restriction of responses rather than to the restriction of stimuli, and it is suggested that the basic factor in all of these results is the degree of response conflict.

CHAPTER THREE

Bivariate Uncertainty
and Information Transmission

IT IS, OF COURSE, quite possible to have a probability distribution
defined in terms of more than one variable. We can have a probability distribution of stimuli and responses, or a probability distribution of stimuli defined in terms of two parameters, such as frequency and intensity of tones. Or we may want to deal with a
probability distribution of pairs of responses or stimuli occurring in
sequence, in which the first term of the pair constitutes one variable
and the second term of the pair the other variable.

One important characteristic of uncertainty as a statistical measure is that no assumptions are made about the metric nature of the
underlying variable. When we talk about the uncertainty of x, x need
not be metric in any sense; it may simply be a method of classification. This property is what gives the uncertainty measure such great
generality, both in application and in mathematical development.
Because of this property, there is no essential difference between a
distribution defined in terms of a single variable and one defined in
terms of two variables. In either case, we simply have a set of probabilities for various categories, and the computation of the uncertainty
is quite unaffected by the way in which we choose to describe the
categories.

BIVARIATE UNCERTAINTY MEASURES

Suppose we have a set of categories defined in terms of two variables, x and y. We can determine the probability of occurrence of each joint category and write a matrix of these probabilities as illustrated in Table 3.1. In our illustration, since x and y each has

Table 3.1

A matrix of probabilities of joint occurrence of a given value of x and a given value of y. The internal entries are the joint probabilities, $p(x, y)$. The marginal sums give values of $p(x)$ and $p(y)$.

		x				
		1	2	3	4	$\Sigma = p(y)$
	1	.08	.02	0	0	.10
y	2	.17	.20	.03	0	.40
	3	0	.03	.18	.09	.30
	4	0	0	.04	.16	.20
$\Sigma = p(x)$		.25	.25	.25	.25	1.00

four categories, we have a total of sixteen joint x and y categories which can occur. To determine the uncertainty of this distribution, we simply use the basic formula of Eq. 2.3, but with a change in notation appropriate to the fact that we now classify the categories in terms of two variables. Thus,

$$U(x, y) = -\Sigma p(x, y) \log p(x, y). \tag{3.1}$$

We call $p(x, y)$ a joint probability, and similarly, the uncertainty computed from such terms, $U(x, y)$, is called a *joint uncertainty*. In the notation system used in this book, a comma between the symbols for the variables always indicates that we are simply dealing with a joint classification of variables, and such terms can always be treated as univariate distributions for purposes of computing uncertainties. In our particular illustration, the actual value of $U(x, y)$ is 2.97 bits, or slightly less than the uncertainty of eight equally probable categories.

We can, of course, also sum the probabilities of Table 3.1 across rows or across columns to obtain the probability distributions separately for x and for y. From these probability distributions we can compute $U(x)$ and $U(y)$, which are respectively for these data, 2.00 and 1.85 bits.

The matrix of Table 3.1 actually has sixteen cells, six of which have zero probabilities of occurrence. In any such matrix the existence of zero cells, or of unequal probabilities of occurrence, indicates that the two variables, x and y, are correlated. In other words, the two variables are not orthogonal. Such a matrix would be orthogonal if each cell had a probability equal to the cross product of the appropriate row and column marginal probabilities, that is, if $p(x, y) = p(x) \, p(y)$. Now we can create a matrix of such probabilities by entering a term $P(x, y)$ in each cell which is equal to the cross produce $p(x) \, p(y)$, and such a matrix has been constructed in Table 3.2. These probabilities are those which would be expected

Table 3.2

The matrix of expected probabilities of joint occurrence of a given value of x and a given value of y. The internal entries are the joint probabilities, $P(x, y) = p(x) \, p(y)$, expected on the assumption of zero correlation between x and y, from Table 3.1. The marginal sums give values of $p(x)$ and $p(y)$.

		x				
		1	2	3	4	$\Sigma = p(y)$
y	1	.025	.025	.025	.025	.10
	2	.100	.100	.100	.100	.40
	3	.075	.075	.075	.075	.30
	4	.050	.050	.050	.050	.20
$\Sigma = p(x)$		.25	.25	.25	.25	1.00

for the data of Table 3.1 if the variables x and y were orthogonal, or uncorrelated. The procedure by which the values of $P(x, y)$ are determined is identical to that for determining expected cell proportions when chi-square, or a contingency coefficient, is to be computed.

The probabilities of Table 3.2 can be used to compute an uncertainty also. Thus,

$$U_{max}(x, y) = -\Sigma P(x, y) \log P(x, y). \tag{3.2}$$

The actual value of this term for our illustration is 3.85 bits. This term is called a *maximum joint uncertainty* because it is the maximum uncertainty which can be obtained with a matrix limited only by the row and column marginal probabilities. In other words, it is the uncertainty obtained when the two variables are orthogonal, so that they have as nearly a rectangular distribution of probabilities as is possible. It should be noted that Eq. 3.2 does not give the maximum uncertainty for any given matrix without regard to the marginal distributions, since a completely equal distribution of probabilities (in our case, $\frac{1}{16}$ in each cell) always gives the largest uncertainty. Thus the *nominal joint uncertainty*, based on assumed equal probabilities, is actually larger than what we are calling the maximum joint uncertainty. The maximum uncertainty is the largest which can be obtained with the real marginal distributions, while the nominal joint uncertainty assumes marginal distributions which do not exist, but are just nominal.

Contingent uncertainty

Now if $U_{max}(x, y)$ is the uncertainty which would be obtained if there were no correlation between x and y, and if $U(x, y)$ is the actual uncertainty obtained for the matrix and becomes smaller the greater the correlation between x and y, then the difference between these two terms indicates the extent to which the uncertainty has been reduced by the correlation between x and y. We can obtain the difference between these two terms, and define a new term

$$U(x{:}y) = U_{max}(x, y) - U(x, y). \tag{3.3}$$

We shall call this term, $U(x{:}y)$, a *contingent uncertainty*, following the terminology of Garner and McGill (1956). It is a measure of the amount of uncertainty reduction due to the contingency or correlation between x and y, and the colon notation will always indicate such a contingent relation. Since $U(x, y)$ is always equal to or less than $U_{max}(x, y)$, the contingent uncertainty must always be non-negative.

The contingent uncertainty, $U(x{:}y)$, can be computed in other ways than that indicated in Eq. 3.3. First, let us note that the probability terms used to compute $U_{max}(x, y)$ are actually cross product terms, and if we substitute these terms in Eq. 3.2, we find that

$$
\begin{aligned}
U_{max}(x, y) &= -\sum_{x,y} p(x)\, p(y) \log p(x)\, p(y) \\
&= -\sum_{x} p(x) \log p(x) - \sum_{y} p(y) \log p(y) \\
&= U(x) + U(y). \tag{3.4}
\end{aligned}
$$

Thus the maximum joint uncertainty which can be obtained in a bivariate matrix, when limited only by the marginal probabilities, is in fact the sum of the marginal uncertainties, just as the nominal joint uncertainty is the sum of the marginal nominal uncertainties.

To obtain a value for the maximum uncertainty, we need only compute the uncertainty of x and the uncertainty of y and sum them; it is not necessary to determine each expected probability, $P(x, y)$. This result, that the maximum uncertainty is the sum of the marginal uncertainties, has an intuitive reasonableness to it. If we have two variables, with known uncertainties, then it should not be possible to combine these two variables in any way such as to obtain a total uncertainty greater than the sum of the two uncertainties with which we start.

Conditional uncertainty

Now let us look at the nature of the term $U(x, y)$. First note that

$$p(x, y) = p_x(y)\, p(x) = p_y(x)\, p(y),$$

where $p_x(y)$ and $p_y(x)$ are conditional probabilities, and indicate the probability of occurrence of a given value of y, in the first case, when the value of x is fixed. In other words, we take each value of x separately and then determine the probability distribution with respect to y, or vice-versa. We thus have as many different distributions of y as we have values of x, and the probabilities of y will sum to 1.0 for each value of x. Tables 3.3 and 3.4 show the data of Table 3.1 in the two conditional probability forms.

Table 3.3

The matrix of the probability of y given a particular value of x.
The internal entries are conditional probabilities, $p_x(y)$,
and for each column of x these must sum to 1.00.

		x			
		1	2	3	4
	1	.32	.08	0	0
	2	.68	.80	.12	0
y	3	0	.12	.72	.36
	4	0	0	.16	.64
	Σ	1.00	1.00	1.00	1.00
		0.9043	0.9162	1.1313	0.9427
		$U_1(y)$	$U_2(y)$	$U_3(y)$	$U_4(y)$

$$U_x(y) = \tfrac{1}{4}(0.9043 + 0.9162 + 1.1313 + 0.9427)$$
$$= 0.97 \text{ bit.}$$

Table 3.4

The matrix of the probability of x given a particular value of y.
The internal entries are conditional probabilities, $p_y(x)$,
and for each row of y these must sum to 1.00.

		1	2	3	4	Σ		
	1	.800	.200	0	0	1.00	0.7220	$U_1(x)$
	2	.425	.500	.075	0	1.00	1.3050	$U_2(x)$
y	3	0	.100	.600	.300	1.00	1.2955	$U_3(x)$
	4	0	0	.200	.800	1.00	0.7220	$U_4(x)$

$$U_y(x) = .10 \times 0.7220 + .40 \times 1.3050 + .30 \times 1.2955 + .20 \times 0.7220$$
$$= 1.13 \text{ bits.}$$

If we substitute the above probability equalities in Eq. 3.1, we obtain, first,

$$
\begin{aligned}
U(x, y) &= -\sum_{x,y} p(x)\, p_x(y) \log p(x)\, p_x(y) \\
&= -\sum_x p(x) \log p(x) - \sum_x p(x) \sum_y p_x(y) \log p_x(y) \\
&= U(x) + U_x(y),
\end{aligned}
\tag{3.5}
$$

where

$$U_x(y) = -\sum_x p(x) \sum_y p_x(y) \log p_x(y). \tag{3.6}$$

If in Eq. 3.1 we substitute $p(y)\, p_y(x)$ rather than $p(x)\, p_x(y)$, we obtain

$$U(x, y) = U(y) + U_y(x), \tag{3.7}$$

where

$$U_y(x) = -\sum_y p(y) \sum_x p_y(x) \log p_y(x). \tag{3.8}$$

A term of the form $U_x(y)$ or $U_y(x)$ is called a *conditional uncertainty* and is the average amount of uncertainty in one variable when the other variable is held constant. We determine this, as the defining equation shows, by first obtaining the uncertainty with respect to one variable separately for each value of the other variable, and then obtaining a weighted average of these various terms, weighted according to the probability of occurrence of the variable held constant. These calculations are shown in detail in Tables 3.3 and 3.4.

By using Eqs. 3.4 and 3.5 to substitute in Eq. 3.3, we find that

$$
\begin{aligned}
U(x:y) &= U(x) + U(y) - U(x) - U_x(y) \\
&= U(y) - U_x(y).
\end{aligned}
\tag{3.9}
$$

If we use Eq. 3.7 instead of Eq. 3.5 to substitute in Eq. 3.3, we would show in addition that

$$U(x{:}y) = U(y) - U_x(y) = U(x) - U_y(x). \tag{3.10}$$

We thus have three different methods of computing $U(x{:}y)$, and for our example the value is 0.88 bit. (All three methods give the same answer except for rounding error.)

By transposing terms in Eq. 3.10, we can see that the contingent uncertainty and the conditional uncertainties can both be regarded as parts of the uncertainty of a single variable. For example,

$$U(y) = U(y{:}x) + U_x(y), \tag{3.11}$$

and

$$U(x) = U(x{:}y) + U_y(x). \tag{3.12}$$

It should be noted that we transposed the notation for the contingent uncertainty, in order to illustrate one way of thinking of the contingent uncertainty. The transposition is quite permissible since the term is a contingency between variables, and the order in which the terms are written is of no more concern than is the order in which we say that x and y are correlated. Thus $U(x{:}y) = U(y{:}x)$.

Now these last two equations can be read as follows: The uncertainty in y can be partitioned into two parts—the uncertainty due to or predictable from x plus the residual uncertainty when x is held constant. Or, alternatively, the uncertainty in x can be partitioned into two parts, the uncertainty due to y plus the residual uncertainty when y is held constant. In this form, the equations are completely analogous to the partitioning of variance in an analysis of variance. In the simple analysis of variance, we break the variance of the dependent variable into a predictable and an error component. The predictable part is the variance due to differences between means, and the error component is the residual variance. Garner and McGill (1956) have shown how completely analogous the equations for uncertainty analysis and variance analysis are.[1]

The nature of the contingent uncertainty

The relation between uncertainty analysis and analysis of variance is so close that uncertainties can be estimated from variances if as-

---

[1] It is of some interest to note that we can simply partition $U(x, y)$ as

$$U(x, y) = U(x{:}y) + U_x(y) + U_y(x).$$

In other words, the total bivariate uncertainty is composed of the contingent (common) uncertainty plus the two conditional uncertainties.

sumptions about the nature of the variance distributions are made. Both the conditional uncertainties and the contingent uncertainties can be estimated from variances. Since the ordinary linear correlation coefficient can be thought of as a ratio between variances, it is also possible to estimate a contingent uncertainty from a correlation coefficient. Although we do not examine these relations exactly here (see Garner and McGill, 1956; Attneave, 1959), it is worth noting that whenever a contingent uncertainty is estimated from variances, the uncertainty estimate is the logarithm of the *ratio between two variances*—a point which helps provide some understanding of the nature of the contingent uncertainty.

A contingent uncertainty is a very useful concept and statistic. By analogy with analysis of variance, it can be thought of as a main effect variance—that is, the predictable variance—although the non-metric uncertainty is used as the measure of variability rather than the metric variance. We have already noted that uncertainty measures require no metric of the variables, while a variance measure does require such a metric. However, since a contingent uncertainty can be estimated from a ratio of two variances (in analysis of variance it is the ratio between total and error variance), we can see that the contingent uncertainty is not simply a non-metric form of a main effect variance. It has somewhat different properties.

A contingent uncertainty is also a measure of correlation. Since the contingent uncertainty can be estimated from a ratio of variances, and since correlation is also a ratio of variances, it might seem that the best interpretation of the contingent uncertainty is simply as a correlation coefficient appropriate to non-metric data, just as the ordinary contingency coefficient is a correlation measure of non-metric data. Yet this interpretation is not quite accurate either. A correlation measure, including the ordinary contingency coefficient, is always a measure of *degree* of relationship between two variables, and can have values ranging from 0 to 1. However, the contingent uncertainty does not have an upper limit of 1; its upper limit is the uncertainty of the variable being predicted (see Eqs. 3.11 and 3.12), and in this sense the contingent uncertainty is much more like the main effect variance, which is also limited by the total variance of the criterion variable.

The best way to interpret the contingent uncertainty is not as a degree of correlation but rather as an *amount* of correlation. It is truly a measure of relatedness, but it measures the amount rather than the degree. It is quite possible, for example, to have two different bivariate matrices, each of which has the same amount of contingent uncertainty but different degrees of correlation. If the amount of uncertainty reduction in x that can be accomplished by knowledge of y is the same in two cases, then the contingent uncertainty is the same, even though the residual uncertainties (conditional or error uncertainties) are quite different. Thus the contingent uncertainty is a measure of how much uncertainty can be predicted with knowledge of a predictor variable, without regard to how much cannot be predicted.

Perhaps we can best understand the particular and unique value of the measure of contingent uncertainty by making a brief contrasting summary of the nature and conditions of the ordinary correlation coefficient, analysis of variance, and the uncertainty measurement. The linear correlation coefficient requires that both the x and the y variables be metric and that the relation between them be reasonably linear. The correlation coefficient is then a measure of degree of relationship and is symmetrical, that is, the correlation between x and y is the same as that between y and x (or either variable can be thought of as the predictor).

In analysis of variance, the dependent or criterion variable, y, must be metric, although the predictor variable, x, may or may not be metric. The main effect variance (the amount predictable) retains the metric of the criterion variable but is a measure of amount of relationship rather than of degree. If we use the analysis of variance terms to compute the correlation ratio, eta, then the original metric requirements remain the same, but we now have a measure of degree rather than amount. Furthermore, the main effect variance, or the eta computed from it, is not a symmetrical measure, since its value may change if we alternatively consider x rather than y as the criterion variable, in those cases where x is also metric.

In uncertainty analysis, neither variable need be metric, although either or both may be. Thus the contingent uncertainty has very general applicability. In addition, the contingent uncertainty is a symmetric measure and doesn't change value if we change the direction of prediction. Still further, and most important, the contingent uncertainty is a measure of amount of relationship rather than of degree, but the amount of contingent uncertainty is in no way determined by the metric (if there is one) of the underlying variable. It is, in a sense, a pure number measure which is applicable to any situation.

These properties have given the contingent uncertainty very great utility. By its completely non-metric character, and by its combination of valuable properties from both correlational and variance analysis, it provides a single measure of relationship which makes possible comparisons between experimental situations which were not previously possible. It is possible to show that two different situations have the same amount of correlation but different degrees of it, or different amounts and the same degree. It is also possible to compare amounts of relationship in hearing versus vision, for example, because the units of measurement do not affect the contingent uncertainty.

INFORMATION CONCEPTS

The discussion relating to bivariate uncertainty measurement has thus far been entirely abstract. We have examined the various uncertainty components which can be calculated from a bivariate distribution in terms of x and y variables only, and the contingent uncertainty has been described simply as a measure of amount of correlation. The reason for developing the material in this fashion is that the mathematical properties of the various terms are general, although the meanings of the terms change when they are applied to different specific situations. Just as uncertainty becomes information when it is reduced, so also does a contingent uncertainty appear to be a positive asset in one situation and yet a liability in another. A conditional uncertainty in one case is equivalent to statistical error or noise, and in another is equivalent to available information.

Information transmission

In communication work, one of the most common uses of the contingent uncertainty is as a measure of information transmission. Suppose we have a communication system, and we want to determine the ability of this system to communicate information. First, we have a source of signals with a known uncertainty which serves as the input to the system. These signals are then transmitted through the system and the receiver reads out each signal as it is sent. We, as external observers, can then determine the output uncertainty of the system, that is, the uncertainty of the distribution of signals read out by the receiver. Now the input uncertainty and the output uncertainty may be the same or different, but just to know these two values does not tell us whether the system has in fact transmitted information, since the output signals may be entirely unrelated to the input signals. Thus we need to know the joint probability distributions of input and output signals, and from these we compute the contingent uncertainty to determine whether and to what extent the system has transmitted information. In this situation we would call the contingent uncertainty *transmitted information*. If the input and output are perfectly correlated, then the information transmission is the same as the input (or output) uncertainty. If correlation is less than perfect, then information transmission is less than input uncertainty.

The contingent uncertainty has been used widely in psychology as a measure of information transmission with various sensory processes. As Garner and Hake (1951) first indicated, it is possible to consider a set of stimuli as the input to a human, and the human's responses as the output of the system. In this context, the human is considered the communication system, the stimuli as the input and the responses as the output. Thus the contingent uncertainty is obtained from a matrix in which stimuli form one variable and responses the other variable, and the information transmitted becomes a measure of discriminating ability of the human subject.

Channel capacity

As I have pointed out previously, the contingent uncertainty cannot be larger than either of the uncertainties of the marginal distributions. This fact means that the measured ability of a communication system to transmit information, or of a human to discriminate, cannot exceed the input or stimulus uncertainty in the particular test situation. It may be, for example, that a human subject can discriminate between various tones to an extent of 4 bits, but if the distribution of stimuli presented to him has an uncertainty of only 3 bits, then the test situation will not show what the capacity of the human is.

Thus information transmission shows only the amount of correlation for a given test situation, and if we want to determine how much information can be transmitted (channel capacity), then we must run a series of tests with differing amounts of input information to determine the maximum information transmission—which in turn is accepted as the channel capacity. Schematically, the outcome of a series of such tests would be like that shown in Fig. 3.1. Each experimental test would have a different stimulus uncertainty, and if the ability of the human to discriminate exceeds the uncertainty of the stimulus, we would expect perfect information transmission, shown as the solid diagonal line. When, however, the stimulus uncertainty exceeds the discrimination ability of the subject, then the information transmission would remain constant regardless of the value of the stimulus uncertainty.

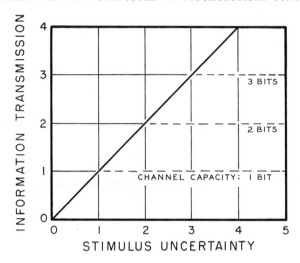

FIG. 3.1. A schematic illustration of the use of information transmission measures to determine the channel capacity of humans for a given discrimination task. As long as the stimulus uncertainty is less than the channel capacity, the experimental result for information transmission would lie on the diagonal line. When stimulus uncertainty exceeds channel capacity, all data would lie on the appropriate horizontal line.

Redundancy

In other contexts, the contingent uncertainty may be a measure of the extent to which information is not provided, if it is used as a measure of the correlation between two variables of an input. Suppose we have a two-variable stimulus to present—frequency and intensity of tone, hue and brightness of light, or size and shape of a visual figure, as examples. If the bivariate matrix of these two stimulus variables shows that all combination of the two variables are not used equally often, then there will be a contingent uncertainty between the variables. This contingent uncertainty now is a measure of the extent to which one variable is redundant with respect to the other. If, to illustrate, the two variables are perfectly correlated, then variable x, say, is completely redundant with respect to variable y. Of course, it is equally true that variable y is completely redundant with respect to x, since the measure is symmetric. By redundancy we simply mean an amount of uncertainty which could be used as information but is not so used because of some constraint between the variables.

The two variables may be the same variable simply repeated. For example, if a series of stimuli is presented, and the values which each stimulus can take are limited by the value of the preceding stimulus, then successive stimuli are correlated. As we noted in Chapter Two, such sequential constraints can be used to decrease the uncertainty of the stimulus just as effectively as a constraint on the number of different categories or on their frequencies of occurrence. To determine the amount of such redundancy, we would form a matrix of the stimuli with the series of stimuli itself being one variable and the same series displaced by one step being the other variable. The contingent uncertainty between the series and the series displaced one step is then a measure of the extent to which the uncertainty of the second of a pair of stimuli is redundant with respect to the first.

The use of measures of redundancy in psychological research has occurred primarily with problems of language or other sequential behavior and with problems of form or pattern perception. Since we shall consider these topics separately in later chapters, we shall not discuss the problems of redundancy much more at this point. There is one aspect of the measurement of redundancy which seems worthwhile mentioning now, however, because it may help to clarify some of the relations we discussed earlier. That problem has to do with whether redundancy is measured with respect to the nominal uncertainty of a variable, or only with respect to the actual uncertainty of a variable, that is, the uncertainty obtained with the marginal frequency distribution.

Communication engineers have usually defined redundancy in terms of the nominal uncertainty. For example, the IRE Standards define redundancy as "the amount by which the logarithm of the *number of symbols* available at the source exceeds the average information content per symbol of the source." In our example of Table 3.1, the 4 x 4 matrix can have sixteen different categories, or 4 bits of nominal uncertainty if all possible categories are used equally often. Since the actual uncertainty of the bivariate distribution is 2.97 bits, we would have a redundancy of 1.03 bits, with this definition.

This amount of redundancy in fact comes from two separate factors: First, note that the actual uncertainty of y is less than the nominal uncertainty. The actual uncertainty is 1.85 bits, and the nominal uncertainty is 2.00 bits. The difference between these (0.15 bit) we shall call *distributional constraint* or *redundancy*, since it is a measure of the extent to which uncertainty is decreased due to the fact that the actual probabilities are not distributed equally.

Second, the contingent uncertainty between the two variables, 0.88 bit, indicates the extent to which the two variables are not orthogonal, or are correlated. We can consider this as *correlational constraint* or *redundancy,* and its value added to the distributional redundancy gives us our total of 1.03 bits of redundancy.

In one sense, all definitions of redundancy reduce to measures of differences between obtained and possible (or nominal) uncertainties of distributions. For example, the total bivariate distribution can be considered only as a single distribution with an actual uncertainty which is less than the nominal uncertainty, just as the uncertainty of our y distribution is less than the total possible, or nominal, uncertainty. Yet, as we have seen, when the distribution is really bivariate, then it is meaningful to speak separately of the distributional constraint on one variable (difference between actual and nominal uncertainty), plus the constraint between variables (the contingent uncertainty). The contingent uncertainty is limited in a very real sense by the actual uncertainty of the separate variables, not just by the nominal uncertainty.

There is little need to continue this discussion here, except to point out that the concept of redundancy cannot be defined too narrowly, or its use will be limited considerably in many areas of application where the concept seems reasonable. We must attempt to be careful in our use of the term, and in particular, to be specific about how we are using it. As I have already done in this chapter, I shall often simply use the term constraint with an appropriate modifier to indicate the particular kind of redundancy we are discussing.

PERCEPTUAL DISCRIMINATION: ABSOLUTE JUDGMENTS

One of the most frequent applications of information concepts in psychology has been the use of the contingent uncertainty as a measure of amount of perceptual discrimination. Garner and Hake (1951) suggested and described the use of the contingent uncertainty as a measure of information transmission with a stimulus-response matrix. Experimentally, a series of stimuli is presented, one stimulus at a time in random order. The subject makes an absolute (categorical) response of some predesignated type to each stimulus. A matrix is then formed with stimuli as the columns and responses as rows, with the cell entry indicating the number or proportion of times that each stimulus category is called each response category. From this matrix the uncertainties of the column and row marginal totals give the stimulus and response uncertainties, respectively. The contingent uncertainty is the amount of information transmitted. The two conditional uncertainties, $U_s(R)$ and $U_r(S)$, are variously called error or equivocation terms. For example, $U_s(R)$ is often called response equivocation and $U_r(S)$ is called stimulus equivocation; or they are called response and stimulus error uncertainties.

To provide a better understanding of the particular value of the information transmission measure and the psychological problems to which it is applicable, perhaps a little personal history of the way in which this author came to recognize the value of information measures can be helpful. Several years before the Garner-Hake paper was published, a group of psychologists was asked a question which was eminently reasonable, but which none of us could answer. The question was this: If we were to use any perceptual or sensory continuum as a method of coding and displaying any information continuum, is it better (in terms of performance) to use a small number of discrete steps on the continuum, a large number of small steps, or even to use the complete continuum with its infinity of steps?

For example, suppose we want to indicate the altitude of aircraft by the size of the symbol used to represent the aircraft. Now the aircraft can have any altitude between fixed limits, and if we are to indicate altitude with complete accuracy, we would need to use a complete continuum of size. However, the human observer who sees the size and makes a judgment of altitude from the size may be more inaccurate with a complete continuum than he would be with a smaller number of discrete steps, and if his judgmental accuracy is poor enough with the complete continuum, we might end up by having poorer overall performance with the complete continuum than with a continuum based upon discrete steps.

In other words, before we could answer the question posed, we needed to know how human discrimination performance was affected by the number of steps used on a given sensory continuum, and discrimination in this case needed to be measured with the absolute judgment procedure. That is, one stimulus is presented at a time and a single categorical or absolute judgment of the stimulus is made.

Now this basic and reasonable question is much more difficult to answer with conventional statistical procedures than it seems at first glance. Suppose we do an experiment in which we maintain the same range of stimulus values, for example, 1 to 40 square millimeters of size, but we use a series of conditions in the experiments varying in respect to the total number of stimulus and response categories. For example, we might use 2, 3, 5, 7, 10, 20, or 40 discrete steps on the continuum. If we carry out this series of experiments and measure number of errors made, the number of errors will be zero for a small number of steps, and will become increasingly large as we increase the number of steps. In other words, a simple error measurement would indicate that performance deteriorates with an increase in the number of steps beyond some minimum value.

Similarly, any measure of correlation will decrease as the number of errors increases, since correlation will be perfect with no errors, but will become smaller as the number of errors increases. Yet it is intuitively clear that there is a sense in which performance can be better with the larger number of categories even though the number of errors has increased or the correlation has decreased, because the increased discrimination which comes with the larger number of steps may be more than enough to offset the increased number of errors. To use an extreme case, suppose we find that five categories give us no errors, but that ten categories give us just 1 percent errors. Now in the second case we have twice as many differentiating steps at a very slight cost in errors, and we might feel that overall performance is better even though the number of errors is greater.

What is needed is some measure of amount of discrimination, or amount of correlation rather than degree of correlation, and it is exactly this property of the information measure that makes it so useful. The contingent uncertainty for the illustration just above would show that the amount of correlation, and by interpretation the amount of discrimination, is better with ten steps and 1 percent errors than with five steps and no errors.

In a first experiment, intended primarily to demonstrate the feasibility of the information measure in absolute judgment, Hake and Garner (1951) determined information transmission for judgments of the position of a pointer on a line, that is, for linear interpolation judgments. They used four different numbers of possible pointer positions, 5, 10, 20, and 50, and two different response conditions. In one response condition, the subjects were always instructed which pointer positions could occur, and were allowed to use no other possible responses. In the other condition, 101 different responses (0 through 100) were allowed and the subjects were not instructed as to how many possible pointer positions there were.

The results of this experiment are shown in Fig. 3.2 and indicate two important things: First, the information measure can show that discrimination ability is not affected by number of possible stimulus categories above some minimum value. In other words, the concept of a channel capacity seems to have some validity for perceptual discrimination work, and it is therefore possible to describe perceptual

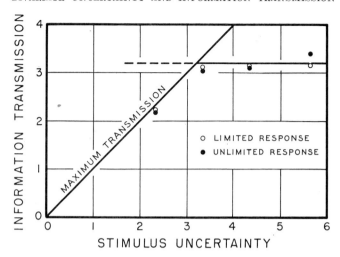

Fɪɢ. 3.2. Information transmission as a function of stimulus uncertainty for judgments of the position of a pointer on a line. With limited response there were as many response categories as stimuli. With unlimited response there were 101 response categories regardless of number of stimulus categories. (Data from Hake and Garner, 1951.)

discrimination ability for a given problem with a single number. Second, the particular value of the information measure is demonstrated by the fact that the two different response conditions led to the same result. Here again the unlimited response condition inevitably leads to greater errors and to lower correlations, but the information measure is unaffected by this fact. The contingent uncertainty between stimuli and responses provides a stable and easily interpretable measure of perceptual discrimination ability.

Since this early experiment, literally scores of experiments have been done to determine the information transmission for particular sensory continua, under many different conditions. Many of these experiments had highly specific purposes in that the utility of a particular information code was being determined. Miller (1956) has summarized much of the basic work in this area, and we will here, like Miller, summarize enough of this work to establish some of the basic principles.

Auditory discrimination

Some of the most thorough work in this area has been done on problems of auditory discrimination. Pollack (1952) first applied the procedure to the absolute judgment of pitch, and his basic results are shown in Fig. 3.3. Here the information transmission measures were obtained by first computing the information transmission separately for each subject, and then averaging these figures. These results confirmed the fact that above a minimum number of stimulus categories over a given range of frequencies information transmission becomes a constant and is no longer affected by number of stimulus categories.

In this particular case, Pollack found information transmission at its maximum (channel capacity) to be about 2.3 bits, which is equivalent to perfect discrimination for five categories. This, of course, is a surprisingly small number of categories for a single continuum, but

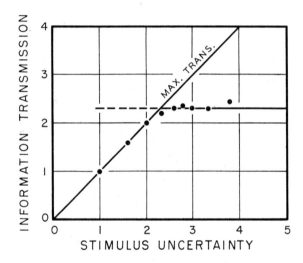

FIG. 3.3. Information transmission for absolute judgments of auditory pitch. (After Pollack, 1952.)

many experiments have since demonstrated that this type of absolute judgment consistently produces such poor discrimination as long as the stimulus varies on only a single sensory continuum. In Pollack's experiment, many different conditions were used, such as variations in the total frequency range, and variations of spacings of the tones in the frequency range. While these factors had some effect on discrimination, for the moment the most important point is that the effects of these variations were very small compared to the value of the maximum information transmission.

Garner (1953) demonstrated much the same result for absolute judgments of loudness, as shown by his data in Fig. 3.4. In that experiment the intensities ranged from 15 to 110 db (re 10^{-16} watt/cm^2) and four to twenty stimulus categories were used. The data plotted in Fig. 3.4 are the average information transmissions for the several subjects, as was done for Pollack's data, and show again that the channel capacity concept is useful in that there does appear to be a maximum discrimination value. In this case, maximum information transmission is about 2.1 bits, a value between four and five tones, confirming the low value found by Pollack for frequency discrimination.

These early results made it clear that there is a constant level of performance which can be specified for a discrimination problem, and

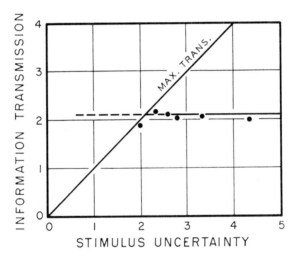

FIG. 3.4. Information transmission for absolute judgments of auditory loudness. (After Garner, 1953.)

that the equivalent number of categories which can be perfectly discriminated with absolute judgments is relatively small. Many other experimenters have in effect made the assumption that the channel capacity concept is legitimate, and thus have determined information transmission at only a reasonably high level of stimulus uncertainty.

Visual discrimination

Relatively few experiments using information measures have been done with purely sensory continua in vision. Halsey and Chapanis (1951) had measured errors of identification for spectral hues, and later Chapanis and Halsey (1956) estimated an information transmission for this task of about 3.6 bits, a value equivalent to about twelve different spectral colors. Conover (1959) later carried out a quite thorough study of absolute judgments of Munsell hues, using maximum saturation hues and a stimulus set of twenty-five hues. He obtained information transmission of about 3.5 bits, a value remarkably close to that previously estimated by Chapanis and Halsey.

These values of information transmission for hue are considerably higher than the values obtained for pitch or loudness judgments, although they are similar to that obtained for linear interpolation judgments. It may be that hue judgments are inherently more accurate, or it may be that hue is not a pure unidimensional variable, due to the existence of strong subjective anchors.

Eriksen and Hake (1955b) have made direct comparisons of the accuracy of absolute judgments of brightness, size, and hue, again using Munsell papers as stimuli. They confirm the fact that hue judgments are somewhat more accurate than are the other judgments, obtaining 2.34 bits of information transmission for brightness, 2.84 for size, and 3.08 for hue. The value obtained for brightness judgments is very nearly the same as those obtained for pitch and for loudness judgments, a fact which suggests that brightness is a unidimensional variable much like these others, where there are no clear subjective anchors such as we have with the psychological primary colors.

Perceptual anchors and the limit of unidimensional discrimination

That the existence of important psychological anchors can increase absolute judgment accuracy is shown in another set of results by Muller et al. (1955), in which they found a quite high value of information transmission for judgments of the angle of inclination of a line, a value considerably higher than that obtained for other single dimensional variables they investigated. For that particular experiment, a line was shown fixed at one end, so that it could be perceived as a line at a fixed position of rotation around a middle point much as the hand of a clock rotates. With this type of stimulus, these authors obtained over 4.5 bits of information transmission, the highest value yet obtained for what appears to be a single stimulus dimension. However, when judgments of this sort are being made, the psychological anchors of the perceived horizontal and vertical are very strong and undoubtedly are critical in obtaining this high value.

Little direct research has been done on the effects of inserting anchors within the range of perceived stimulus values, but the extent to which such procedures would increase information transmission can be deduced from the evidence at hand, and from the logical nature of the problem. Suppose, to illustrate, that we are requiring judgments of pitch, and that we can obtain 2.3 bits of information transmission regardless of the frequency range of the stimuli. Now if we use a total range from 200 to 5000 cps, but present an anchor at 1000 cps, we are dividing the total range into two logarithmically equal ranges, and from either of these we should obtain the same 2.3 bits of information transmission. The insertion of the anchor, which will allow the subject to make an initial dichotomous judgment, will not, however, double the information transmission but will simply add 1 bit—exactly the amount of information the anchor gives. If five pitches below 1000 cps can be distinguished, and five above, then the anchor will allow ten pitches to be discriminated. Thus to double the range, or to provide an anchor which effectively does the same thing, does not double the information transmission but simply increases it by 1 bit.

Suppose we assume that any single stimulus continuum can, without anchors, provide 2.3 bits of information transmission. We would have this amount for judgments of lengths of line, or extent, for example. Now the linear interpolation judgment of the Hake-Garner variety is simply a judgment of extent (distance from one end of the line to the marker), except that a second anchor is introduced to define the other end of the scale. Thus if only one anchor (necessary to define starting point for extent) is used, we would expect 2.3 bits of information transmission, but we would obtain 1 bit more with the second anchor. We should then have 3.3 bits of information transmission, a value close to the 3.2 bits actually obtained. If we add one more anchor, to define an extra interval, we would expect just 1 more bit. The third interval, however, would not add 1 more bit because it would not double the number of discriminations. We would have to add two more intervals to obtain the second extra bit.

This reasoning helps explain the 4.5 bits of information transmission obtained by Muller et al. for judgments of angle of inclination, since if the vertical and the horizontal each provide strong anchors, then the basic value of 2.3 bits would hold for a single quadrant, and four quadrants would give two bits more of information transmission, or 4.3 bits—a value very close to the 4.5 bits actually obtained.

This discussion perhaps explains why it is so very difficult to obtain high information transmission with a single psychological dimension. Even when anchors are used to improve discrimination, the improvement occurs as a logarithmic function. If 2.3 bits of information transmission can occur with each of two ranges on a continuum, then the use of both ranges together does not double the information transmission, but only adds 1 more bit. As we shall see in the next chapter, however, the use of two simultaneous *dimensions,* instead of doubling the range of a single dimension, does lead to a doubling of information transmission, not just the addition of 1 more bit.[2]

In summary, this section states that information transmission studies used to measure perceptual discrimination have shown that the concept of a channel capacity as a limiting information transmission value is valid for this type of problem. In addition, they have shown with remarkable consistency that the maximum number of perfectly identifiable categories on a unidimensional continuum is about five, but that this number of categories can be increased by using sensory or perceptual continua in which there exist strong psychological anchors (such as hue and angle of inclination). For sensory continua not having these natural anchors, transmission can be increased by the use of direct stimulus anchors. Nevertheless, unidimensional discrimination is fundamentally limited in amount by its very nature in a way which does not limit multidimensional discrimination.

Channel capacity as an abstraction

In interpreting the channel capacity as a measure of discrimination, we have spoken as though the measured channel capacity indicates the maximum number of stimulus categories which can be discriminated with perfect accuracy. It is convenient to treat channel capacity in this fashion, and it leads to no serious error of interpretation. However, this treatment is not quite accurate, since the empirical functions obtained do not in fact show the kind of sharp break in the idealized information transmission functions which are indicated in Fig. 3.1.

If these idealized functions were perfectly valid, then we could with complete accuracy use the information transmission which is obtained with a high stimulus uncertainty to infer that if the number of indicated categories had actually been used, we would have obtained perfect information transmission. However, the empirical functions ob-

---

[2] Direct comparative judgment is far more precise than the absolute judgment discussed in this section. For example, Jacobson (1950, 1951) estimates information capacities for the eye and the ear in thousands of bits, when these estimates are based on differential sensitivity data. These orders of magnitudes are so vastly different that it is clear that the processes are not the same. It also seems clear that actual performance figures of the order estimated by Jacobson could never be obtained in practice, because these estimates were obtained from differential sensitivity data—data obtained from a procedure in which there are as many anchors (standard tones or lights) as there are tones to be judged.

tained always show that in the region of the expected sharp break, the transition from perfect transmission (when stimulus uncertainty is lower than channel capacity) to stable transmission (when the channel capacity has been reached) is not sharp, but rather is gradual. This gradual change indicates that if, to illustrate, we have a channel capacity of 2.3 bits and we actually present the equivalent five stimulus categories, then we will obtain an information transmission of slightly less than 2.3 bits.

Thus when we interpret the channel capacity to indicate an equivalent number of perfectly identifiable categories, we are using the channel capacity concept only as an abstraction, an abstraction which does not quite correspond to reality but is a convenient fiction. The fact that the abstraction does not exactly correspond to reality is not just an unfortunate empirical finding but is a result of the nature of the perceptual process. In any judgmental process of this sort, the identifications made to any particular stimulus value will tend to be normally distributed. At least, there will be no sharply truncated distribution of responses, but the frequency of response to any given stimulus will be maximum at the equivalent value and will tail off gradually for response values farther removed from the correct one. This fact means that when the smaller number of indicated values is actually used, there will still be some small number of errors, so that the response equivocation never quite becomes zero. However, if stimulus uncertainty matches the channel capacity, the response equivocation must be zero in order for information transmission to equal the stimulus uncertainty. If the responses are truly normal in their distribution, there would be no condition under which response equivocation would be truly zero, since there would always be some small region of overlapping responses.

Thus to use the channel capacity to indicate the maximum number of perfectly identifiable categories is not really quite correct, but it is convenient to do so, and doing so leads to no serious error. The reservation that such a use is an abstraction should, however, be kept in mind.

FACTORS AFFECTING INFORMATION TRANSMISSION

In the preceding section we have dealt only with the major psychological findings regarding absolute judgments of unidimensional stimuli. I have deliberately emphasized the relative stability of the channel capacity, and the fact that this capacity is unaffected to any serious degree by various experimental factors. However, we should not leave this material without more discussion of the ways and the extent to which the channel capacity can be influenced. While many of these effects are not large, nor do they change the principles stated above in essence, they are nevertheless real.

Discriminability

The inherent discriminability of the set of stimuli presented for judgment is an experimental factor directly relevant to the concept of information transmission. As is clear from the nature of the matrices from which a contingent uncertainty is computed, the amount of information transmitted is directly related to the degree of overlap between distributions of responses for various stimuli. The amount of overlap between these distributions will be influenced by the inherent discriminability of the stimuli being judged. One way in which this discriminability can be affected is by the total range of stimulus values selected for judgment. It is obvious that if, in judgments of pitch, a frequency range between 1000 and 1002 cps is used, there will be little if any information transmission because of a complete failure of discrimination with too small a range. In fact, Munson and Karlin (1954) have actually suggested using the largest stimulus separation which leads to zero information transmission as the measure of the difference threshold, a suggestion which has considerable merit.

Within more realistic ranges of stimulus values, the effect of range still exists but is quite small. This effect has been shown as an incidental aspect of many different experiments, but in particular Pollack (1952) showed a 0.2 bit increase in information transmission when the upper range for frequency was increased from 500 to 8000 cps and the lowest frequency was held at 100 cps. Eriksen and Hake (1955a) as well as Alluisi and Sidorsky (1958) have shown similar effects when the range of visually judged sizes was increased. In the Eriksen and Hake experiment, for example, the average increase in information transmission when the range of areas was approximately doubled was 0.16 bit.

Another way in which information transmission can be affected is by the particular spacing of the stimuli within the range. Ideally, as Garner and Hake (1951) pointed out, these stimuli should be spaced equally according to a criterion of discriminability and these authors described a scale of equal discriminability for this purpose. Garner (1952) compared, for loudness judgments, two distributions of stimuli, one evenly spaced on a decibel scale (corresponding roughly to an equal discriminability scale) and one with stimuli concentrated in the upper intensity range. He found approximately 0.20 bit better transmission with the even spacing of stimuli. Pollack (1952) had used a variety of spacings of stimuli and also found that the best information transmission occurred with roughly equal spacing of stimuli on a logarithmic scale of frequency.

Thus these factors do affect information transmission, but one cannot help but be impressed with their relative lack of effect as much if not more than with their effect. The experimental effects do exist, but they are not large.

The relative lack of effect of the total stimulus range is particularly important since it makes so clear that psychological judgments are not really absolute in the sense that a single stimulus value generates in the sensorium a direct and equivalent value. Rather, all judgments seem to be made with respect to the total range of stimuli in a particular experimental situation. It is perhaps unfortunate that the term absolute judgment has been used for the method which so clearly demonstrates that perceptual judgments are not absolute. The confusion was created because absolute means both categorical as well as without regard to an outside reference. The response made in this type of experiment is absolute in contrast to relative, or comparative, but it is clear that the perceptual process is far from absolute. Perhaps we can say that categorical judgment experiments have shown that perceptual processes are not absolute.

Learning

Another factor which we have not treated in a major way is that of learning. Most of the experiments reported here have made use of a preliminary training period, and casual inspection of data has indicated no serious effect of training or practice. It is usually assumed that learning does not play an important part in determining information transmission or channel capacity.

Yet when attempts have been made to give extreme amounts of practice, some discrimination learning does occur. Hartman (1954), for example, practiced subjects on pitch judgments two sessions a week for 8 weeks. He also used four different ranges of frequencies. His data show that for his largest range of frequencies information transmission increased from 1.32 bits to 2.20 bits. Since this latter figure is very close to the value obtained by Pollack, it seems reasonable that Pollack's training and indoctrination procedure had eliminated any serious effect of learning during the course of his experiment. For Hartman's smallest pitch range, the increase was much less—from

1.06 to 1.40 bits over the total period of training. In this condition, discriminability was apparently so poor that even large amounts of training could not substantially improve it.

In an experiment on color identification using Munsell colors varying in hue, saturation, and value, Hanes and Rhoades (1959) practiced one subject on approximately fifty different color chips over a period of 5 months, and were able to reduce the subject's errors to about 3 percent. However, forgetting was quite rapid, and within 3 months after the end of the training, errors were back to about 25 percent.

It is clear, in other words, that training over extended periods of time can substantially improve information transmission—a fact which helps explain the almost uncanny accuracy of some people in industry who are required to make such accurate judgments of color and even taste.

Compatibility

In the last chapter we mentioned that while reaction times increase with an increase in stimulus uncertainty, the compatibility of the response in relation to the stimulus is such a strong factor that high compatibility can eliminate the reaction-time effect. Several experiments have shown that stimulus-response compatibility is important in determining information transmission as well. Fitts and Seeger (1953), Alluisi and Martin (1958), and Alluisi and Muller (1958) have all shown the importance of this factor. We need not dwell on this topic now, since our concern here is with information measurement. We mention these relations, however, to make it clear that in psychological work information measurement has been very valuable, and has even led to some important conceptions concerning human perceptual behavior. Information variables, however, are not the only determiners of performance, and any full understanding of behavior can use information concepts only as part of a total set of useful concepts.

SPEECH DISCRIMINATION

In Chapter Two we saw that perceptual accuracy, when measured in terms of percent correct identifications, decreased as the stimulus uncertainty increased; and in particular, the accuracy of speech identification decreased as the number of words in the message vocabulary increased. Yet in this chapter we have seen that discrimination performance, when measured in terms of information transmission, increases with an increase in stimulus uncertainty at least until some

asymptotic level is reached, at which point we assume we are measuring a channel capacity. These two statements appear to be contradictory if it is assumed that both errors and information transmission are equivalent indicators of perceptual discrimination. As I
pointed out earlier in this chapter, however, in the absolute-judg-
ment type of experiment, errors must necessarily increase with an increase in number of stimulus categories, and yet the information
transmission measure can indicate that there has been actual improvement in discrimination ability, or at least stable discrimination.

The paradigm within which speech intelligibility is measured is
not unlike that in which we measure the accuracy of identification of
tones, of colors, of sizes, or of angles of inclination. A single stimulus
is presented at a time and the subject is required to label it as one
from a predetermined set of possible alternatives. In speech work, the
label is the word itself, while in the perceptual work the label is
often quite arbitrary—a number, a letter, or an artificial naming system such as that used with Munsell colors.

Since the experimental paradigm of speech intelligibility work is
so like that of the absolute judgment work, it is remarkable that so
very little analysis of speech intelligibility in terms of information
transmission has been done. The different experimental backgrounds
of the two types of work may be partially responsible. It is also true
that there are certain difficulties in applying the information transmission measure to speech intelligibility work when small sizes of
vocabulary are used. When we are obtaining loudness judgments, for
example, it is quite simple to select four intensities over a specified
range—and these same four intensities can be used throughout the
particular experiment. In a speech experiment, however, we cannot
select just four monosyllables since we cannot be sure that the results
we obtain are independent of language sampling factors. Therefore,
in the usual experiment, a single set of words is not ordinarily used.
Rather, on each presentation the subject is told which words are possible on that presentation, and the set of possible words is changed
over the course of the experiment so that, insofar as possible, all words
are paired with all other words in the set. This sort of precaution is
necessary to prevent artifactually high (or low) accuracies due to
chance factors in using groups of words which are highly discriminable from each other, but not from words used in other sets.

Nevertheless, it might be well to examine the work on speech intelligibility to see if the experimental results concerning the effect of
stimulus uncertainty are really so different from those obtained in
the typical absolute judgment experiment. While no data are available

to us to enable exact computations of information transmissions, we are able to estimate these measures by making some assumptions. Figure 3.5 shows the estimated information transmissions from the Miller, Heise, and Lichten data discussed in Chapter Two.

To obtain these estimates, I assumed that the response uncertainty would be the same as the stimulus uncertainty—an assumption which will not be seriously in error. Then I assumed that the percent correct figure gives us the largest single category of response and that all the errors are then distributed randomly among the other possible alternatives. To illustrate, if I have four stimulus categories, I assumed a response uncertainty of 2.0 bits. And if, for a given condition, 40 percent of the words were correctly identified, I assumed a distribution of responses per stimulus word of 40, 20, 20, and 20 to give us a conditional uncertainty (or response equivocation) of 1.92 bits. This value subtracted from the response uncertainty gives us an estimated information transmission of 0.08 bit.

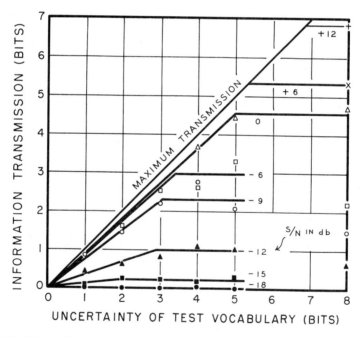

Fig. 3.5. Information transmission for monosyllables heard in noise. Each set of points is for a different signal-to-noise ratio as indicated. (Data estimated from Miller, Heise, and Lichten, 1951.)

These estimated information transmissions plotted in Fig. 3.5 certainly suggest a reasonable set of relations. For a signal-to-noise (S/N) ratio of −18 db we have 0 information transmission regardless of the uncertainty of the test vocabulary, even though the original percent correct figures ranged from 51 (for two-word vocabularies) down to 5 (for thirty-two word vocabularies). In other words, at this low S/N ratio, there is no information transmission and no discriminability. As the S/N ratio is increased, information transmission also increases. Similarly, as long as there is any information transmission possible, it increases with an increase in stimulus uncertainty—a result in line with the results on absolute judgments and a result which leads to a contrary interpretation of the effect of stimulus uncertainty. Performance does not decrease but rather improves. The data presented here are skimpy for the purpose, but they strongly suggest that there is an asymptotic value for each S/N level; that is, for each S/N ratio we can specify a channel capacity—a result that seems eminently reasonable. Thus we should be able to specify the effects of the noise by stating a single number which is the channel capacity for that noise level.

In order to look at the problem from this point of view, I have replotted the data of Fig. 3.5 in Fig. 3.6, this time plotting information transmission as a function of the S/N ratio. Values obtained from test vocabularies which are too small to allow maximum information transmission (that is, are below channel capacity) are also plotted here, and they are the low values which occur for small S/N ratios. Even with these values plotted, however, it is not at all unreasonable to draw a single function to represent all of the data—a function which specifies a single value of (maximum) information transmission as a function of noise level. Furthermore, the intercept of the function on the abscissa allows us to state the S/N ratio below which no information transmission can be obtained—in this case at −16 db. In this conclusion we are using the Munson-Karlin criterion of zero information transmission to define a threshold.

Before we conclude too readily that this method of dealing with speech intelligibility work is fully valid, we should look at the consequences of the assumptions I made in computing the information transmissions. First, in assuming that response uncertainty is the same as stimulus uncertainty we are assuming a maximum possible value, since any unequal distribution of responses can only lower the value. Thus if the assumption is incorrect, its result is that we estimate information transmissions slightly too high, but it would

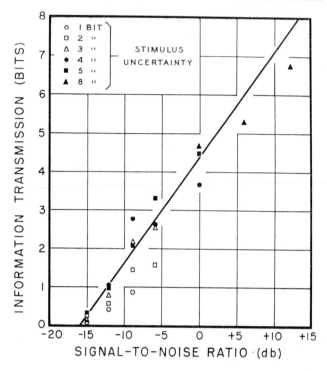

Fig. 3.6. Information transmission for monosyllables heard in noise as a function of the signal-to-noise ratio. Each set of points is for a different size of test vocabulary as indicated. (Data estimated from Miller, Heise, and Lichten, 1951.)

take considerable error of this sort to change the conclusion that information transmission increases with an increase in size of test vocabulary.

My second assumption was that the errors were distributed equally among all the possible incorrect categories. This assumption has the effect of maximizing the computed conditional uncertainty or response equivocation, and thus of minimizing the estimated information transmission. Furthermore, this effect is strongest when a large number of categories is used. Thus if an error due to this assumption were corrected, the effect would be to increase still further the information transmissions obtained with high stimulus uncertainties. Since the effect of this assumption is opposite to the effect of the assumption concerning response uncertainty, errors due to the two assumptions will tend to cancel. However, it seems reasonable that the second assumption is more seriously wrong than the first. Therefore, we might expect that more accurate measures of this effect would not show a clear channel capacity, but rather that the functions of Fig. 3.5 would continue rising to the maximum information transmission possible with the type of stimulus materials available. We will see in the next chapter that when stimulus uncertainty is increased by increasing the number of stimulus dimensions, a simple channel capacity is not indicated. Since speech can hardly be considered a unidimensional stimulus, an expectation of further rise in the functions of Fig. 3.5 does not seem unreasonable.

A word about the maximum information transmission possible with this type of stimulus material is also in order. There is not an indefinite number of choices for most stimulus materials, particularly words. Since Miller, Heise, and Lichten used monosyllables, the maximum vocabulary is quite limited. They mention using an original list of a thousand monosyllables, which certainly is near the maximum possible number. Such a list corresponds approximately to a maximum stimulus uncertainty of 10 bits, so that no information transmission figure could exceed this amount. The function drawn in Fig. 3.6 could not continue indefinitely upwards if the S/N ratio were increased, because the limit of stimulus uncertainty would be reached. If the actual linear function in Fig. 3.6 is extrapolated to 10 bits of information transmission, the equivalent S/N ratio is +20 db—suggesting that perfect intelligibility occurs at that level. Once again the data are very skimpy for these estimates, but they suggest a falling off at the high end, with the possibility that the upper limit of information transmission is reached in a more gradual manner—that is, the upper limit of 10 bits is reached as an asymptote rather than as a discrete break in the function.

There is little point in discussing this problem further since we have so little data to go on.[3] My main intent here has been simply to show that information transmission measures very probably can simplify speech intelligibility work and lead to more uniform concepts. Accurate measures of information transmission might very well show, for example, that different types of stimulus words (for example, dissyllables rather than monosyllables) give the same information transmission under the same noise conditions, since it is quite possible to have different percent correct figures but the same information

---

[3] I. Miller (1957) actually published information transmission measures for nonsense passages heard in noise. Unfortunately, his assumption that all errors were in a single category is very unreasonable. When his data are recomputed with the assumptions used here, the results are quite similar. No complete matrices of confusions were shown.

transmissions. It seems not unreasonable that errors made to monosyllables are more random than errors made to dissyllables, with the result that the response equivocation to dissyllables can be less than that to monosyllables. Pair confusions would be much more expected with dissyllables, and a simple measure of percent correct ignores a result which is strongly indicative of perceptual discrimination.

The purpose of this discussion on speech intelligibility is to make clear that there are few results if any which indicate that performance is poorer with larger stimulus uncertainties—as long as information measures are used to measure both performance and stimulus uncertainty. While it is true, as I showed in the last chapter, that percent accuracy decreases with an increase in stimulus uncertainty, it is not true that total discrimination performance decreases. The information measures are far more meaningful in measuring discrimination performance than are the much less meaningful measures of errors.

Stimulus effect, response effect, or independence of information?

In Chapter Two we discussed at some length the question of whether the effect on perceptual accuracy of number of stimulus categories was primarily a stimulus or a response effect. Since the evidence is quite good that the number of stimulus categories can be limited just as effectively after the perceptual act as before, we concluded that the effect was primarily due to a restriction on responses.

In the present context of discussion of information transmission and channel capacities, this question certainly changes its form, if it does not disappear altogether. The question was originally raised to attempt an explanation of the fact that perceptual accuracy became better with a smaller number of stimulus categories, and the concern was whether this improvement was due to a perceptual set established before the actual stimulus presentation. However, as we have seen in this chapter, the *amount* of stimulus discrimination does not get better as the number of stimulus categories is decreased. Insofar as the channel capacity concept is valid, a decrease in stimulus uncertainty leads to no change in performance until stimulus uncertainty becomes less than the channel capacity; and in that case the amount of perceptual discrimination decreases because of the limitation of stimulus uncertainty. Thus there is really no effect to be explained; there is no improvement in discrimination with smaller uncertainty, and thus no perceptual selective set to assume.

Actually, we can look at this problem from a slightly different point of view, and that is to consider the stimulus presentation and the restriction of the set of possibilities as two separate communication acts, each of which is designed to provide information to the subject in the experiment by reducing his uncertainty concerning the particular stimulus presented. One of these acts provides information unambiguously, and the other provides further information, but normally in an ambiguous fashion.

To illustrate, let us assume that a subject is trying to decide which of 1024 monosyllables is presented in noise. Let us also suppose that the S/N ratio at which our subject must work is −6 db, and further that the data of Fig. 3.5 are valid to determine how much information can be transmitted through the human in noise. From this figure, we see that our best estimate of the channel capacity is 3 bits with this amount of noise. Now we can ask whether we can get all of the information (10 bits) transmitted if we give our subject 7 bits unambiguously by restricting his set of stimuli (or responses) and requiring him to obtain the other 3 bits through noise. If the channel capacity concept is perfectly valid, our answer would be an unequivocal yes, since, if we give 7 bits, then all of the remaining 3 bits would be transmitted through noise, and our subject would have the required total of 10 bits. The actual data of Fig. 3.5, however, indicate that we could not achieve the total of 10 bits with such a procedure, since we find that with 3 bits of stimulus uncertainty the subject can only transmit 2.5 bits, and our total would then be just 9.5 bits rather than the required 10 bits. Therefore, unless the channel capacity concept is completely valid, we know that we cannot divide the transmission task in this fashion and hope to come out even.

What are the conditions under which we would expect the channel capacity concept to be perfectly valid, and thus for us to be able to achieve the full required information transmission by two such communicative acts? They are, simply, that the two communicative acts provide completely independent information. If any two communicative acts provide completely independent information, then the total information provided is simply the sum of the two separate amounts of information. Suppose, for example, that, in listening to the monosyllables in noise, I can determine that the correct word is "no," "blow," "crow," or "flow." If the original set of words had 10 bits of uncertainty, then I have received 8 bits from listening to the word. Now if I am given another 8 bits by being told that the correct word is "may," "blow," "crow," or "cry," I still cannot narrow the choice down to just one word, even though altogether I have been given 16 bits of information, and only needed 10 bits. The reason is simply that the two communicative acts duplicated information.

We can argue in this vein that in speech work the two communicative acts are not completely independent, since at values of stimulus uncertainty below the channel capacity perfect information transmission does not occur. It is interesting, in addition, to compare other types of absolute judgment experiments to see whether the communicative acts do provide more nearly independent information.

In the usual absolute judgment experiment with a single sensory dimension, the range of the stimulus values is kept constant, but the number of stimuli and responses used to cover this range is made smaller or larger. Under these circumstances, the channel capacity concept holds very well, and we get perfect information transmission with low values of stimulus uncertainty, and a constant information transmission for high values of stimulus uncertainty (with a smoothed transition area). Perhaps this result is due to the particular way in which the number of categories is restricted. Suppose, to illustrate, that in loudness judgments we change the number of stimulus categories by keeping the same intensity spacing, but by restricting the range of intensities. We know restricting the range of stimuli has a small but real deleterious effect on information transmission; therefore, if we reduce stimulus uncertainty by restriction of the range of stimulus values, we would obtain channel capacity functions for loudness judgments similar to those shown for speech in Fig. 3.5. In other words, we would not expect maximum information transmission to occur for low values of stimulus uncertainty, but the transmission values would lie consistently below the line for maximum transmission.

Why this should occur can be seen more clearly if we describe a hypothetical experiment which is more closely analogous to the type of experiment done with speech. Suppose we require a subject to make absolute judgements of twenty loudnesses, spaced 5 db apart on an intensity scale. We know that we will get a channel capacity of about 2.3 bits. Now we present our subject a particular stimulus, let us say "5," and then also tell him that the stimulus comes from the set "1" through "10." This latter act gives the subject 1 bit of information, but it will not appreciably change his judgmental accuracy, because he already was quite sure that it was in the lower half of the stimuli. Thus we were simply duplicating information. Suppose instead, however, that we tell him that the correct stimulus was an odd-numbered one. Now once again we are giving him exactly 1 bit of information, but in this case it will not tend to duplicate what he already knew, and he will be able to improve his accuracy considerably.

In general, then, the first question that must be asked about the effects of restriction of stimulus set is whether the two communicative acts provide independent information. And it is clear that many methods of restriction of stimulus set will not provide information independent of that which the subject gets from the direct perceptual act.

There is still a question which can be asked concerning whether restriction of the set before stimulus presentation is more effective than restriction after stimulus presentation, and that is whether prior knowledge of the set of stimuli allows the subject to attend selectively in such a way that he obtains independent information. Note that we are not asking whether the subject can improve his performance by having a smaller stimulus uncertainty, since we know that he cannot. If anything, performance becomes worse with smaller stimulus uncertainties. However, it is still possible that prior knowledge of the stimulus set allows the subject to determine which information he gets (even though the amount of it does not change), so that the information he gets from the direct perceptual act is independent of, and thus additive to, the information he gets by restriction of his set of stimuli. Furthermore, it is possible that restriction of the set before the stimulus presentation will allow the subject to obtain independent information, while restriction after the stimulus presentation will not allow it.

RESPONSE CATEGORIES AND RATING SCALES

Information transmission measures have also been used for determining the optimum number of rating categories for use in rating scales. Bendig and Hughes (1953), for example, measured information transmission for ratings of familiarities of twelve countries, with 3-, 5-, 7-, 9-, or 11-category scales. Bendig (1954) used the same procedure with ratings of preference for twenty foods. In both of these cases there was only a slight increase in information transmission up to at least the eleven categories used.[4] In these experiments, information transmission was quite small, being no more than 0.24 bit for ratings of countries and 0.32 bit for ratings of food.

Later Garner (1960) presented some illustrative data in a discussion of this problem, in which ratings of handwriting for legibility were

[4] In both of these experiments the data as presented by the authors show a moderate increase in information transmission. My statement that only a slight increase was found is based on their data after I corrected them for statistical bias, a problem which is particularly acute when relatively small numbers are spread over many categories. This correction for bias, known as the Miller-Madow correction (Miller, 1955), corrects for bias in either univariate or bivariate distributions. The correction for bias in the contingent uncertainty is equal to $(k-1)(r-1)\log_2 e/2n$, where k and r are the numbers of columns and rows.

obtained with four to twenty rating categories. Even when these information transmissions were corrected for bias there was a slight but steady increase in information transmission throughout the range of values used, up to about 0.50 bit for twenty rating categories, as shown in Fig. 3.7.

These few experiments show that the concept of a channel capacity is not appropriate, in the sense that there does not appear to be a maximum information transmission which remains stable with higher levels of response uncertainty. And there is good reason why there should not be a channel capacity for this problem, even though superficially rating scales are so very similar to absolute judgments.

In the absolute judgment paradigm, the number of stimuli is normally varied concomitantly with the number of responses—although Hake and Garner (1951) have shown that if more responses than stimuli are allowed, the information transmission is unaffected. Thus the interpretation that the measured channel capacity indicates the maximum number of *stimulus* categories which can be judged with no error is legitimately related to the nature of the experiments, and such a conclusion has been shown experimentally to be valid.

The rating-scale problem, however, is such that the number of items to be judged is fixed by the nature of the problem and is ordinarily not free to be changed. Thus we are not free to select just three or

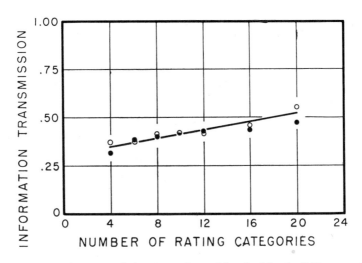

FIG. 3.7. Information transmission for ratings of handwriting legibility as a function of the number of rating categories. The open circles are for individual ratings, and the filled-in circles for pooled ratings. (After Garner, 1960.)

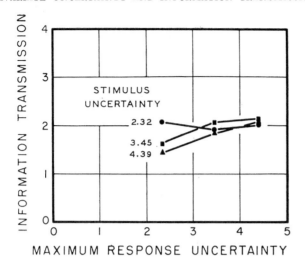

Fig. 3.8. Information transmission for absolute judgments of visual size with different numbers of response and stimulus categories. (Data from Eriksen and Hake, 1955a.)

two stimuli as being representative of the entire set, as in reality is done with the absolute judgment problem. The rating scale problem is, in essence, the problem of determining how many rating categories are necessary to allow the rater to demonstrate all of the discriminability between stimuli, or rated objects, that exists. Typically, for the usual rating problem, this fact would mean that at least as many rating categories should be used as there are rated objects, and, ideally, ranking of the objects should be used, since as long as no two items are identical on the rating continuum, there is some discriminability between them and it will appear if sufficient ratings are made.

That this relationship is not unique to the nature of the materials usually found in rating-scale problems has been shown by Eriksen and Hake (1955a) who used absolute judgments of visual size with an orthogonal design involving five, eleven, or twenty-one stimulus categories and five, eleven, or twenty-one response categories. The results they obtained are shown in Fig. 3.8. When stimulus uncertainty was at a minimum (five categories, or 2.32 bits), the number of response categories had no appreciable effect on information transmission. This result confirms the earlier result of Hake and Garner, since in all these cases the number of responses possible was always equal to or greater than the number of stimuli. However, when there are, for example, twenty-one stimuli, then maximum information transmission is obtained only when an equal number of response categories is allowed. The loss in information transmission when only five response categories are used rather than twenty-one, with twenty-one stimulus categories, is over 0.50 bit, which is an appreciable proportion of the maximum transmission obtained.

INFORMATION TRANSMISSION RATE

Thus far in this chapter we have discussed information transmission per stimulus presentation. That is to say, we have not been concerned with how often a discriminative act is made, or at which rate, but only in the discrimination evidenced in each separate judgment. With this outlook, it has been clear that information measures provide a very meaningful way of describing discrimination accuracy.

It is, of course, quite possible to discuss information rate rather than information transmission per stimulus, and the equations describing rate of information transmission differ from those shown here only in providing a time variable in the equations. If, for example, we have an information transmission of 3 bits per stimulus, and five such discriminations are made per second, then our information rate is 15 bits per second. And in the usual physical communication system the critical factor in describing the performance of the system, or the system's capacity, is the rate of information transmission. Thus the channel capacity of a telegraph system would be described as so many bits per second. One of the great values of the information measure in describing a physical communication system has been the fact that information transmission per item and number of items per second are reciprocally related, so that the channel capacity of the system can be stated as a single number without separately specifying rate of signal presentation and information per signal.

It has been tempting for psychologists to attempt to transfer the concept of a channel capacity for information rate to human behavior, and the original work on reaction times was done with this sort of thing in mind. Thus the linear relation between stimulus uncertainty and reaction time can be used to determine the amount of time required per bit of uncertainty, and from it a rate of information transmission. However, a direct translation from the reaction time function to information rate is not as useful as at first glance it seems, primarily because of the awkwardness of the non-zero intercept constant in this function. In other words, time and stimulus uncertainty are inversely related only if the function is linear and has an intercept of zero time for zero uncertainty. To illustrate, the function in Fig. 2.6, from Hyman's data, shows approximately 360 msecs reaction time required for 1 bit of stimulus uncertainty, but 520 msec for 2 bits of uncertainty. Thus if a 1-bit stimulus were presented twice in succession we would expect to require 720 msec. This value is substantially more than the reaction time required for a single 2-bit stimulus, and it is clear that time and stimulus uncertainty are not exchangeable in any simple fashion.

A variety of experiments has demonstrated that there is no simple channel capacity for rate of information transmission in humans, even for a highly specific experimental situation. To a large extent these experiments will be discussed in parts of the book where the content seems to be appropriate. Two experiments are directly relevant to this point, however, and clearly establish that time and uncertainty per stimulus are not equivalent for humans. Klemmer and Muller (1953) had subjects press keys in response to flashing lights, and they systematically varied both rate of presentation and stimulus uncertainty per presentation. They found that maximum rate of information transmission occurred when the stimulus uncertainty was at its maximum regardless of the rate of stimulus presentation. Furthermore, the optimum rate of stimulus presentation was two or three stimuli per second regardless of the stimulus uncertainty. In other words, the two variables of uncertainty per stimulus and rate of stimulus presentation were essentially independent insofar as human performance was concerned. Later, Alluisi, Muller, and Fitts (1957) confirmed this result with both verbal and motor (key pressing) responses to visually presented Arabic numerals, finding that information transmission rate for humans is much more a function of stimulus uncertainty than it is of rate of stimulus presentation.

An experimental attack on a practical application problem of these concepts has recently been carried out by R. R. Riesz and R. L. Deininger at the Bell Telephone Laboratories. They were concerned with the keying time required by telephone operators with push-button keying; that is, the "dialing" is done by successive pushes of buttons rather than by rotation of a dial such as is found on most home telephones. They tested a series of four different conditions, differing in length of the keyed number and the number of alternatives per number. They used lengths of 11, 8, 6, and 5 digits and allowed 4, 7, 13, and 22 alternatives, respectively. Each of these four composite conditions provides telephone numbers of approximately

22 bits of total uncertainty. (These researchers used letters of the alphabet rather than actual numbers so they could easily vary number of alternatives.) The total keying time required for each of the four conditions was measured, and this time was broken into two separate parts. The prekeying time was the delay between presentation of the number and the beginning of keying. The keying time was the time actually required for keying after the operator had begun to key. The results of this experiment are shown in Fig. 3.9.

These results confirm the fact that maximum rate of performance occurs when each separate stimulus has the maximum uncertainty. In fact, the actual keying time itself shows a very slight effect of the stimulus uncertainty. For example, the actual keying time per letter keyed was 0.61 sec for four alternatives (eleven letters keyed), and it was 0.82 sec for 22 alternatives (five letters keyed). This difference in speed for the two cases is not enough by far to offset the difference in stimulus uncertainty.

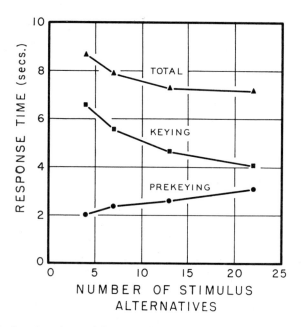

FIG. 3.9. Keying time for push-button telephones as a function of the number of stimulus alternatives. The total uncertainty of the telephone number was held constant at approximately 22 bits by varying the length of the number inversely to the number of alternatives per unit. (Data from Riesz and Deininger, 1960, personal communication.)

The prekeying time itself is somewhat equivalent to reaction time, since it is the time before any action commences. It increases with the number of stimulus alternatives, just as reaction time increases with stimulus uncertainty. This increase, however, is not enough to offset the loss in total keying time required for the longer numbers. It is interesting to find that prekeying time increases with increased stimulus uncertainty, even though the total number uncertainty is essentially the same for all conditions. Apparently the initial delay is more a result of the uncertainty of the first response than it is of the total uncertainty.

It appears, then, that there are psychological factors involved in carrying out any timed task which are quite independent of information variables. Even though reaction time is a function of stimulus uncertainty, there are limiting factors involved in the carrying out of successive motor responses which are quite unrelated to information as such. There is, in other words, a limit on how fast any sequence of acts can be carried out, and this limit is almost entirely independent of how much information is being processed, but is only dependent on how many actual motor acts per second are required. Apparently the intercept constant in the reaction time function provides a very real limiting factor.

Perhaps the word of caution is necessary, and perhaps not, but it is clear that while information measurement is very meaningful for some types of psychological problem, it is not meaningful for other types. Time is a variable which can operate quite independently of information variables, so that the concept of a channel capacity for information rate does not have the same utility as the channel capacity concept has as a measure of ability to discriminate between stimuli. Therefore, it is my opinion that measurements of information rate can be meaningful only for determining transmission rates for very specific situations—so specific that little psychological generality is possible.

ANXIETIES AND EXPECTANCIES

Two other uses of information measurement are worth mentioning here, although not in great detail because they are somewhat peripheral to the major topics discussed.

First, information measures have been used somewhat effectively in studies of anxiety. Frick (1953) used correlation of successive acts of rats in Skinner boxes to show that rats experimentally made anxious had their regular pattern of behavior disrupted. While Frick did not use strictly informational measures, the principle of correlating responses with previous responses is basically the same as that involved in using the contingent uncertainty as a measure of sequential constraint. Later, Eriksen and Wechsler (1955) had subjects make absolute judgments of visual size, some under anxiety conditions, and some under normal conditions. They found that the anxious subjects had lower response uncertainties than non-anxious subjects, but the same information transmission measures. Thus the effect of anxiety was not an impairment of perceptual discrimination, but was, rather, a stereotyping of responses—that is, the subjects did not use all responses equally often. This procedure of differentiating between response effects and perceptual effects would seem to have interesting possibilities. Still later, Kuethe and Eriksen (1957) showed that the nature of the anxiety effects experimentally induced depended on the basic personality of the subject.

The other application of information concepts is in the area of probability matching behavior in expectancy experiments. Grant, Hake, and Hornseth (1951) had showed that when subjects are asked to guess which of two events will occur, and when these two events occur with unequal probabilities, then the subjects will guess each event in approximately the same proportion as the event actually occurs. This result, which has led to the "probability-matching hypothesis" has generated a considerable amount of research to determine why the phenomenon happens, and the conditions under which it does not. The concern about the phenomenon is that such behavior does not conform to a particular type of optimum game strategy, since the maximum number of correct guesses will always occur when the subject guesses the more probable event 100 percent of the time. In other words, it is assumed that subjects are in fact trying to maximize their "hits."

Grant (1954) has suggested the possibility of more use of information concepts and measures in dealing with this type of problem, and more recently Siegel (1959) has proposed a specific mathematical model which assumes that there is some value to the subject in his generating a set of responses which match the information content of the stimuli.

COMMENTARY

The uneasiness which I expressed at the end of Chapter Two has begun to wane. The reason is primarily that with the bivariate information measure we can use information concepts to specify both the nature of the stimulus and the nature of the response; and, even more importantly, to specify the relation between them. In Chapter Two, when dealing only with the univariate measure of uncertainty, we could use uncertainty to specify the stimulus or the response, but not both. Such a limitation circumscribes the utility of the measure in two important ways.

First, the use of uncertainty measures to specify only a property of the stimulus or the response requires that we use some other measure to indicate its effect on performance. Ordinarily, however, there is nothing inherent in the nature of the performance criterion to suggest how stimulus uncertainty should be related to performance. Number of trials to criterion in a learning experiment need at best be monotonically related to stimulus or response uncertainty. And the use of errors in a discrimination experiment is a woefully inadequate performance criterion. The use of the information measure for performance as well as for stimulus specification shows all of the categorical discrimination which the human subjects demonstrate, while an error criterion cannot. All errors are not equally wrong, and the information measure is at least sensitive to the relative distribution of errors.

Actually, we might be concerned here with the limitation of the information measure itself, since it also does not preserve all of the discrimination which subjects can exhibit. It is not sensitive even to ordinal, much less to higher metric, properties of the responses, and in some experimental problems this lack can be quite severe.

Second, the use of uncertainty measures to specify only the stimulus or response uncertainty does not lead to any insights into the nature of the psychological process. It does not, for example, suggest that there can be such a thing as a fixed amount of discrimination which is independent of stimulus uncertainty. Yet when we use information measures to specify the stimulus, the response, and the relation between them, we are able to ask and to answer questions which were not questions at all before. The property of the contingent uncertainty in specifying an amount of relation, rather than a degree of relation, has been immensely helpful in discrimination work.

While errors can be used to measure relative performance, they cannot indicate an absolute level of performance as the measure of information transmitted does. The measure of information transmitted, with its associated concept of channel capacity as a stable amount of discrimination, has led to important insights into the nature of perceptual discrimination.

The idea that there can be an amount of discrimination which is invariant under a wide range of stimulus uncertainties is new and has considerable utility. To be able to specify discrimination performance with a single number is certainly valuable, and we have seen that this can be done with simple sensory continua. Furthermore, there is some real possibility that it can be done with more complex stimuli such as speech, although here the problems are more involved. Certainly an elaboration of the concept of information transmission can be expected to lead to further insights about the nature of perceptual processes.

SUMMARY

When we have a bivariate matrix of data, there are several uncertainty terms which can be computed in addition to the univariate measures of uncertainty which are still appropriate to the marginal distributions.

Joint uncertainty, $U(x, y)$, is a simple measure of average uncertainty with respect to joint categories of the two variables, x and y.

Nominal joint uncertainty is the uncertainty of the matrix based on the assumption that all joint categories occur equally often. It is the sum of the two marginal nominal uncertainties.

Maximum joint uncertainty, $U_{max}(x, y)$, is the maximum uncertainty which the matrix can have when limited only by its row and column marginal distributions. It is numerically equal to the sum of the row and column marginal uncertainties.

Conditional uncertainty is the uncertainty in one variable when the other variable is held constant, averaged over all values of the second variable. There are two such conditional uncertainties, $U_x(y)$ and $U_y(x)$, for the bivariate matrix.

Contingent uncertainty, $U(y:x)$, is a measure of the amount of relation between the two variables, and is numerically equal to the difference between the maximum joint uncertainty and the joint uncertainty. It is a symmetric term, and specifies the amount of uncertainty in y which can be predicted from knowledge of x, or conversely.

The contingent uncertainty can be interpreted as a measure of transmitted information or as a measure of redundancy. In this chapter it is considered primarily as a measure of transmitted information, and is used to determine amount of perceptual discrimination. When used this way, it shows that for unidimensional perceptual continua there is a channel capacity such that no further increase in stimulus uncertainty leads to a concomitant increase in information transmission.

This channel capacity, or limiting amount of discrimination, is quite stable and low for most unidimensional continua, having a value of about 2.3 bits. This value, which is equivalent to five stimulus categories, is stable under ordinary perceptual conditions but can be increased by the use of perceptual anchors. For stimulus continua which have natural anchors, the value is correspondingly larger.

As an approximation, it can be shown that there is a single channel capacity for speech heard in noise which is a function of the noise level. Thus it is possible to specify a single number for speech intelligibility in noise—a number whose value might well be influenced by the nature of the words and other speech parameters.

The channel capacity concept indicates that as stimulus uncertainty increases, information transmission also increases until some stable value is reached, beyond which no further improvement occurs. This way of looking at the effect of stimulus uncertainty changes the question concerning whether the effect of restriction of stimulus categories on discrimination is due to restriction of the stimulus or to restriction of the response, since there is no deterioration in discrimination as the stimulus uncertainty is increased. The question can, however, be phrased in another manner, which is to ask whether the information provided by the communication act which restricts the number of categories is independent of the information provided by the direct discriminative act, since only under conditions of independence will the two amounts of information be additive. It is suggested that the two acts will provide independent information if the subject is able to attend selectively to certain aspects or dimensions of the stimuli—a possibility which should be more real with multidimensional stimuli than with unidimensional stimuli.

CHAPTER FOUR

Multivariate Uncertainty and Multidimensional Information Transmission

We saw in the last chapter how uncertainties can be used to measure the amount of relation or correlation between variables, and that the equations involved in this type of measurement are quite analogous to those involved in analysis of variance. One of the great values of information measurement, and of concepts derived from it, has been the ability, not only to measure the amount of relation between variables, but also to determine sources of relation. In other words, it is possible to partition a total variability into component parts and determine the extent to which variability or uncertainty is related to each of several variables. These techniques, which have gone under the general name of multivariate uncertainty analysis, have provided not only a statistical tool but also a frame of reference for the analysis and understanding of several classes of psychological problem.

There are two general approaches which can be used in multivariate uncertainty analysis: The uncertainty of a single variable can be partitioned into predictable and error components, or the uncertainty of a total matrix can be partitioned. We shall use the first of these approaches in this chapter, and the second of them in Chapter Five. Each approach has its particular merits and is most appropriate to certain kinds of experimental problem.

MULTIVARIATE PARTITIONING OF UNCERTAINTY

The partitioning approach was first developed by McGill (1954) and its relation to analysis of variance was shown by Garner and McGill (1956). The basic equation from which this approach starts is Eq. 3.11, in which it is shown that the uncertainty of a variable y can be partitioned into two parts, that part which is predictable from x (the contingent uncertainty) plus the residual or error uncertainty (the conditional uncertainty, in general terms).

That equation assumes the meaningfulness of only two variables in the classification of possible events. Suppose, however, that there are three variables, that, by the nature of the variables, one of them, y, is sensibly the variable to be predicted, and that the other two, w and x, are the variables from which the prediction is made. We can call the first variable the criterion, and the other two variables the predictors. Remembering that in uncertainty analysis no metric of the underlying variable is assumed, we can momentarily consider our two predictor variables as a single variable, which we shall write (w, x)—the comma notation again indicating that the two variables are being treated as a single joint variable. Thus, Eq. 3.11 can be rewritten as

$$U(y) = U(y{:}w, x) + U_{wx}(y). \tag{4.1}$$

$U(y)$ is still the uncertainty of the single variable y, $U(y{:}w, x)$ is the predicted uncertainty which we shall call a *multiple contingent uncertainty*, and $U_{wx}(y)$ is the *multiple conditional uncertainty* (error uncertainty in most applications). In the multiple contingent uncertainty notation the comma is retained between the two predictor variables to indicate again that they are being used as a single joint variable. Again, the colon indicates that a contingent relation is involved and that the relation is symmetric. In other words, we could just as well write $U(w, x{:}y)$, which would imply that the joint term (w, x) is being predicted from the term y. Since rarely do we use a single term to predict two terms, we will equally rarely write the multiple contingent uncertainty in this reversed form. Nevertheless it should be remembered that any contingent uncertainty is in fact symmetric. The multiple conditional uncertainty, $U_{wx}(y)$, is the uncertainty of y when just one value of (w, x) has been used at a time, and then a weighted mean of the uncertainty has been computed. The comma notation between w and x is dropped for this term because the subscripted notation is not used in any other way and no ambiguity can result.

While we will shortly cease spelling out in probability form the exact meaning of each of the terms we discuss, it might be well to define the multiple conditional uncertainty.

$$U_{wx}(y) = -\sum_{w,x} p(w, x) \sum_y p_{wx}(y) \log p_{wx}(y). \qquad (4.2)$$

Here the $p(w, x)$ are the probabilities of the joint occurrence of a given value of w and a given value of x. The multiple contingent uncertainty is normally calculated by subtracting the multiple conditional uncertainty from the uncertainty of y, that is, by transposition,

$$U(y{:}w, x) = U(y) - U_{wx}(y). \qquad (4.3)$$

Partial contingent uncertainties

Now suppose we want to partition the uncertainty of y in a more detailed fashion by determining the extent to which y can be predicted from w and from x separately. Clearly, we need to determine the components of the multiple contingent uncertainty in a more detailed way. The simplest way to see the nature of the terms involved is to add and subtract terms so as to maintain the equality of Eq. 4.3, and then to regroup the terms into meaningful new ones.

$$\begin{aligned} U(y{:}w, x) &= [U(y) - U_x(y)] + [U_x(y) - U_{wx}(y)] \\ &= U(y{:}x) + U_x(y{:}w) \qquad (4.4a) \\ &= U(y{:}w) + U_w(y{:}x). \qquad (4.4b) \end{aligned}$$

The last form of this equation is what would have been obtained if $U_w(y)$ had been added and subtracted rather than $U_x(y)$. This equation shows that the multiple contingent uncertainty can be partitioned into two parts—the uncertainty which can be predicted from one variable alone plus the uncertainty which can be predicted from the second variable when the first variable is held constant. (When simple contingent uncertainties of the form $U(y{:}w)$ or $U(y{:}x)$ are computed from three-variable matrices the third variable is ignored, that is, the matrix is collapsed over that variable.)

Terms of the form $U_x(y{:}w)$ and $U_w(y{:}x)$ are called *partial contingent uncertainties* and they are quite analogous to the partial correlation coefficient except that again they are measures of amount of relationship rather than of degree. Such terms can be computed by subtraction of the two conditional uncertainty terms as indicated in Eq. 4.4, or they can be computed in a more direct fashion by, say, first computing the value of the contingent uncertainty between x and y for each value of w, and then obtaining a weighted average of all of the separate values of $U(x{:}y)$, weighted according to the probability of occurrence of each value of w. In other words, with a slightly more exact notation,

$$U_w(y{:}x) = \sum_w p(w_i)\ U_{w_i}(y{:}x). \tag{4.5}$$

Here $U_{w_i}(y{:}x)$ means that the contingent uncertainty between x and y has been computed for just one value of w. Now since a simple two-variable contingent uncertainty must always be zero or positive, the partial contingent uncertainty must always be equal to or greater than zero also. This fact in turn means that the multiple contingent uncertainty must always be equal to or greater than either of the simple contingent uncertainties which can be obtained with the same matrix of probabilities. To summarize these relations,

$$U_w(y{:}x) \geq 0 \tag{4.6a}$$
$$U_x(y{:}w) \geq 0 \tag{4.6b}$$
$$U(y{:}w, x) \geq U(y{:}w) \tag{4.6c}$$
$$U(y{:}w, x) \geq U(y{:}x). \tag{4.6d}$$

Partitioning of the multiple contingent uncertainty in the form shown in Eq. 4.4 is one way of looking at the multiple prediction problem. If we want to predict the uncertainty of one variable from two others, we first determine how much prediction can be obtained from one predictor variable alone and then determine how much *extra* prediction can be obtained from the second predictor variable after the effects of the first predictor variable are held constant. If the two predictor variables are themselves correlated, it is obvious that when we add the prediction from the second predictor we must use a term which partials out any prediction which has already been measured from the first predictor variable.

Interaction uncertainties

We can partition the multiple contingent uncertainty in a more detailed manner by adding, subtracting, and grouping further terms to those of Eq. 4.4. For example,

$$U(y{:}w, x) = U(y{:}x) + U(y{:}w) + [U_x(y{:}w) - U(y{:}w)]$$
$$= U(y{:}x) + U(y{:}w) + U(\overline{wxy}). \tag{4.7}$$

The first two terms on the right of this equation are the two simple contingent uncertainties. The third term, $U(\overline{wxy})$ is an *interaction uncertainty*, and is the amount of the uncertainty of y which is predictable from unique combinations of w and x. At a first-order level, it is quite analogous to the interaction variance in analysis of variance—that is, it is analogous to a two-variable interaction. The reason for the notation used here for the interaction is not immediately apparent, and depends on a proof which will be given in Chapter Five. It will be shown that in uncertainty analysis there is a unique interaction term in a three-variable matrix regardless of which term is used as the criterion variable. At the moment, however, the term should be considered as a predictability term for predicting y from unique combinations of x and w.

The interaction uncertainty can be written in these two ways:

$$U(\overline{wxy}) = U_x(y\!:\!w) - U(y\!:\!w) \qquad (4.8a)$$
$$= U_w(y\!:\!x) - U(y\!:\!x). \qquad (4.8b)$$

Equation 4.8a is obtained by adding terms to Eq. 4.4a and Eq. 4.8b is obtained by adding terms to Eq. 4.4b. With either of these equations, it is clear that the multiple contingent uncertainty can be partitioned into the uncertainty predictable from x alone plus that predictable from w alone plus that which can be predicted from unique combinations of the two variables.

Now all of the terms on the right side of Eq. 4.8 must be positive. Therefore the interaction uncertainty is the difference between two terms which are both positive. This means that whether the interaction uncertainty is positive or negative depends on the relative magnitudes of two positive terms. There is nothing about the general form of these equations which makes it impossible to obtain a negative interaction uncertainty, and such negative terms do occur. If, for example, the simple contingent uncertainty between x and y is larger than the partial contingent uncertainty between the same terms, then the interaction uncertainty will be negative. The nature of the partial contingent uncertainty clarifies also the conditions under which the interaction may be negative. Since the partial contingent uncertainty subtracts out any contingent uncertainty between, say, x and y, which is due to the fact that the two predictor variables are themselves correlated, the partial term may be smaller than the simple contingent uncertainty only when the predictor variables are correlated.

At first glance these relations suggest that the analogy between analysis of variance and uncertainty analysis is tenuous at best, since it is usually assumed that the interaction variance must always be positive. As Garner and McGill (1956) have shown, however, a positive interaction variance is assured only if the predictor variables are orthogonal, the usual requirement for an experimental design using analysis of variance. If the same requirement is made for uncertainty analysis, then it is equally assured that the interaction uncertainty will be positive. The proof of this statement lies in the fact that there is a unique interaction term for the three-variable matrix, as will be shown later. Thus,

$$U(\overline{wxy}) = U_y(x:w) - U(x:w). \tag{4.8c}$$

In this form, we can see that the interaction uncertainty must be zero or greater if x and w are orthogonal, since if these predictor variables are orthogonal the contingent uncertainty between them is zero and the interaction uncertainty becomes identical to $U_y(x:w)$, which is equal to or greater than zero.

In order to clarify the meaning of the interaction uncertainty, and the situations in which it can exist, a look at several simple examples (Tables 4.1 to 4.4) is useful. The first three of these tables use an

Table 4.1

A matrix of probabilities in which all of the multiple contingent uncertainty $U(y:w, x)$ is associated with the simple contingent uncertainty $U(y:w)$. The uncertainty of y is 1 bit, which is the same as the contingent uncertainty between y and w.

	x_1w_1	x_2w_1	x_1w_2	x_2w_2	Σ
y_1	.25	.25	0	0	.50
y_2	0	0	.25	.25	.50

eight-cell matrix obtained from three dichotomous variables, in which y is treated as the criterion variable and w and x are the predictor variables. Table 4.1 shows a matrix of probabilities in which all of the predictability in y is due to the contingent uncertainty between y and w; and the other contingent uncertainty, $U(y:x)$, and the interaction uncertainty, $U(\overline{wxy})$, both have zero values. In this matrix, y is perfectly correlated with w, and is entirely uncorrelated with x either when the matrix is summed across w, or when we take a single value of w at a time. In other words, the partial contingent uncertainty, $U_w(y:x)$, is also zero.

In the second matrix of probabilities shown in Table 4.2, all of the multiple contingent uncertainty is due to the interaction uncertainty, and the two simple contingent uncertainties, $U(y:w)$ and $U(y:x)$, are zero. This result is due to the fact that when we collapse the matrix across w to obtain the matrix of x and y, we have no correlation; and, likewise, when we collapse across x to obtain the matrix of w and y

Table 4.2

A matrix of probabilities in which all of the multiple contingent
uncertainty $U(y\!:\!w, x)$ is associated with the interaction
uncertainty $U(\overline{wxy})$. The uncertainty of y is 1 bit,
which is the same as the interaction uncertainty.

	x_1w_1	x_2w_1	x_1w_2	x_2w_2	Σ
y_1	.25	0	0	.25	.50
y_2	0	.25	.25	0	.50

we have no correlation. Yet within each value of w, the contingent
uncertainty between x and y is 1 bit, and within each value of x the
contingent uncertainty between w and y is 1 bit. In other words, the
two partial contingent uncertainties, $U_w(y\!:\!x)$ and $U_x(y\!:\!w)$, each
has a value of 1 bit. The difference between this partial contingent
uncertainty and the simple contingent uncertainty of zero is 1 bit—
the value of the interaction uncertainty.

Table 4.3 shows a matrix in which each of the simple contingent

Table 4.3

A matrix of probabilities in which the interaction term $U(\overline{wxy})$
is negative. The two contingent uncertainties, $U(y\!:\!w)$ and
$U(y\!:\!x)$, are each $+1$, and the interaction is -1, making
a sum for the multiple contingent uncertainty of $+1$.

	x_1w_1	x_2w_1	x_1w_2	x_2w_2	Σ
y_1	.50	0	0	0	.50
y_2	0	0	0	.50	.50

uncertainties has a value of 1 bit, and the interaction uncertainty has
the same value but is negative. Clearly in this case the multiple contingent uncertainty has a value of 1 bit (its maximum, since $U(y)$ is
1 bit), and is composed of three parts. The two positive parts add up
to $+2$, and the negative interaction subtracts 1 bit to leave the correct total. In this case since x and w are perfectly correlated, the prediction in y we obtain from x is the same as the prediction we obtain
from w, and there is no way of determining which of the two simple
contingent uncertainties is the "true" one. The negative term simply
tells us that some prediction has been duplicated and must be corrected, but it can only correct the total prediction; it cannot determine
its particular locus.

Table 4.4 shows a slightly more complicated matrix of probabilities in which we now have a sixteen-cell matrix composed of dichotomous values of w and x and four possible values of y, corresponding to the four possible combinations of w and x. The particular matrix shown has almost equal amounts of prediction from each of the two simple contingent uncertainties as well as from the interaction uncertainty—as close as they could be made without using more decimals in the probabilities. This matrix corresponds fairly closely to that in Table 4.2, where all of the prediction was in the interaction term.

Relatively slight changes in these probabilities can produce quite different patterns of uncertainties. If, for example, there were no equivocation (that is, if the term $U_{wx}(y)$ were 0), then we would have had a total of two bits for the multiple contingent uncertainty, 1 bit each from w and from x, and the interaction would have been 0. This relation would result from the fact that each predictor variable alone could perfectly dichotomize the criterion variable. The value x_1, for example, could lead equally often to values of y_1 and y_4, and x_2 could always lead to values of y_2 and y_3. The value w_1 would lead to y_1 and y_3, and w_2 could lead to y_2 and y_4. Thus if x is used to predict first, it would narrow the possibilities of y down to two, and then the value of w would narrow y down to just one value. To illustrate, if we first know that the value is x_1, we then know that y is either y_1 or y_4. Then if we know that w has a value of w_2, we know that y is either y_2 or y_4. The common value of y, y_4, is then the correct value.

Table 4.4

A matrix of probabilities in which the multiple contingent uncertainty
is due almost equally to the three components,
$U(y{:}w)$, $U(y{:}x)$, and $U(\overline{wxy})$.

	x_1w_1	x_2w_1	x_1w_2	x_2w_2	Σ
y_1	.22	0	0	.03	.25
y_2	.03	0	0	.22	.25
y_3	0	.22	.03	0	.25
y_4	0	.03	.22	0	.25
Σ	.25	.25	.25	.25	

$$U(y{:}w, x) = 2.0 \; - 0.53 = 1.47 \text{ bits}$$
$$U(y{:}w) \quad = 2.0 \; - 1.53 = 0.47 \text{ bit}$$
$$U(y{:}x) \quad = 2.0 \; - 1.53 = 0.47 \text{ bit}$$
$$U_w(y{:}x) \quad = 1.53 - 0.53 = 1.00 \text{ bit}$$
$$U(\overline{wxy}) \quad = 1.00 - 0.47 = 0.53 \text{ bit}$$

Suppose, on the other hand, that the matrix of Table 4.4 were the same as it is except that within each column the probabilities were .125 for each of the two non-zero cells. This matrix would then be, for all practical purposes, identical to that of Table 4.2, and we would have 1 bit of total predictability of y, all of which would be in the interaction term. With such a matrix, the multiple conditional uncertainty (equivocation) would be 1 bit, so that the multiple contingent uncertainty would also be 1 bit (2 bits of y-uncertainty minus the equivocation). Each value of x would lead equally often to each of the four values of y, so that no prediction from x alone is possible. Similarly, the w variable would not discriminate. Unique combinations of w and x would, however, still allow dichotomization of the y variable, with the result that the interaction uncertainty would contain all of the prediction.

These particular matrices were used to illustrate some principles concerning interaction uncertainties which I shall now summarize:

1. A positive interaction is always an indication that the distributions of probabilities with respect to the y, or criterion variable, overlap, such that knowing just the independent values of the two predictor terms does not differentiate as well as does knowing the particular combination of the values. Thus if there are as many values of y as there are combinations of values of the predictor terms, and if each value of y occurs uniquely and differently for each combination of w and x, there can be no positive interaction term, since such a situation cannot produce overlapping distributions. Just one cell in each column is filled, and the cell is different for each column. Overlapping distributions can be produced in one of two ways.

First, if we have fewer y values than there are combinations of w and x, as in Tables 4.1 through 4.3, we can have overlapping distributions unless some columns never occur, as in Table 4.3. Thus in matrices like those of Tables 4.1 and 4.2 it is possible to have positive interactions, and whether or not we have them depends on the particular pattern of the probabilities.

Second, we can have overlapping distributions even when there is one value of y for each combination of values of w and x if the equivocation is greater than zero, as in Table 4.4. In this table, there would have been no interaction term if there had been no equivocation. The particular pattern of results then will determine whether there is a positive interaction term and how important it is.

2. The prerequisite condition for a negative interaction term is

simply that the two predictor variables must be correlated. As we have pointed out, a negative interaction term is essentially a correction for the correlation between the predictor variables, and as such does not have the same meaning as a positive interaction term. It cannot, of course, occur alone, as the positive interaction term did in Table 4.2, since the multiple contingent uncertainty must be zero or greater. Thus a negative interaction uncertainty can only occur in conjunction with positive simple contingent uncertainties, and Eqs. 4.8 show that a negative interaction term cannot be larger in absolute magnitude than the *smallest* simple contingent uncertainty involved in the matrix. Including the contingent uncertainty between the two predictor variables, there are three simple contingent uncertainties in a three-variable matrix, and if any of these is zero, the interaction cannot be negative; and a negative interaction uncertainty cannot be numerically larger than the smallest of any of the three.

Thus a positive interaction term is meaningful as a measure of amount of prediction, and can occur alone or in combination with positive contingent uncertainties. But a negative interaction term is meaningful only as part of a total pattern of prediction, in which the total must always be positive, and the negative interaction term can only be interpreted as a correction appropriate to the total.

Higher-order interactions

Our discussion of the interaction term involved in a three-variable matrix has been moderately detailed because a three-variable matrix is the smallest which can have an interaction, because the three-variable interaction has been the most widely used, and because the principles involved are also applicable to interactions found in higher order matrices.

Suppose that we have a four-variable matrix, in which the variables v, w, and x are the predictors, and y is again the criterion. Remembering that we can always keep the three predictor variables grouped and deal with them as a single variable, we can write, following Eq. 4.1,

$$U(y) = U(y:v, w, x) + U_{vwx}(y). \tag{4.9}$$

Thus our general equation concerning the partitioning of the uncertainty of y into a predictable and an error part is not changed. This equation differs from Eq. 4.1 only in that we label our predictor in a three-variable manner rather than as two variables.

We can also partition the multiple contingent uncertainty into components in the same manner as in Eq. 4.4, and momentarily we will consider w and x to be a single joint variable. Then,

$$U(y{:}v, w, x) = U(y{:}w, x) + U_{wx}(y{:}v). \qquad (4.10)$$

The term $U(y{:}w, x)$ is, of course, exactly what it has been all along, and the term $U_{wx}(y{:}v)$ is a partial contingent uncertainty just as before. Our general partitioning statement is still true, in that the predictable uncertainty in y is partitioned into that predictable from the joint variable (w, x) plus that predictable from v when (w, x) is held constant. Its calculation is exactly as before except that combinations of (w, x) are used to obtain the contingent uncertainty between y and v rather than values of a single variable.

Now since the multiple contingent uncertainty $U(y{:}w, x)$ can itself be partitioned, then

$$U(y{:}v, w, x) = U(y{:}w) + U_w(y{:}x) + U_{wx}(y{:}v), \qquad (4.11)$$

and we have shown that the total prediction in y can be broken into that predictable from w, plus that predictable from x when w is held constant, plus that predictable from v when w and x are both held constant. In other words, we keep adding the prediction from new predictor terms, but must remember to use partial contingencies so as to add prediction which is independent of that already accounted for.

It should be clear, of course, that several other equations analogous to Eq. 4.11 can be written, depending on which variable we account for first. We might, for example, account for prediction from v first, then from x with v held constant, then from w with x and v held constant. In all, there are six equations of the form of Eq. 4.11, one for each of the six possible orders of three things.

Equations in this form can be expanded to any number of predictor variables by simply adding on the next partial contingent uncertainty with all previous variables held constant. For example, if we add a new predictor variable, u, then we can write

$$U(y{:}u, v, w, x) = U(y{:}w) + U_w(y{:}x) + U_{wx}(y{:}v) + U_{vwx}(y{:}u). \qquad (4.12)$$

Such additional terms can be added on as long as the nature of the particular problem makes it profitable to do so, and as long as the actual calculations can be carried out.

However, to go back to Eq. 4.11, let us once again add and subtract terms so as to maintain the equality, but also to be able to identify the component terms involved in the complete multivariate analysis,

$$U(y:v, w, x) = U(y:w) + U(y:v) + U(y:x)$$
$$+ [U_w(y:x) - U(y:x)] + [U_w(y:v) - U(y:v)]$$
$$+ [U_x(y:v) - U(y:v)]$$
$$+ [U_{wx}(y:v) - U_x(y:v)] - [U_w(y:v) - U(y:v)]$$
$$= U(y:w) + U(y:v) + U(y:x)$$
$$+ U(\overline{ywx}) + U(\overline{yvw}) + U(\overline{yvx})$$
$$+ [U_x(\overline{yvw}) - U(\overline{yvw})]$$
$$= U(y:w) + U(y:v) + U(y:x)$$
$$+ U(\overline{ywx}) + U(\overline{yvw}) + U(\overline{yvx})$$
$$+ U(\overline{yvwx}). \tag{4.13}$$

Thus the total multiple contingent uncertainty can be broken into a series of simple contingencies plus interaction terms. When prediction is made from three variables, there are three simple contingent uncertainties—one for each variable. Then there are three three-term interactions, each including the criterion variable, y, in combination with the three possible pairs of the three predictor variables. Finally, there is a four-term interaction, which is the prediction due to unique combinations of the three predictor variables. Once again, the notation $U(\overline{yvwx})$ is used because in fact there is a unique interaction of this form for the four-variable matrix, but in this situation it can be interpreted as the prediction from unique combinations of the three predictor variables.

To generalize to larger numbers of predictor variables, any multiple contingent uncertainty can be partitioned into a series of simple contingent uncertainties (one for each predictor variable), plus interaction terms. There will be as many three-term interactions as there are pairs of the predictor variables. There will be as many four-term interactions as there are triplets of the predictor variables, as many five-term interactions as there are quadruplets of the predictor variables, etc. To illustrate, if we have six predictor variables, there will be six simple contingent uncertainties, fifteen three-term interactions (because there are fifteen pairs of six variables), twenty four-term interactions, fifteen five-term interactions, six six-term interactions, and one seven-term interaction.

Obviously we seldom need to carry out an analysis using as many terms as this, and often, even if the number of predictor variables is relatively large, we can make simplifying assumptions about some of the terms and either group them or ignore them.

It should be noted that the four-term interaction is a difference between two other terms, just as the three-term interaction is, but it is now a difference between two interaction terms, one of which is itself a partial interaction term since (in the case here) it is a measure of the $\overline{yvw}$ interaction with x held constant. Obviously, if we had added and subtracted different terms in Eq. 4.13, we would have found that the four-term interaction can be one of several differences, depending on which term is held constant. Thus,

$$
\begin{aligned}
U(\overline{yvwx}) &= U_x(\overline{yvw}) - U(\overline{yvw}) \\
&= U_v(\overline{ywx}) - U(\overline{ywx}) \\
&= U_w(\overline{yvx}) - U(\overline{yvx}) \\
&= U_y(\overline{vwx}) - U(\overline{vwx}).
\end{aligned} \tag{4.14}
$$

A four-term interaction is somewhat more difficult to interpret than the three-term interaction, since it is not as restricted. It is the difference between terms, each of which may be positive or negative, and as such is not guaranteed to be positive even if all three predictor variables are orthogonal. It serves as a general corrective term, but it may be correcting for interaction terms which are duplicative.

Multivariate criteria

This discussion so far has always assumed that the criterion itself is a single variable, and that the predictor variables are two or more in number. Typically in psychological work this is the situation. It is not necessary that it be so, however, and we shall be discussing some psychological research where it has not been so. It might be worthwhile, therefore, to look at the uncertainty components involved when the criterion as well as the predictor is multivariate. (It should be clear that the foregoing analysis would not change if we simply had a multivariate criterion, but a univariate predictor. The entire analysis would simply be reversed.)

Let us suppose that x and y are criterion variables and that v and w are predictor variables. Now our basic equation partitioning the criterion uncertainty is

$$
U(x, y) = U(x, y : v, w) + U_{vw}(x, y). \tag{4.15}
$$

This equation, and its terms, are identical to those of Eq. 4.1 except that the criterion variable is now the joint variable (x, y). The conditional uncertainty, $U_{vw}(x, y)$ can now be partitioned, following the form of Eq. 3.5 by simply keeping the subscripted notation.

$$
U_{vw}(x, y) = U_{vw}(x) + U_{vwx}(y). \tag{4.16}
$$

Thus the conditional joint uncertainty can be partitioned into a conditional uncertainty of x plus the conditional uncertainty of y when x is held constant, when in both cases the predictor variables,

v and w, are held constant. And, of course, the equation can be reversed in form so that we first take out the conditional uncertainty of y, and then the conditional uncertainty of x with y held constant.

The *joint multiple contingent uncertainty* can also be partitioned, following the form of Eq. 4.4, so that

$$U(x, y{:}v, w) = U(x, y{:}v) + U_v(x, y{:}w). \tag{4.17}$$

The two terms on the right of this equation can be expanded, and then by adding and subtracting terms appropriately, it can be shown that

$$\begin{aligned}
U(x, y{:}v, w) = {} & U(x{:}v) + U(y{:}v) + U(x{:}w) + U(y{:}w) \\
& + U(\overline{vwx}) + U(\overline{vwy}) + U(\overline{vxy}) + U(\overline{wxy}) + U(\overline{vwxy}).
\end{aligned} \tag{4.18}$$

Thus the total predictability of the joint criterion variable (x, y) from the joint predictor variable (v, w) can be broken into a series of simple contingent uncertainties plus several interactions. There are four contingent uncertainties, representing the four combinations of the two criterion variables and the two predictor variables. Then there are four three-term interactions involving the pairing of each predictor variable with the pair of criterion variables and each criterion variable with the pair of predictor variables. In addition, there is a four-term interaction involving unique combinations of all four variables.

In most practical applications involving joint multiple contingent uncertainties, there are factors inherent in the nature of the criterion and predictor terms which make some of the analytic terms more meaningful than others. For example, if a two-dimensional stimulus is used, and the required response is two-dimensional in the same fashion, then those contingency terms involving stimuli and responses of the same sort would be more important than those involving stimuli of one sort but responses of another. We shall refer to contingent uncertainties involving equivalent stimuli and responses as *direct contingencies,* and those involving non-equivalent stimuli and responses as *cross contingencies.* To illustrate more concretely, suppose that sixteen visual stimuli are generated by orthogonal combinations of four hues and four sizes; and the subject responds with two numbers, the first indicating hue and the second indicating size. The two matrices involving stimulus hue and response to hue, and stimulus size and response to size would lead to direct contingencies. However, the matrix involving stimulus hue and response to size would lead to a cross contingency, as would the matrix involving stimulus size and response to hue.

For a complete multivariate analysis of any situation involving two predictor and two criterion variables, each of the above terms should be computed. However, in most situations there are factors which make it obvious that some of the terms will at best be negligible and thus can be safely ignored. There are other situations, however, where the interactions cannot safely be ignored. For example, if two stimulus variables influence each other, then a complete analysis might well be necessary.

COMPONENTS OF PREDICTABILITY

Multivariate uncertainty analysis, and concepts derived from it, have been used in many areas of psychological research. The techniques have proved particularly valuable in analysis of language and other forms of sequential behavior. Most of these topics will be discussed separately, however, and we shall not go into them now. If we continue in the vein of emphasizing phenomena which are primarily perceptual in nature, then we can distinguish two basically different uses of multivariate analysis. The first of these involves the use of multivariate uncertainty analysis primarily as a statistical tool in helping to identify sources of predictability. In this sense, multivariate uncertainty analysis has a role not unlike that of multivariate correlational analysis, and in fact they have often been used as alternative techniques. The chief value of uncertainty analysis in this sense lies simply in its non-metric character, which makes it amenable to many experimental problems which are not easily handled with correlational analysis.

Almost invariably in such use the criterion variable has a fixed number of alternatives, and the multivariate analysis simply adds more predictor variables in an attempt to identify sources of predictability. For example, Frick and Miller (1951) used basically these techniques to analyze the sequential behavior of rats before and after reinforcement for a particular pattern of behavior. They analyzed sequences of responses up to length 4, and showed that behavior became more sterotyped, that is, more predictable, as a result of the reinforcement schedule.

In a similar fashion, Senders and Sowards (1952) and Senders (1953) analyzed sequences of binary responses made by human observers in a psychophysical experiment, as a result of different expected proportions of each response. Analyzing sequence lengths as great as four, they found systematic increases in predictability as a function of the number of preceding responses used to predict the next response.

Still in a similar manner, Lincoln and Alexander (1955) used a multivariate uncertainty analysis of sequences of tapping responses made by humans under instruction to tap one of eight positions at a time in as random a manner as they could. Since these authors present a fairly detailed analysis of the various prediction components, it is possible to identify three separate sources of predictability for the responses on the basis of the two previous responses used as predictors. Total predictability—the multiple contingent uncertainty—was 0.56 bit. Prediction from the previous response alone gave 0.25 bit of uncertainty, and prediction from the second previous response alone gave 0.17 bit of uncertainty. Since these two values for the simple contingent uncertainties add up to only 0.42 bit, there was a positive interaction term with a value of 0.14 bit. Thus the amount of prediction that comes from the second previous response alone is just slightly more than that which comes from unique combinations of the two preceding responses, and in this case considerable error would have resulted if the interaction uncertainty had been ignored or assumed to be trivial.

The experiments described so far in this section have used responses as the criterion variable and responses prior to the one under consideration as the predictor variables. Multivariate uncertainty analysis has been heavily used in such situations because of the importance of prior behavior on the behavior at any instant. However, it is not necessary that multivariate uncertainty analysis be concerned exclusively with prior behavior as the predictor variables. Garner (1953), for example, in the research on absolute judgments of loudness used multivariate uncertainty analysis to identify sources of predictability in the responses. In this case, of course, the stimulus itself is the most important predictor variable. But it is possible and profitable, as this experiment showed, to use a prior *stimulus* as another variable in the experiment, and even to include the subject as an analytic variable. To cite one case only, with twenty stimuli and twenty responses, information transmission from stimuli to responses is approximately 1.6 bits. When subjects are also included as a predictor variable, the multiple contingent uncertainty rises to 2.0 bits, and when the preceding stimulus is included in addition, the total predictability rises to 2.3 bits of uncertainty. It was also possible to show that the extent to which subjects and preceding stimuli contribute to total predictability depends on the number of stimulus categories used—the more categories, the greater the importance of these extra variables.

McGill (1957b) used multivariate uncertainty analysis in determining the relative importance of the preceding response in a psychophysical judgment as a function of the noise level. His subjects were required to identify one of four tones differing in frequency and at different noise levels. McGill then determined the information transmission with respect to just the stimuli and then also with respect to the previous response. His data, which are shown in Fig. 4.1, show that the extent to which the previous response can be used to predict the next response depends on the noise level, and thus on the amount of prediction which can be obtained from the stimuli alone. This result is very reasonable, since it suggests that behavior depends on previous behavior most when it is the least stimulus structured.

Edwards (1956) has used multivariate information analysis with decision making experiments involving different amounts and probabilities of reward. He used both preceding events and the outcomes of these events as predictor variables. In a later paper, Edwards (1961) also used the multivariate analysis with data from a proba-

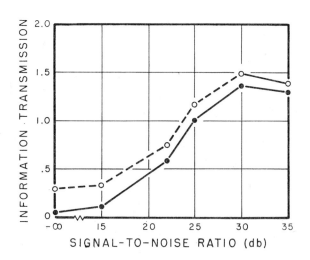

FIG. 4.1. Multiple information transmission for judgments of frequency of four tones as a function of signal-to-noise level. The bottom curve is the simple contingent uncertainty between responses and stimuli. The top curve is the multiple contingent uncertainty in which responses are predicted from stimuli and from the previous response. (After McGill, 1957b.)

bility learning experiment, again using preceding stimuli and preceding guesses (responses) as predictor variables. In both of these cases Edwards used multivariate analysis in a fairly detailed manner, separately identifying sources of prediction from different variables and from combinations of variables.

These several illustrations of the use of multivariate analysis as a statistical technique have been presented both to demonstrate the use of the technique in this manner, and also as a means of emphasizing and contrasting the use of multivariate analysis solely as a statistical technique and its use as an analytic model which not only aids in the analysis of data but in the design of the experiment as well.

We noted earlier that, in the uses discussed so far, the addition of extra predictor variables in no way changes the nature of the criterion variable. The extra predictor variables are added simply to account for uncertainty which cannot be accounted for on the basis of the primary predictor variable. Thus there would be little point in adding predictor variables unless the error uncertainty with fewer variables is moderately large. Since the maximum value of the multiple contingent uncertainty is limited by the uncertainty of the criterion variable, and since this value is not affected by the number of predictor variables, it is clear that the addition of predictor variables is useful only if a moderate amount of the criterion uncertainty remains to be accounted for. There are other situations, however, in which the addition of predictor variables increases the potential magnitude of the multiple contingent uncertainty, and we shall discuss these situations now.

MULTIDIMENSIONAL STIMULUS JUDGMENTS

In an ideal communications system, it is possible to state a channel capacity for information transmission, either for single events or for rate of information transmission, and the form in which the information comes should make no difference. In other words, information is the commodity to be processed, and as long as the total amount of the commodity remains below the capacity of the system, the system can process all of it. However, as I pointed out in Chapter One, the distinction which MacKay (1950) makes between logon and metron information content is very meaningful when we deal with human organisms as information processors. At least roughly speaking, we can identify metron content as the precision of perceptual judgment on a single sensory dimension—the type of process we discussed in Chapter Three. When dealing only with metron content, we were able to draw the conclusion that there is a fixed upper limit of information transmission which cannot be exceeded even with further increases in input or stimulus uncertainty. In other words, the concept of a channel capacity for human perceptual discrimination seems quite justified as long as we are dealing only with metron information content, that is, as long as stimulus uncertainty changes only with respect to a single sensory or perceptual dimension. Furthermore, the channel capacity for metron information is remarkably small, rarely exceeding 3 bits for a single dimension.

We also saw in Chapter Three that when dealing with rate of information transmission it is not possible to exchange rate for stimulus uncertainty and maintain the same rate of information transmission. In a sense, number of stimulus presentations per second is a form of logon information in that it represents independent successive presentations of the information. In equation form,

$$\text{Rate} = nU(S), \tag{4.19}$$

where $U(S)$ is the uncertainty per stimulus presented, and n is the number of stimuli presented per unit time. Now these two terms can vary reciprocally to maintain the same rate, but when we carry out the experiment with human performance, the two terms do not turn out to be equivalent. In order to maintain a high rate, we must have relatively large stimulus uncertainty and relatively few presentations per second. In other words, there seem to be limiting time factors involved in human performance which are not exchangeable with stimulus uncertainty.

In this section, we shall discuss the general question of ways and means of maximizing information transmission in human perceptual performance, and in particular we shall examine the experimental results which are obtained when stimulus information is varied by changing the number of stimulus dimensions along with, or instead of, changes in uncertainty per stimulus. In the multivariate analytic terms we discussed earlier in this chapter, we shall be concerned with experiments which have been set up to determine information transmission from several predictor or stimulus variables.

In most of these experiments, increases in logon content of the stimulus are accompanied by equivalent increases in the response uncertainty, and usually in a form which allows multivariate analysis of the response as well as of the stimuli. For example, when we combine stimulus changes in pitch and in loudness, it is customary to have a response system which responds differentially and identifiably with these two parameters. This characteristic of such experiments is not, of course, mandatory. It is quite possible to have five pitches combined orthogonally with five loudnesses, and to assign an arbitrary number from 1 to 25 to each of the resultant tones. We can even assign fewer than twenty-five numbers, as Eriksen and Hake (1955b) did for judgments of visual stimuli. Such procedures would make considerable difference in the analysis of the results and in the interpretation of the results.

Odor and taste

One of the most straightforward experiments involving multidimensional stimulus presentation and analysis was carried out by Beebe-Center, Rogers, and O'Connell (1955). They measured information transmission for absolute taste judgments of concentrations of salt and sucrose. When various numbers of sucrose steps were used alone, a maximum of 1.69 bits of information transmission was obtained. When various saline solutions were used alone, an information transmission of 1.70 bits was obtained. Then sixteen compound solutions were used, consisting of all of the combinations of four concentrations of salt and four of sucrose. From the matrix of absolute judgments obtained, a total information transmission of 2.25 bits was computed. This figure corresponds to a joint multiple contingent uncertainty such as that partitioned in Eq. 4.18.

From the total matrix these authors then constructed two submatrices, one corresponding to the 4 x 4 matrix for judgments of salt alone, and the other to the 4 x 4 matrix for judgments of sucrose alone. The two direct contingent uncertainties obtained from these matrices were 1.14 and 1.00 bits respectively, adding to a total of 2.14 bits, just slightly less than the total of 2.25 bits of multiple information transmission. Now the two submatrices give two of the four contingency terms involved in the total—the salt-salt and the sucrose-sucrose terms. The other two contingency terms (cross contingencies) would be obtained from a salt-sucrose matrix and from a sucrose-salt matrix, in which in each case the first term is the stimulus variable and the second is the response variable. Thus the sucrose-salt matrix would give a measure of the amount of correlation between judgments of salt and amounts of sucrose. The fact that the two direct contingency terms give a sum nearly equal to the total contingent uncertainty means that the cross-contingency terms and all of the interactions are negligible. In other words, even though the judgments were combined in the task, they were apparently quite independent.

Notice, however, that the total information transmission for the two-dimensional judgments is substantially larger, by about 0.5 bit, than the information transmission obtained for either stimulus dimension alone. And yet the total is not as large as the sum of the transmissions when each dimension has been used separately. This sum is 3.39, considerably larger than the value of 2.25 bits obtained from compound judgments. Thus it would appear that the use of two stimulus dimensions gives greater total information transmission than can be obtained with one dimension, but when the two dimensions are used, the information transmission from each dimension alone is considerably reduced.

Similar results have been obtained for judgments of odor. Engen and Pfaffmann (1959) had shown that about 1.5 bits of information transmission can be obtained for judgments of odor intensity. However, when odor intensity and quality were used together, these same authors (1960) found that quality gave about 3.5 bits of information transmission while intensity gave only approximately 0.3 bit. Since odor quality is itself a multidimensional stimulus, the rather high figure for it is not too surprising. And the unusually low figure for judgments of intensity is to some extent due to the fact that the intensities were made equivalent in physical dilution terms, not in terms of judged intensity. Nevertheless these results confirm the fact that greater information transmission can be obtained from multidimensional stimuli, although at the cost of lower information transmission per dimension.

Visual position

It will be recalled that Hake and Garner (1951) had shown that the channel capacity for judgments of position on a line was approximately 3.2 bits of uncertainty. Klemmer and Frick (1953) and Osborne, Quastler, and Tweedell (1955) have obtained judgments of positions of dots in a square. In other words, they have used two spatial dimensions rather than one. These two sets of data for single dot judgments are shown as the circles in Fig. 4.2, and the agreement between the two experiments is quite remarkable. Furthermore, the Klemmer and Frick transmission figures were computed from the total matrix, and thus their data are for the total multiple contingent uncertainty. The Osborne et al. data were computed from matrices for the two dimensions separately, so that they were using only the direct contingency terms. The good agreement between these data (as well as some direct checks which Osborne et al. made) indicates again that judgments of the two dimensions are quite independent.

The channel capacity for this type of judgment is approximately 4.4 bits of uncertainty. Since the channel capacity for judgments of a

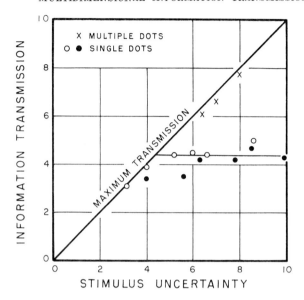

Fig. 4.2. Information transmission for absolute judgments of positions of dots in a square. Multiple-dot data and open circles are from Klemmer and Frick (1953). Filled-in circles are data from Osborne, Quastler, and Tweedell (1955).

single dimension is 3.2 bits, we once again have the result that information transmission is greater with two dimensions than with one, but at a cost in information transmission for each dimension separately. The total increases, but the component contingent uncertainties decrease.

The x's plotted in Fig. 4.2 are some transmission data from the Klemmer and Frick experiments in which more than one dot were presented simultaneously. They presented as many as four dots simultaneously on a 3 x 3 grid, thus greatly increasing the number of possible stimuli. Their results show that total information transmission can be considerably increased by this method, and in fact was close to being perfect. This procedure of presenting more than one stimulus at a time is as much a method of increasing the dimensionality of the stimulus as is the procedure of having a single stimulus vary simultaneously in more than one dimension, and we shall have more to say about this problem later. It should be noted, however, that the information transmission figures computed by Klemmer and Frick for the multiple-dot data are total information transmissions, since they treated each dot pattern as a single stimulus. Thus these computations include all of the discrimination exhibited by the subjects.

Osborne et al. also report some experiments in which dial readings were used. They found that when a single dial of 360° was used, about 4.2 bits of information transmission were obtained, and when subjects were required to report on two dials presented simultaneously, about 6.3 bits were obtained. Thus the multiple presentation increased the total information transmission, but with a decrease in the information transmission per dial. Similar results were obtained when more dials were used, or when two or three pointers on a single dial were used. The pattern seems to be clearly established that *an increase in the dimensionality of the stimulus increases total information transmission, but decreases information transmission per dimension.*

An experiment involving both the dimensionality problem and the rate problem was reported by Klemmer (1956). In this experiment subjects were required to track a randomly moving target by touching the successive stimuli with a stylus. The target was presented in one or two dimensions, and changed as rapidly as the subject responded to it (that is, the task was self-paced). Since the subjects were instructed to respond with complete accuracy, and the target changed only after a correct response, all of the information presented is transmitted. The variation is only in the rate at which it is transmitted. The results of this experiment, with information transmission rate being the dependent variable, are given in Fig. 4.3. These two curves show that

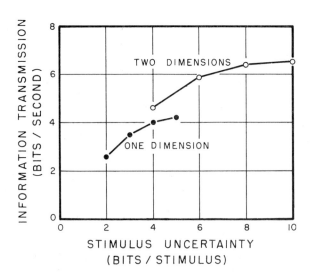

FIG. 4.3. Information transmission rate as a function of stimulus uncertainty for one- and two-dimensional tracking. (After Klemmer, 1956.)

if stimulus uncertainty in bits per stimulus is the same, information transmission rate is better when the stimulus uncertainty is two-dimensional rather than one-dimensional, and we have confirmation of the general result that information transmission is better with multidimensional stimuli.

These results also confirm those mentioned previously that maximum information rate occurs with maximum stimulus uncertainty. In other words, in this self-pacing task, while there was some increase in stimulus rate with a decrease in stimulus uncertainty, the increased stimulus rate is not sufficient to offset the lowered uncertainty per stimulus. As a concrete example, when the uncertainty per stimulus was 2 bits in the one-dimensional task, the subjects responded at a rate of 1.32 targets per second, with a resultant information transmission rate of 2.64 bits per second. When the stimulus uncertainty was increased to 4 bits per stimulus, the subjects responded at a rate of 1.00 targets per second. Thus a doubling of the stimulus uncertainty did not lead to a halving of the stimulus rate, but only to a decrease of about 24 percent. In other words, as we have seen before, actual stimulus rate tends to be fairly stable, so that information transmission rate is at a maximum when stimulus uncertainty is at a maximum.

In one sense, this result with respect to rate constitutes a contradiction of the more general result. Rate itself can be considered a dimensionality problem, since successive stimuli can be considered successive independent dimensions or logons. However, when logon content is increased by increasing the number of successive stimuli, it is not as effective as is metron content for maximizing performance. When logon content is increased either by increasing the dimensionality of a single stimulus or by increasing the number of simultaneously presented stimuli, then it is a more effective means of obtaining high information transmission than is increasing metron content of the stimulus.

Auditory stimuli

Several experiments on stimulus dimensionality with regard to auditory discrimination have been carried out by Pollack and his co-workers. Pollack (1953) first combined judgments of pitch and loudness. Under the particular conditions of this experiment, with unidimensional tests, he obtained 1.8 bits of information transmission for pitch and 1.7 bits for loudness judgments, giving a sum of 3.5 bits. When simultaneous pitch and loudness judgments were made, the total information transmission was 3.1 bits, again confirming the result of an increase in information transmission when two dimensions are used, but at a decrease in information transmission per dimension.

When information transmission for just pitch and just loudness were computed from the two-dimensional judgment data, the transmissions were 1.6 and 1.3 bits respectively. The sum of these direct contingency terms is 2.9 bits, just slightly under the total information transmission. Thus for multidimensional stimuli in taste, visual perception, and audition we have evidence that the two dimensions are judged quite independently.

There is something of a dilemma in this finding. The evidence from the multidimensional judgments themselves consistently has indicated that for all practical purposes two simultaneous judgments have gone on together with little or no interaction between them. Yet the evidence also shows that the accuracy of judgment of each dimension is decreased by the requirement of a simultaneous judgment. Thus clearly the addition of another stimulus variable affects accuracy of judgment of the single variable, but not in a manner which produces a direct interaction between the two judgments.

Pollack and Ficks (1954) later carried out a series of experiments involving as many as eight simultaneous auditory dimensions. Real ingenuity was required to find eight different dimensions, and these authors accomplished it by using an alternating noise and tone. The eight dimensions were frequency of the tone, frequency range of the noise, intensity of tone, intensity of noise, rate of interruption, percentage of time that tone was on rather than noise, total signal duration, and apparent direction of source of sound. Each of these variables was dichotomous. This experimental condition was compared with one using six dimensions but with two, three, or five steps per dimension. The results show that all of these conditions except that involving six binary dimensions (which gave slightly lower information transmission) gave nearly the same total information transmission—about 7.0 bits. This value, of course, is considerably higher than what has been obtained for any single dimension and is exceeded only by the multiple dot data of Klemmer and Frick. This amount of information corresponds to approximately 128 differentiable auditory signals, and is of an order that comes closer to our intuitive feelings about the kind of discriminations we make in the everyday world.

That such signals can be used in a more realistic way was shown by Sumby, Chambliss, and Pollack (1958), who devised a set of auditory signals to be used as an alphabet. They employed four stimulus variables, with two, three, or five alternatives per variable. Their results showed that three alternatives per variable gave the best performance, agreeing with the suggestion in the Pollack and Ficks results, that three levels per dimension are better than two. Certainly at this stage it seems that maximum information transmission will be obtained with humans when no more than three alternatives are used with a single variable, but with many variables involved.

Overlearned stimuli

Such a conclusion must be modified for certain kinds of perceptual problem. Just as we noticed in the last chapter that extended practice can lead to substantially higher information transmission for unidimensional stimuli, we must realize that certain types of stimuli are thoroughly overlearned by the ordinary subject before the experiment. Anderson and Fitts (1958) used this type of stimulus in presenting nine numerals as stimuli, along with colors and spatial position. Numerals are, of course, thoroughly overlearned form stimuli, and information transmission with them will be very great, and to a considerable extent unrelated to the number of alternatives actually used in the experiment.

In the first part of their experiment, these authors required judgments of either nine alternative numerals or nine alternative colors. For each type of judgment, three, four, five, or six stimuli were presented adjacently and simultaneously. The total information transmission about numerals or colors is given in Fig. 4.4 as a function of the

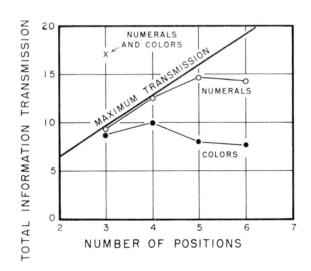

FIG. 4.4. Information transmission as a function of the number of simultaneously presented stimulus positions for judgments of numerals or colors. The single point is for judgments of both numerals and colors together. (Data from Anderson and Fitts, 1958.)

number of simultaneously presented stimuli. With numerals, information transmission is very nearly at its maximum with as many as five different positions presented at once, but with colors, somewhat less information transmission is obtained with a maximum at four different stimuli. In discussing the Klemmer and Frick data, I pointed out that the use of several stimuli simultaneously is a means of increasing the dimensionality of the stimulus. In the former case, since the multiple dots were presented on the same visual matrix, each dot was not separately identifiable and thus could not be treated in analysis as a single variable. These authors simply treated each possible dot pattern as a single stimulus in their data analysis. In the present case, however, the Anderson and Fitts method of presentation allows the possibility of a complete multivariate analysis in which each stimulus position is treated as a separate variable. The data plotted in Fig. 4.4 represent, for each condition, the sums of the information transmissions obtained for each stimulus position separately. In other words, these data are the sums of the direct contingency terms, and do not include any information transmission which would come from cross contingency terms, or from interactions.

Now previous experiments with taste, visual dots, and auditory perception have suggested that the dimensional judgments involved are quite independent, and that the cross contingent uncertainties and the interaction terms are relatively unimportant. However, the fact that the two curves in Fig. 4.4 both show an actual drop in total information transmission with an increase in the number of position variables leads to the suspicion that the cross contingent uncertainties and the interaction uncertainties may not be negligible, and that the reason for the drop in information transmission with an increase in number of variables is that more of the information transmission is lost by not taking account of these other terms. Table 4.5 is a very simple illustration of a pattern of data which are not unrealistic but in which the total joint multiple contingent uncertainty is considerably larger than the sum of the two direct contingencies. In that table, we are assuming that x is, by the nature of the experiment, directly related to v, and that y is directly related to w. To make the illustration concrete, we can assume that v is the first stimulus position and w is the second position. Then x is the stated response to the first stimulus position, and y is the stated response to the second stimulus position. Now this pattern of hypothetical data assumes that whenever both stimuli are the same, the response is completely accurate for both stimulus positions; but when the two stimuli are different, v_2w_1, or

Table 4.5

A matrix of probabilities in which the joint multiple contingent uncertainty $U(x, y:v, w)$ is substantially larger than the sum of the two direct simple contingencies, indicating that the cross contingencies and interactions are important.

	v_1w_1	v_2w_1	v_1w_2	v_2w_2	Σ
x_1y_1	.25	0	0	0	.25
x_2y_1	0	.20	.05	0	.25
x_1y_2	0	.05	.20	0	.25
x_2y_2	0	0	0	.25	.25

$$U(x, y:v, w) = 2.0 - 0.36 = 1.64 \text{ bits}$$
$$U(x:v) \quad\quad = 1.0 - 0.47 = 0.53 \text{ bit}$$
$$U(y:w) \quad\quad = 1.0 - 0.47 = 0.53 \text{ bit}$$

v_1w_2, occasional reversals in the responses occur. With this actual pattern of data, the sum of the two direct contingencies is 1.06 bits, which is 0.58 bit less than the joint multiple term.

To refer back to the Anderson and Fitts experiment, if subjects produced a moderately high number of reversal errors (that is, reversal with respect to position), then the sum of the direct contingencies could underestimate the total multivariate information transmission. Suppose, for example, that the stimulus was "red," "yellow," "blue" in successive positions. If a response of "yellow," "blue," "red" occurs more often than a response like "green," "violet," "orange," then there will be significant cross contingency terms as well as interaction terms.

However, to return to the actual experiment, Anderson and Fitts also presented to their subjects simultaneous color and numeral combinations at three stimulus positions. In other words, they were using six stimulus variables: color and form at each of three positions. The information transmission obtained under this condition, when color and form each had nine alternative values, is shown in Fig. 4.4 as the "X." Its value is 17 bits. When color was used alone with three positions, information transmission was 8.8 bits, and when numerals were used with three positions, information transmission was 9.4 bits. The sum of these two values is 18.2 bits, which is 1.2 bits more than that obtained with the compound color-form stimuli. Thus we once again have evidence that the addition of extra stimulus dimensions increases total information transmission, but at some cost in information transmission per dimension.

Correlated stimulus dimensions

The experiments we have been discussing have all involved orthogonal, or uncorrelated, stimulus dimensions. It is the lack of correlation which makes possible the increase in information transmission since the total number of possible stimuli is increased by the addition of new variables. If the response schema is also appropriately changed, then increased information transmission is at least possible, even if it has been at a maximum with one variable, since the maximum possible has been increased with the addition of another variable. Typically in these experiments, the response schema is one appropriately identifying each of the several variables. For example, in the Anderson and Fitts experiment, responses separately identified position, color, and form. Such a response schema is, of course, necessary for a multivariate *response* analysis, since only with such a schema can we determine which response variable is appropriate to which stimulus variable.

The results of these experiments have suggested that maximum information transmission is obtained when a large number of stimulus dimensions is used, with a relatively small number of alternatives per dimension. Throughout these experiments runs the implication that an observer who is to be an efficient information transmitter must be able to conceptualize the perceptual problem in terms of a large number of discrete dimensions, and that the use of a large number of alternatives per dimension can only serve to confuse him.

An experiment reported by Eriksen and Hake (1955b), however, shows that this is not the only means by which multidimensional stimuli can be used to increase the information transmission of humans. In their experiment they used size, hue, and brightness as the stimulus variables, and had twenty stimulus alternatives for each of these variables. The response schema used by them was an arbitrary code number from 1 through 20. Now when each stimulus dimension was used singly, the average information transmission was 2.75 bits, which is equivalent to about seven stimulus categories. Thus the twenty stimulus and response categories were considerably more than the demonstrated perceptual discriminability showed was necessary, and the response uncertainty was considerably greater than the information transmission achieved. In other words, the information transmission possible with twenty categories was much greater than that achieved.

In a second series of judgments, these authors paired the three variables in the three possible ways, but in a correlated manner. That is to say, each color was paired with a particular size, or each size was paired with a particular brightness, and this pairing remained the same throughout the experiment. Such a procedure in no way increases stimulus uncertainty, since the total number of stimulus alternatives remains the same—twenty. Since the response schema was not changed, the maximum information transmission possible remained the same. The actual average information transmission obtained for the three pairs of variables was 3.43 bits, an improvement of 0.68 bits over the unidimensional judgments.

Then in a third series of judgments, all three variables were used simultaneously, again in a completely correlated manner. With this series of judgments, information transmission was 4.11 bits, an improvement of 1.36 bits over the unidimensional judgments. Since twenty response categories allow a maximum of 4.32 bits of information transmission, it is also clear that the use of the three correlated stimulus dimensions produced nearly perfect discrimination for the series of twenty stimuli. (4.11 bits is equivalent to seventeen or eighteen categories.)

Eriksen (1952) had also shown that search time on a visual display was decreased if the number of dimensions on which the objects differed was increased. In a similar type of experiment, Green and Anderson (1955, 1956) found that visual search time for a particular number on a display was decreased if color or size were used as additional cues. Eriksen (1957) would argue that these results are due to the fact that there is a gain in discrimination, and thus in information transmission, as long as the various perceptual dimensions *can* lead to independent responses. In other words, it does not seem to matter that the actual stimuli are correlated as long as the perceptual dimensions are to some extent uncorrelated.

It should be noticed that the Eriksen and Hake result shows approximately the same amount of information transmission for three variables as do other experiments using comparable stimuli. Thus increasing the dimensionality of the stimuli in a correlated manner seems to be an effective means of increasing information transmission —with the proviso that the total number of stimuli and of responses be sufficiently large to allow the improvement in information transmission to occur. In other words, the critical factor involved in all of these experiments is perceptual independence of the stimulus dimensions. *As long as the dimensions are perceptually independent, then addition of new dimensions will increase total discrimination and information transmission.*

SPEECH DISCRIMINATION

Some of these concepts concerning perceptual discrimination have existed in the literature on linguistics for some time. In particular, Roman Jakobson in the late 1930's was beginning to express the idea that the most adequate description of speech as an auditory stimulus was to use as many specific features or dimensions as possible, with as few discriminations (alternatives) per dimension as possible. These ideas were spelled out with concrete suggestions concerning the possible dimensions which might be used by Jakobson, Fant, and Halle (1952). Lotz (1950) had suggested eight possible distinctive features—gravity, nasality, vocality, saturation, continuity, voice, glottalization, and tenseness—and had also suggested that binary opposition is the primary patterning principle. Halle (1954) also made explicit that the optimum discrimination system is one which has as many dimensions as possible with the minimum of two alternatives per dimension.

This emphasis, of course, sounds quite like the inevitable conclusion which comes from the research on multidimensional stimulus judgments, and it is interesting to note, as an aside, that the beginnings of this emphasis preceded the introduction of formal information measurement to the world of science. It is at times tempting to assume that information concepts created and solved psychological research problems, whereas it is clear that these concepts have been very useful, but not entirely indispensable.

I mentioned in Chapter Three, in our discussion of speech discrimination, that it is quite possible that speech will not show a simple channel capacity, even though our procedure for estimating information transmission actually suggests such a limiting information transmission for each level of noise. While the channel capacity concept seems to be valid for single perceptual dimensions, it is not necessarily valid when stimulus uncertainty is increased by increasing the number of stimulus dimensions instead of by increasing uncertainty per dimension. The linguists suggest that speech is actually composed of a multidimensional system of stimulus parameters. If speech must be considered as a multidimensional stimulus, then a restriction on the number of words in the test vocabulary becomes a mixture of dimensional restriction and of uncertainty per dimension, and the resultant changes in information transmission should not indicate a simple channel capacity.

Miller and Nicely (1955) have carried out a direct experimental test of some of these ideas concerning the nature of the speech stimulus. They studied discrimination of sixteen different consonant sounds by forming nonsense syllables with the vowel *a* as in *father* serving as the common vowel sound which was preceded by each of the sixteen consonants. They determined patterns of confusions for these sounds under several different conditions of noise masking and frequency distortion. We shall be concerned here only with the noise-masking experiments.

For purposes of analysis, each of the consonants was classified according to each of five different linguistic features: voicing, nasality, affrication (whether articulators are closed completely), duration, and place of articulation. Each of these features was treated as a binary opposition except place of articulation, for which three alternatives were used—front, middle, and back. Both the stimulus words and the response words could be classed according to each of these features, and confusion matrices for each feature could be set up to determine information transmission for each feature separately. Such computed terms correspond to what we have called the direct contingent uncertainties. Total information transmission was also computed for the entire matrix of stimuli and responses.

The results of this experiment for different signal-to-noise ratios are shown in Fig. 4.5. Each curve shows the information transmission for each of the five stimulus features as a function of the noise level. These curves differ in two important respects. First, each feature has

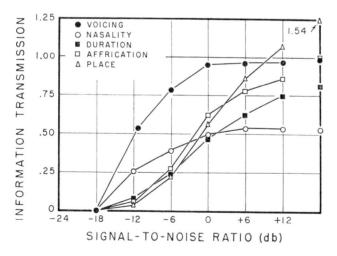

Fig. 4.5. Information transmission as a function of signal-to-noise level for five different speech features. The maximum possible information transmission for each feature is shown at the right. (Data from Miller and Nicely, 1955.)

a different maximum information transmission which depends on the number of consonants which have each of the two or three alternatives. These maximum uncertainties are shown on the right hand margin of the graph. For example, nasality has a low maximum uncertainty because only two consonants, "m" and "n," are nasal. On the other extreme, place of articulation, with its three possible alternatives, has a maximum uncertainty of 1.54 bits. Thus the maximum information transmission which can be achieved with each of the features differs.

Second, the noise level at which maximum information transmission is achieved for each feature differs also. For example, both voicing and affrication have maximum uncertainties of 1.0 bit, but this maximum has been nearly achieved for voicing at a signal-to-noise ratio of 0 db, while for affrication it still has not been achieved at a signal-to-noise ratio 12 db greater.

The total information transmission, computed from the complete matrix, was 3.55 bits at a signal-to-noise ratio of +12 db. The sum of all of the direct contingent uncertainties at this same level is 4.21 bits. In this case, then, the several dimensions are not operating independently, and it is impossible that they should since the stimulus dimensions themselves are partially correlated. The degree of this correlation, and thus redundancy, can be seen in the fact that the sum of the maximum possible transmissions per dimension is 4.89 bits, while the sixteen different stimuli can transmit only 4.0 bits. Miller and Nicely argue, however, that since the proportionate discrepancy between total transmission and sum of the direct contingent uncertainties is approximately the same for maximum uncertainties and for obtained information transmissions, then the *perceptual* dimensions are independent, even though the stimulus dimensions themselves are not. This argument cannot be made unequivocally, but is certainly reasonable. The point being made by Miller and Nicely is similar to that which came out in the Eriksen and Hake experiment with correlated stimulus dimensions. The critical factor seems to be the independence of the perceptual dimensions, not the independence of the stimulus dimensions as actually presented.

Nevertheless, these data make it clear why there should be some doubt about the possibility of there being a simple channel capacity for speech at any given noise level. A set of words is certainly multidimensional in character, and the different dimensions themselves do not have the same channel capacity at any given noise level. Thus it would be difficult to increase a test vocabulary (and thus stimulus uncertainty) without at the same time increasing dimensionality of the stimuli. However, if dimensionality is increased, we have little reason to expect the channel capacity concept to be valid.

INDEPENDENCE OF INFORMATION AND RESTRICTION OF SET

In Chapter Three, we considered the effect of stimulus uncertainty in terms of two communicative acts, one being the act of the restriction of the set of possible alternatives, and the other being the direct perceptual act in which the specific stimulus is presented to the subject. We noted then that in order for these two communicative acts to be jointly maximally effective, the information obtained from them should be independent.

This problem is of considerable interest in connection with multidimensional stimuli, because of the possibility of deliberately selecting restricted sets which make use of the human's greater ability to obtain information from multidimensional stimuli than from unidimensional stimuli. Suppose, to use a concrete example, we consider the stimulus dimensions used by Eriksen and Hake mentioned above. These authors used twenty categories each of size, hue, and brightness, but when they combined these dimensions, they combined them in a perfectly correlated manner. Now we can consider the twenty combined stimuli as being selected from an original set of eight thousand stimuli —all of the possible combinations of each of the twenty values of each of the three dimensions. We could select twenty stimuli from this set in many different ways, and the effect of restriction of stimulus set would be quite different depending on the manner in which we selected the stimuli.

Suppose first that we select twenty stimuli which are all identical in hue and brightness, but which differ only with respect to size. Now we know that information transmission for the single dimension is approximately 2.75 bits. But suppose that we select the twenty stimuli which Eriksen and Hake actually used—twenty stimuli which varied maximally in all three stimulus dimensions. In this case, the obtained result shows that we would get 4.11 bits of information transmission—a considerably greater amount than we obtained with the first 20 stimuli selected.

Suppose we consider this experiment as one involving two communicative acts. The subject starts with an original uncertainty of approximately 13 bits (eight thousand possible stimuli). By our statement that the correct stimulus is one of twenty (4.3 bits), we give the subject 8.7 bits of unambiguous information. Then his perceptual judgment reduces the uncertainty still more, 2.75 bits in one case, and 4.11 bits in the second. In the former case the total is considerably below the required 13 bits, while in the latter it is almost the amount required. Thus we may conclude that the two communicative acts provided independent information in the latter case, but not in the former.

Now this hypothetical experiment is exactly like the type of experiment carried out with speech work to determine the effect of stimulus uncertainty on accuracy of perception of speech in noise. In Pollack's (1959a) experiment, for example, the subject starts with a stimulus set of known size, and then is told (either before or after the direct perceptual act), that the correct word is contained in a smaller subset. Insofar as speech is multidimensional in nature, however, the particular subset of stimulus words selected should have an important bearing on the accuracy. Presumably the selection is done on a random basis, so that the average accuracy will be better than the poorest possible, but poorer than the best possible. It would be interesting to see whether selecting words which differ in one, two, three, or more dimensions would lead to greater information transmission than selection on the basis of fewer dimensional differences. It seems almost certain that such an experiment with speech would show results similar to those of Eriksen and Hake. We will discuss this problem of selection of stimuli on discrimination further in the next chapter.

The question of whether some of these effects are primarily stimulus effects or primarily response effects can be very meaningful in this context as well. It may be, for example, that a perceptual set can be established which is selective with regard to stimulus dimensions, but not simply with regard to sets of stimuli which vary on many dimensions. In other words, sets of stimuli selected on the basis of maximum variation of several stimulus dimensions may show no difference in terms of restriction before or after the stimulus presentation; but sets which restrict the possible stimuli to those varying on a single dimension may show a difference depending on when the restriction is carried out. It seems plausible, for example, that if I know ahead of time which of several dimensions to attend, I might improve my performance; whereas if I must attend to all in order to be sure that I attend to the correct one (and am not told which is correct until after the stimulus presentation), then I might do more poorly.

Such a possibility seems particularly plausible when we consider the experimental results obtained with multidimensional stimuli: Information transmission is greater for multidimensional stimuli than for unidimensional stimuli but at a cost in information transmission per dimension. Thus requiring a subject to attend to several dimensions simultaneously does produce a lower judgmental accuracy per dimension, and some of this lost accuracy might be regained if the subject knows ahead of time which particular dimension to attend.

To illustrate the plausibility of this suggestion, suppose that we select two stimuli which the subject must discriminate, and that these two are selected from the sixteen possible with four dichotomous variables. In one case we restrict the set to xxxo or xxxx. If these patterns of x's and o's are presented visually, spaced so widely apart that the subject cannot look at all of them at once, then clearly it is to the subject's advantage to know ahead of the stimulus presentation what these two stimulus possibilities are, since he can then look at the last position and get perfect discrimination. And with these stimuli, restriction after the stimulus presentation would be much less valuable, since he might have looked at the wrong element (dimension) of the stimulus.

Suppose, on the other hand, that the restricted set of stimuli is xxxx or oooo. In this case it would not matter where the subject looked, since any stimulus dimension would give him perfect discrimination. Thus with this set of restricted stimuli it should make no difference whether the set was restricted before or after the stimulus presentation. In the former case, restriction before the stimulus would have been better because it would have permitted useful selective attention; while in the latter case the selective attention was of no value.

The nature of these restricted sets—that is, the nature of the redundancy—will be discussed in some detail in the next chapter, but there is one point to emphasize here: That is that the second set of stimuli is far better for discrimination purposes than the first set (just as was true for the Eriksen and Hake correlated stimulus dimensions). Thus selections which are optimum for discrimination purposes should not show a difference in set restriction before or after the stimulus presentation, but selections which are poor for discrimination purposes should show an advantage in set restriction before the stimulus presentation.

This illustration, with the use of a mechanical type of selective attention (actually looking in a different direction), seems clear cut. The result is a little less obvious if a subject must selectively attend to a single dimension of a unitary stimulus, such as the color of a stimulus which varies in size and brightness, where the selective attending cannot be done on a mechanical basis. It would seem more than profitable to investigate the role of multidimensional stimuli with this type of problem.

COMMENTARY

The experiments discussed in this chapter induce a clear principle concerning human perceptual discrimination: *Discrimination is best when the stimuli to be discriminated vary simultaneously on many different dimensions.* As we saw in the last chapter, it is difficult to obtain very large information transmissions with single perceptual dimensions. Quite large values have been obtained with multiple stimulus dimensions, however—values which correspond somewhat better to our intuitive feelings about the discrimination complexity actually required and carried out by humans in the ordinary course of their lives. Anderson and Fitts, for example, using stimulus variables which in themselves provide high information transmissions—several simultaneous stimuli differing in both form and color—were able to show that 17 bits of information transmission can be obtained with single brief exposures. This value corresponds to perfect discrimination between over 131,000 alternative stimuli—a truly large amount of discrimination.

This experiment, contrasted with other multidimensional stimulus experiments, shows that even though the general principle can be stated that discrimination is at a maximum with many dimensions, there is still a very meaningful experimental problem of determining the particular types of stimulus dimension, which when compounded lead to maximum discrimination. Anderson and Fitts used colors, which we had previously seen are highly discriminable, and numerals, which are a thoroughly overlearned type of visual form. When used jointly, these stimulus dimensions provide great discrimination. In addition, several experiments reported here suggest that the most effective means of increasing the number of stimulus dimensions is actually to present several stimuli simultaneously but spatially separate. Such a procedure, of course, can easily be used only with visual stimuli, although Broadbent (1958) describes auditory research which makes use of the principle of simultaneous stimulation from several spatially separate sources.

It is interesting to note that information transmission is not greatly improved when successive presentations of individual stimuli are used, and yet each successive presentation can be considered another dimension in the same way that the spatially separate stimuli can be considered as separate dimensions. The crux of the matter may not be, however, the form in which the stimuli are presented, but rather the form in which the response is made, since such experiments invariably require as many discrete responses as there are discretely presented stimuli. Perhaps the problem is not unlike that described by Miller (1956) in showing that the memory span for binary digits is greatly increased if the subjects are taught to recode the digits into meaningful groups—thus using a single response system with greater uncertainty, but with fewer actual responses required.

A simple channel capacity concept is clearly inappropriate when stimulus uncertainty is increased by increasing the dimensionality of the stimuli rather than by increasing the number of steps on a single continuum.[1] A curve relating information transmission to stimulus uncertainty under conditions of increased dimensionality will show a gradual increase in information transmission, possibly reaching an effective asymptotic value with a very large number of dimensions. There certainly will be, however, no reasonably sharp break in the function such as occurs with unidimensional stimuli. Most of these experiments have shown that increased dimensionality leads to increased information transmission, but at the cost of a decrease in transmission per dimension.

This latter fact, which explains why there will be no sharp break in the function, also suggests the possibility that there could be a definite drop in the function if the information input becomes too great. (The Anderson and Fitts data actually show such a drop, although we cannot be sure that the effect is due to information overload rather than insufficient analysis.) The reason for this possibility lies in the fact that increased dimensionality has a detrimental effect as well as an advantageous effect, and it is quite conceivable that the addition of one more dimension, say, might decrease information transmission for each dimension more than the gain due to the extra dimension. If such a result were true, it would provide some understanding of the human's information processing, and would imply that the limiting capacity is a capacity to deal with dimensions, not a capacity to deal with number of alternative stimuli on a single dimension.

[1] This principle, while apparently quite firmly based on experimental evidence presented in this chapter, may be limited in generality. It is quite possible that the channel capacity concept is valid even with increased dimensionality if very short stimulus presentations are used. This problem is discussed further in Chapter Six.

It seems to me that the importance of multidimensional stimuli can hardly be overemphasized in research. Not only does the number of dimensions seem to be the critical factor in terms of total information transmission, but it seems like a most real possibility that the entire question of perceptual selective sets has to do with the dimensionality of the stimuli as restricted. As we have noted before, some experiments have indeed shown that restriction of the set of alternatives before the stimulus presentation may be better than restriction after the presentation. Thus we know that there can be some advantage to allowing a perceptual set to operate. I suspect that the critical factor concerns whether the nature of the stimuli selected for the restricted set allows selective attention to dimensions.

This whole question of the particular set of stimuli selected cannot be overemphasized. All sets of stimuli selected from the same population of stimuli are not equivalent, and the particular set selected can have as important a bearing on experimental results as the total amount of restriction. Selection by dimensions is different from selection on a single dimension, and experiments on this problem must take this factor into account. It is not sufficient, in other words, to specify the amount of restriction, or redundancy, but it is important also to specify the particular nature of the restriction. I shall discuss this problem more fully, from a slightly different orientation, in Chapter Five.

SUMMARY

When a matrix is defined in terms of more than two variables, and one of the variables, y, can be considered a criterion, and the others, w, x, etc., can be considered the predictors, the uncertainty of the criterion variable can be partitioned into several parts, some of which are new uncertainty terms.

Multiple contingent uncertainty, $U(y:w,x)$, is the total amount of uncertainty in y which can be predicted from joint values of w and x.

Multiple conditional uncertainty, $U_{wx}(y)$, is the total amount of uncertainty in y which cannot be predicted from w and x. This, plus the multiple contingent uncertainty, equals the total uncertainty in y.

Partial contingent uncertainty, $U_x(y:w)$, or equivalent forms, is the prediction of the uncertainty in y which is provided by w after the prediction provided by x is partialed out. It is the average contingent uncertainty between y and w for fixed values of x.

Interaction uncertainty, $U(\overline{wxy})$, is the amount of prediction of the uncertainty of y provided by unique combinations of w and x. This term, which may be negative with non-orthogonal predictor variables, when added to the two contingent uncertainties, provides all the multiple contingent uncertainty. Interaction terms also exist for four or more variables.

Joint multiple contingent uncertainty, $U(x, y:v, w)$, is the total amount of the uncertainty of a joint criterion variable which can be predicted from a joint predictor variable.

Multivariate uncertainty analysis has been used to some extent primarily as a statistical tool for analyzing sources of predictability. More importantly for our purposes, however, it has provided a framework within which to ask questions concerning the nature of perceptual discrimination.

Many different experiments have shown that discrimination, as measured by information transmission, is greater for multidimensional stimuli than for unidimensional stimuli. When, however, multidimensional judgments are required, the amount of information transmission obtained per dimension is less than if the dimensions had been used alone, even though the total information transmission is increased. Furthermore, the greater information transmission occurs even if the stimulus dimensions are correlated.

Analysis of information transmission for speech suggests that speech is a multidimensional stimulus, that the number of levels per dimension is two or three, and that discriminations between speech sounds are independent.

It seems very probable that when stimulus uncertainty is decreased by restricting the set along dimensional lines, rather than by restricting without changing number of dimensions, perceptual sets which are selective to dimensions can be established. Thus restriction of the set before stimulus presentation (rather than after) should be more effective when the restriction decreases the number of dimensions to which attention must be directed.

CHAPTER FIVE

The Partitioning
of Structure and Meaning

IN THE PRECEDING CHAPTERS, we have used information concepts from a particular point of view: We have been concerned primarily about the extent to which the uncertainty of one variable can be predicted from, or related to, other variables. In dealing primarily with perceptual discrimination problems, this approach is relatively straightforward and not unlike other methods of dealing with these problems except that we use a measure with greater generality.

In this chapter we shall start looking at problems from a somewhat different point of view. We shall be looking at the total constraint in an entire system of variables, and will be concerned not just with the extent to which one set of variables can predict another, but also with the relations within the prediction variables themselves. To look at problems this way gets us very close to what we call meaning, and allows us to consider psychological problems in which the idea of meaning is not at all remote. In later chapters, for example, we shall be concerned with such things as pattern perception, the nature of verbal learning, and concept formation. However, talking about meaning is a tenuous undertaking because of the ambiguity of the term itself.

Most writers on information measurement have at least tacitly assumed that the amount of information is not related to information in the ordinary or lay sense of the word, and in particular that it

138

is not related to meaning in the psychological sense. This lack of relation between information in the technical sense and meaning has been explicitly stated by many authors, and the point seems to have been accepted, since at least one recent dictionary specifically states that in communication theory information is a quantity measured without regard to meaning.

Information concepts deal with very special kinds of relations, and these relations are primarily statistical and probabilistic in nature. This fact has led writers like Bar-Hillel (1955) to make a special point of explaining that semantic information is not the same thing as statistical rarity of signals, and that information theory has little relevance to many semantic and linguistic problems. Semantics must deal with the particular relations between symbols and events, and not with statistical ensembles of messages.

At first glance the complete separation of information measurement from problems of meaning seems reasonable, since there are some very real differences between the kinds of problems dealt with. Yet most of us feel no intuitive objection when Pinkerton (1956) uses information concepts in describing musical melodies, and implies that the lower information content of nursery tunes makes them less meaningful than more complicated music. Meyer (1957) makes this relation specific in identifying meaning in music with uncertainty of the melodic pattern. Pinkerton actually stated that there is probably an optimum amount of uncertainty in the melodic pattern for music to be ideal—and again he is clearly implying that ideal music is meaningful music.

When Pinkerton states that there is an optimum amount of uncertainty in melodic patterns, he is suggesting that human subjects would be able to state a preference for one melody over another, and that such preferences would be related to the sequential uncertainty of the melodies. Thus there is the clear implication of human preference and perhaps value which is directly related to information measurement. While Pinkerton actually did not carry out any experiments involving human judgments, Berlyne (1957a, 1958a,b) has carried out similar types of experiments involving preferences for visual figures. He gave subjects various pictures or pairs of pictures and they were free to choose how long they looked at each. He found that his subjects preferred to look at the more complex pictures. More recently, Jones, Wilkinson, and Braden (1961) allowed subjects to choose various sequential patterns of lights over a 12-hour period, and they found that subjects preferred (chose more often) the more complicated series of lights, and that the longer they were in the experiment, the greater their preference for the complicated patterns. Jones et al. also clearly established that the critical variable was the predictability of the light, not just variation, by showing that highly predictable but changing patterns were chosen less often than the less predictable patterns.

I am not attempting to argue that these experiments are unambiguously related to meaning. But it is clear that these experiments involve preference and value judgments of human subjects, not just their ability to perform tasks of discrimination, speed of reaction, tracking of targets, etc. In other words, information concepts and measurement are not just relevant to the experimenter as a means of specifying the stimulus or of measuring responses and correlations between stimuli and responses. Information and uncertainty of events are directly perceived by subjects and affect the preference or value of the events to the subjects. Whether such preferences are related to meaning is a question which I will not attempt to answer completely, but I will try to show that there are some aspects of the problem of psychological meaning which can be dealt with directly by use of the various information concepts and methods of measurement.

THE NATURE OF MEANING

Certainly one of the major difficulties in dealing with psychological problems of meaning has been the extreme ambiguity of the term itself. The term *meaning* has meant many things to many people, and while the various connotations of the term are all related to some extent, occasionally they become diametrically opposed, and we find different authors coming to apparently opposite conclusions about the role of meaning in human behavior only because of differences in definitions of the term. Whenever we try to use scientifically a term which has common everyday meaning we run into difficulty because for everyday usage it is not necessary to have sharply defined terms. Furthermore, the connotations and contexts of usage of the term meaning are so many and varied that it is probably impossible to categorize in any final manner the various uses of the term. Nevertheless, certain distinctions of usage can be made and will help to clarify the role which information measurement has in dealing with meaning.

Structure and signification

Certainly one of the major points of confusion has been between meaning as structure of any closed system of events and meaning as the signification of any particular event. This is basically the distinction which Bar-Hillel was concerned about, and yet the difficulty is not unique to or caused by information concepts.

By *signification,* I mean the particular specifying or indicating relation for any single event or symbol. The signification of the word *house* is the actual structure, or its dictionary definition, or all the associations which the word brings to mind. Signification is any or all of the relations which are unique to the particular word. In a language system, each word used has its own signification. If one language system is being learned when another is already known, the word in the old language which is the equivalent of the word in the new language is, for this situation, its signification. When I say that *chien* means *dog,* then I am using the word *means* as *signifies.*

It is clear that the signification of each word, or other symbol or event, can be specified without regard to all the other symbols which exist in the closed system. I do not need to know the entire French language to know that *chien* is the equivalent of *dog,* or that *maison* signifies *house.* Thus meaning in the sense of signification is the actual equivalence relation for any single event and is not related to the statistics of the entire set of events.

By *structure* I mean the totality of the relations between events. When we say that a picture composed of randomly located dots is meaningless, we imply that we see no relations between the dots and that, therefore, the picture has no structure. If the same total number of dots is rearranged, however, we can perceive structure and the picture becomes meaningful. Similarly, a foreign language may be meaningless to us, but if we learn how to translate the foreign language into our own, it becomes meaningful because it has acquired a relational structure. Meaning in this sense again refers to the entire set of relations not just to the significations of each individual word. A particular word may be meaningful in the sense of signification, but the entire language becomes meaningful only if some structure is perceived in the total set of symbols. I am definitely not implying that meaning as structure is simply the sum of the significations of the individual words, but rather that the structure is itself meaningful.

We cannot talk about structure without talking about an entire set of events, and the totality of the relations between the events can be specified as an amount. It is, using information measurement, possible to state that one system of symbols or events is more structured than another system. When we say that one thing is more meaningful than another, we imply that more structure exists or is perceived. Thus meaning as structure can be quantified, and the information concepts are quite appropriate for its quantification.

On the other hand, meaning as signification cannot be quantified other than to say that it exists or does not exist. The signification of a word is the actual identifying relation, and it cannot exist in lesser or greater degree. It is simply a statement of the nature of a relation, and while the nature of the relation can be changed, this change is qualitative and cannot be quantified. To a child, the signification of the word *honesty* may be very simple, while to an adult it may be very complex. But this change is not one of quantity of signification, but rather of quality.

Nevertheless, psychologists have often tried to quantify meaning as signification. They have tried to state that a particular nonsense syllable, for example, is more meaningful because it leads to a greater number of associations in a given period of time. Is it realistic, however, to state that a word which leads to many associations because it is ambiguous is more meaningful than a word which leads to only a single association because of its lack of ambiguity? The signification of a word is the actual set of equivalences or associations, and there is no reasonable way in which meaning in this sense can be quantified.

Internal and external meaning

Another needed distinction about the nature of meaning is between internal and external meaning. The structure of a set of events may be internal or it may be external. When we talk about the structure of a set of dots in a picture, we are talking about the relations between the dots themselves, and not about the relations between the pattern of dots and some external object or event. It is not necessary, however, that the relations be entirely internal to the dots themselves. If, for instance, the dots are on a radar scope and represent actual aircraft flying in a real geography, the total system of dots can again be meaningful because of their external reference. The several dots on the scope at any one time may have no apparent internal structure at all, but they are nevertheless meaningful because of their relation to the real world of aircraft. The totality of the relations between the dots on the scope and the real aircraft provides structure and meaning, as long as there is a high correlation between the two sets of events.

The distinction between internal and external meaning can be seen most easily in talking about an actual language system. If I am learning the French language, I need to learn the total set of relations between my native language, English, and the new language. The extent to which these relations are invariant is the extent to which there exists an external structure for the language. At the same time, I must learn something about the internal structure of French. The symbols in any language are correlated, so that there is a structure of the language which is entirely internal to the language system itself.

Amount of structure, internal or external, can be identified with the amount of correlation between events. Insofar as one set of words is correlated with another set of words—in this instance, English words correlated with French words—then we have external structure. If there existed no equivalences between English words and French words, then English could not provide external structuring for French and vice versa. Anyone who has struggled through the learning of a foreign language is well aware of the fact that the correlation between words is not perfect, and thus that the use of one language to provide external structuring for another is at best imperfect.

Also, insofar as the language symbols (letters, sounds, or words) are correlated with each other, we have internal structure. Once again, the amount of this internal structure will be related to the degree of correlation. A set of symbols in which certain invariant relations hold between the symbols is highly structured, and one in which there exist no relations between the symbols is not structured at all.

That the internal and external structure of a language can be perceived quite independently is easily seen when we realize that we can recognize that a particular language being spoken is French, or German, or Spanish, without our having any understanding of what is actually being said. What we are recognizing is the internal structure of the language, and if languages had no internal structure we could not tell one from another without knowing the actual translation of the words. French is French, whether we can understand it or not, and it is obviously different from German.

The distinction between internal and external meaning need not be confined to meaning as structure. Signification can also be internal or external. For example, the signification of the French word *maison* may be the English word *house,* and here the signification is external since we are using a word from one language system to signify a word from another language system. Even if we don't know the translation of the word *maison*, it is quite possible for us to become familiar with those words which usually precede or follow this word in the French language itself. Those adjectives which are normally associated with the word *maison* are as much its signification as is the English equivalent. Thus signification can also be internal or external.

Other authors have suggested or implied some of the distinctions I am making here. Meyer (1956), for example, distinguishes between what he calls designative and embodied meaning, and his *designative meaning* is what I am calling external meaning, while his *embodied meaning* is what I am calling internal meaning. In both cases, however, Meyer is referring to my signification meaning—the actual equivalence relation. Royce (1959), on the other hand, identifies meaning with structure, both internal and external. I will not go this far, however, since signification must clearly be considered as one aspect of meaning.

I feel, to summarize, that meaning can be either signification or structure, and that it can be either internal or external. Furthermore, all of the four combinations of these variables exist. Thus we can have external signification or internal signification; and we can likewise have external structure or internal structure. I do not, then, feel that structure is the only kind of meaning, but rather that it represents the only kind of meaning which can be sensibly quantified.

In the rest of this chapter, and in subsequent chapters, we will use information concepts in measuring the amount of structure. We will use these concepts for both internal and external structure or meaning, and will see that the two types of structure can be advantageously considered as a single quantity—a quantity which can exist as a total amount and which can be allocated to one or the other subvariety of structure.

It should be remembered throughout, however, that we are not talking about meaning as signification, and it is very easy to forget the distinction. Structure is something which can exist in an amount, and as such puts limits on meaning as signification. For example, when I mentioned that we can learn the characteristic structure of French and recognize it as different from German, I was talking about an amount which can be learned, but the specific relations which are learned are the significations. Both French and German may, and probably do, have approximately the same amount of internal structure. Thus they do not differ in the amount of structure or meaning. However, the particular relational rules or equivalences are different and the learning of these is what makes it possible for us to distinguish the two languages even when we don't understand them. Of course, if there were no amount of internal structure, then there would be no rules to learn.

In other words, within any fixed system of symbols or events, structural meaning is prerequisite to signification meaning. Unless correlation exists between a symbol system and another symbol system or a system of real events, there can be no external signification. Unless the symbols themselves are correlated, there can be no specific rules by which the internal signification can be learned. Thus the following discussion, concerned entirely with structural meaning, is a discussion of the extent and amounts of meaning, but not with the particular relational rules.

STRUCTURE AND TOTAL CONSTRAINT

I have identified meaning with the amount of structure which exists and is perceived in a system of variables. There are many ways in which this structure can be measured and quantified, but here we are concerned primarily with information and uncertainty measures as ways of specifying the amount of structure.

I shall use the term *constraint* to refer to the amount of inter-relatedness or structure of a system of variables as measured in informational terms. As with meaning and structure itself, I shall distinguish between *total constraint, internal constraint,* and *external constraint,* and shall develop some of the mathematical relations which exist between these forms of constraint in any system of variables.

Total constraint of three variables

To begin this discussion, we shall use an alternate approach to the multivariate uncertainty analysis. It will be remembered that, in Chapter Three, when discussing bivariate probability distributions, we noted that the contingent uncertainty could be obtained by first obtaining the maximum possible uncertainty for the bivariate matrix when limited only by the row and column marginal totals, and subtracting from this figure the obtained uncertainty of the matrix. In an entirely similar manner we can determine the maximum uncertainty for a matrix formed by three or more variables, and then can subtract from this total the actual obtained uncertainty to obtain a measure of total constraint.[1]

First, for the three-variable case, with variables w, x, and y, the probability of occurrence for any cell in the three-variable matrix is $p(w)\,p(x)\,p(y)$ if there are no correlations between any of the variables, that is, if all three variables are orthogonal. From this relation it is clear that

$$U_{\max}(w, x, y) = U(w) + U(x) + U(y). \tag{5.1}$$

Now the probability of occurrence for any cell, given the actual correlations between variables, is $p(w)\,p_w(x)\,p_{wx}(y)$, or any equivalent form. From these relations,

$$
\begin{aligned}
U(w, x, y) &= U(w) + U_w(x) + U_{wx}(y) &\text{(5.2a)}\\
&= U(x) + U_x(y) + U_{xy}(w) &\text{(5.2b)}\\
&= U(y) + U_y(w) + U_{wy}(x) &\text{(5.2c)}\\
&= U(w, x) + U_{wx}(y) &\text{(5.2d)}\\
&= U(x, y) + U_{xy}(w) &\text{(5.2e)}\\
&= U(w, y) + U_{wy}(x). &\text{(5.2f)}
\end{aligned}
$$

We can use Eq. 5.1 in combination with any of these equations to obtain the components of the total constraint. If we use each of the last three forms of Eq. 5.2, then we obtain the following identities:

$$
\begin{aligned}
U(w{:}x{:}y) &= U_{\max}(w, x, y) - U(w, x, y)\\
&= U(y{:}w, x) + U(w{:}x) &\text{(5.3a)}\\
&= U(w{:}y, x) + U(y{:}x) &\text{(5.3b)}\\
&= U(x{:}w, y) + U(w{:}y). &\text{(5.3c)}
\end{aligned}
$$

In this equation, $U(w{:}x{:}y)$ is the total constraint in this system of three variables, and the colon notation again is used because we are in fact dealing with the same sort of thing as we were with a contingent uncertainty, which is simply the total constraint in a system of two variables. The order in which the terms are written is of no significance.

This equation shows that total constraint can be divided into two parts, one of which is the multiple contingent uncertainty between one variable and the other two, and the other of which is the contingent uncertainty between these latter two variables. If we now expand the various multiple contingent uncertainties, we find that

---

[1] The mathematical relations which we will discuss here have been developed by various authors, chiefly McGill (1954), Garner and McGill (1956), Garner (1958), and Watanabe (1954, 1959, 1960). Specific references will ordinarily not be made, since the material has for the most part been drawn on in a very general way.

$$U(w\!:\!x\!:\!y) \,=\, U(y\!:\!w) \,+\, U(y\!:\!x) \,+\, U(w\!:\!x) \,+\, U(\overline{wxy}). \qquad (5.4)$$

Regardless of which form of Eq. 5.3 we expand, we obtain the same equation, and it is in this form that we have the proof that there is a unique interaction term for the three-variable matrix. Thus, stated verbally, the total constraint is the sum of the contingent uncertainties between the three pairs of variables plus the interaction uncertainty for the matrix.

If we now simply transpose terms in Eq. 5.3,

$$U(y\!:\!w,\, x) \,=\, U(w\!:\!x\!:\!y) \,-\, U(w\!:\!x). \qquad (5.5a)$$
$$U(w\!:\!y,\, x) \,=\, U(w\!:\!x\!:\!y) \,-\, U(x\!:\!y). \qquad (5.5b)$$
$$U(x\!:\!w,\, y) \,=\, U(w\!:\!x\!:\!y) \,-\, U(w\!:\!y). \qquad (5.5c)$$

Thus the multiple contingent uncertainty for any of the three variables used as a criterion is the total constraint for the three-variable matrix less the contingent uncertainty between the two predictor variables. If, for example, in a particular experiment the two stimulus variables are made to be orthogonal, then the multiple contingent uncertainty for predicting the response will contain all of the total constraint. Thus if in the experiment we use two orthogonal stimulus variables to predict the response variable, we are using all of the constraint possible. However, if from the same set of data we use one of the stimulus variables as the criterion, then the multiple contingent uncertainty must be lower unless responses are orthogonal to the stimulus variable used as a criterion.

As an example, when Garner (1953) used multivariate uncertainty analysis to determine the extent to which preceding stimuli and the immediate stimuli can be used to predict the response, I was using all of the total constraint, since I had made the sequence of stimuli such that the stimuli were orthogonal with respect to preceding stimuli. If, however, I had used preceding stimuli plus the response to predict the immediate stimulus (the stimulus being judged), then the multiple contingent uncertainty would have been smaller because of the contingent uncertainty between responses and the preceding stimulus.

In other words, while the simple contingent uncertainty is a completely symmetric term, the multiple contingent uncertainty is not. With the two-variable contingency, the amount of uncertainty in x which can be predicted from y is the same as the amount in y which can be predicted from x. But not so with three variables. The variable y is not necessarily as predictable from w and x as is x from w and y. Eq. 5.5 shows that we need only know the simple contingent uncertainties in order to know which of the three possible multiple contingent uncertainties will be largest and by exactly how much. Since there is only the unique interaction term, then differences between the multiple contingent uncertainties are due only to differences in the simple contingent uncertainties.

Higher-order total constraints

Similar relations exist if we have more than three variables in our matrix. Suppose, in a four-variable matrix, we have variables v, w, x, and y. Now we have a larger maximum uncertainty by the addition of the variable v, and also an expanded term for the actual uncertainty.

$$U_{max}(v, w, x, y) = U(v) + U(w) + U(x) + U(y), \qquad (5.6)$$

and

$$U(v, w, x, y) = U(v) + U_v(w) + U_{vw}(x) + U_{vwx}(y). \qquad (5.7)$$

Subtracting the actual uncertainty from the maximum uncertainty,

$$U(v:w:x:y) = U(v:w:x) + U(y:v, w, x), \qquad (5.8)$$

and

$$U(y:v, w, x) = U(v:w:x:y) - U(v:w:x). \qquad (5.9)$$

Each of the above equations could be written in many different forms depending on which variable is used first, or which are considered predictor and which criterion variables. In words, however, once again we can state that the multiple contingent uncertainty, $U(y:v, w, x)$, is the total constraint in the four-variable matrix, $U(v:w:x:y)$, minus the total constraint in the three-variable matrix, $U(v:w:x)$, formed by the three predictor variables. Or, the uncertainty available for predicting any one variable is the total constraint in the matrix less the constraint or total contingency involving just the variables from which the prediction is being done.

It is of some interest to see how this approach to the multivariate uncertainty analysis comes out when we deal with the multiple criterion case. If x and y are the two criterion variables and v and w are the two predictor variables, then[2]

$$U(x, y:v, w) = U(v:w:x:y) - U(v:w) - U(x:y). \qquad (5.10)$$

Here we see that the joint multiple contingent uncertainty is the total constraint in the four-variable matrix minus the contingencies between each pair of grouped variables.

---

[2] The expansion of $U(x, y:v, w)$ necessary for a detailed proof is given in Eq. 4.18.

These relations can be generalized to any number of variables by writing equations of the form of Eqs. 5.9 and 5.10. Any multiple contingent uncertainty can be considered to be the total constraint in the mutivariate matrix minus the total constraint involved in each set of grouped variables. Of course, each of the terms in these equations can be expanded to see individually all of the simple contingency terms plus the various interactions. In many cases such spelling out of the terms is of little value, since each interaction cannot be individually identified as a quantity. However, one form of expansion of Eq. 5.8 is of general interest:

$$U(v\!:\!w\!:\!x\!:\!y) = U(v\!:\!w) + U(x\!:\!v, w) + U(y\!:\!v, w, x). \quad (5.11)$$

In this form, we can see that the total constraint involved in any multivariate matrix can be broken into a series of contingency terms. First we take the contingent uncertainty between two of the terms, then we add the multiple contingent uncertainty in which a third variable is predicted from the two already considered, then we add the multiple contingent uncertainty in which the fourth variable is predicted from the three already considered. The equation in this form can be expanded to any number of variables, by always simply adding the extent to which the next variable considered can be predicted from those already considered. This expansion in a sense allows us to determine the additional contribution to total constraint which can be obtained by considering one additional variable.

Needless to say, the above procedure cannot be used to state that one variable is more important than another, since the order in which variables are used will have considerable effect on the amount of prediction obtainable from them. This problem is identical to that found with multiple correlations, where the problem of assessing the relative contribution of each predictor variable is hopeless unless the predictor variables are orthogonal, that is, unless their contributions to total prediction are independent.

INTERNAL AND EXTERNAL CONSTRAINT

We can speak of the total constraint in any system of variables in a completely abstract way, without identifying the nature of any of the variables involved. When, however, we want to distinguish between internal and external constraint, we must be more specific in distinguishing the function of the variables, since internal constraint refers entirely to the constraint within a system of symbolic variables, while external constraint refers to the constraint existing between this system of variables and some external referent system of variables.

In order to clarify the nature of the relations between the three types of constraint, we will use a slightly different method of describing the variables. First, we will use x to refer to a group of variables, x_1, x_2, x_3 $\cdots$ x_n. We are interested in the relations between these x variables, and these relations will form the internal constraint. Then we will use the term y to designate the external or referent variable, and we shall be interested in the relation between the full group of x variables and the y variable as a measure of external constraint. The y variable need not be truly a unidimensional variable, but we will treat it as one. The point is simply that we are interested in the y variable only insofar as it relates to our system of x variables.

To make this distinction more meaningful, we can think of the x variables as the predictor variables and y as the criterion variable. We are then interested in the relations within the predictor variables and also the relation between the predictor variables and the criterion variable. Alternatively, we can consider the x variables to be the stimulus variables in an experiment. They might be, for example, the color, form, and size of a set of visual stimuli. The y variable is then the response, which might itself be multivariate, but might just as easily be a single set of designating numbers, letters, or words. Here again we are interested in the relations within the set of stimulus variables and the relation between these stimulus variables and the response variable.

To become more specific, suppose we have a system of four x variables, x_1, x_2, x_3, and x_4, which are combined orthogonally, and which are used as a set of stimulus variables to which an external response, y, must be made. Now we have altogether five variables, and we can specify the total constraint in this set of five variables and also break this total constraint into two parts following the form of Eq. 5.8:

$$U(y{:}x_1{:}x_2{:}x_3{:}x_4) = U(y{:}x_1, x_2, x_3, x_4) + U(x_1{:}x_2{:}x_3{:}x_4). \quad (5.12)$$

In this form, and with this notation, we can see that the total constraint in the sytem of five variables can be broken into two parts, one of which is the multiple contingent uncertainty for predicting y from the four x variables, and the other of which is the total constraint within the set of x variables themselves. These two parts can be readily identified as the two types of structure or constraint we are concerned with; the multiple contingent uncertainty is the external constraint, and the total constraint within the set of x variables is the internal constraint.[3]

In our particular case we specified that the four x variables are orthogonal; therefore there is no internal constraint. The total constraint in the system of five variables then equals the external constraint. If we have a unique referent (y value) for each x value, then the amount of external constraint is equal to the y uncertainty, which in turn is equal to the total uncertainty of the x variables. With this condition of a unique referent for each x value, we can write the more general relation

$$
\begin{aligned}
U(y:x_1:x_2:x_3:x_4) &= U_{\max}(y, x_1, x_2, x_3, x_4) - U(y, x_1, x_2, x_3, x_4) \\
&= 2[U(x_1) + U(x_2) + U(x_3) + U(x_4)] \\
&\quad - [U(x_1) + U(x_2) + U(x_3) + U(x_4)] \\
&= U(x_1) + U(x_2) + U(x_3) + U(x_4) \\
&= U(y).
\end{aligned}
\tag{5.13}
$$

Thus the total constraint equals the total uncertainty of the x variable, which in turn equals the uncertainty of the y variable.

Redundancy and the interchange of constraint

The example we have just been using, if we think of the x variables as stimulus variables, allows us to say that all possible stimuli have been used and thus that there is complete orthogonality of the stimulus variables and no internal constraint. If all stimuli are not used, however, then we introduce what we are calling internal constraint. Let us continue this discussion by seeing what effect selection of stimuli has on these constraints; and to make our discussion still more concrete, let us make each of the x variables dichotomous, so that sixteen possible stimuli can be formed from the four x variables. And again we will have a unique y value (response) for each possible stimulus.

---

[3] For our purposes it is normally unnecessary to consider the internal structure of the y variable. To do so, however, does not change the basic nature of these relations, but simply adds the internal constraint of the y variable. This relation can most easily be seen by transposing terms in Eq. 5.10. If y_1 and y_2 are the two y variables, and x_1 and x_2 are the x variables, then

$$
U(y_1:y_2:x_1:x_2) = U(y_1, y_2:x_1, x_2) + U(y_1:y_2) + U(x_1:x_2).
$$

Thus the total constraint is the contingent uncertainty between the two sets of variables plus the constraint within the y variables plus the constraint within the x variables. If the y variable is not differentiated into its subvariables, then that term simply disappears.

Let us suppose now that we do not use all of the sixteen possible stimuli, but only four of them. And let us further suppose that we select four stimuli such that each of the two values of each x variable still occurs half of the time. In other words, we select our four stimuli so that the uncertainty of each x variable remains 1 bit. With one response for each of the four stimuli, our uncertainty of y has been reduced to correspond to the actual uncertainty of x, not to the maximum uncertainty of x (which was previously the same as the actual uncertainty of x). Now our total constraint is

$$
\begin{aligned}
U(y:x_1:x_2:x_3:x_4) &= U_{max}(y, x_1, x_2, x_3, x_4) - U(y, x_1, x_2, x_3, x_4) \\
&= [U(x_1, x_2, x_3, x_4) + U(x_1) + U(x_2) + U(x_3) + U(x_4)] \\
&\quad - U(x_1, x_2, x_3, x_4) \\
&= U(x_1) + U(x_2) + U(x_3) + U(x_4) \\
&= U_{max}(x_1, x_2, x_3, x_4). \quad (5.14)
\end{aligned}
$$

Thus the fact that we now use only four of the sixteen possible x categories has not changed the total constraint in the five-variable matrix. It can be seen in general that the process of selecting fewer than the maximum possible number of stimulus categories will not change the total constraint (when the referent variable is included in the matrix), as long as the stimuli are selected in such a way that each stimulus variable has the same uncertainty as it did originally. If the stimuli are selected so that the uncertainty of one or more variables decreases, then Eq. 5.14 shows that the total constraint decreases by exactly the same amount.

Now this process of using fewer categories than can exist given the uncertainties of the individual variables is what produces redundancy, and basically these equations show us how redundancy affects total constraint: *Redundancy has no effect on total constraint as long as each variable retains its maximum uncertainty.*

However, the fact that the total constraint remains unaffected by the introduction of redundancy does not mean that the constraint remains in its original form.

$$
\begin{aligned}
U(y:x_1:x_2:x_3:x_4) &= U(y:x_1, x_2, x_3, x_4) + U(x_1:x_2:x_3:x_4) \\
&= U(x_1, x_2, x_3, x_4) \\
&\quad + [U_{max}(x_1, x_2, x_3, x_4) - U(x_1, x_2, x_3, x_4)]. \quad (5.15)
\end{aligned}
$$

This equation shows that the multiple contingent uncertainty (external constraint) is the same as the actual uncertainty of the stimulus (which is the same as the actual uncertainty of the response), but now the internal constraint within the set of four x variables is no longer zero, since the actual uncertainty is less than the maximum possible uncertainty. In our concrete example, the introduction of the redundancy of 2 bits has not changed the total constraint, which is still 4 bits. But it has had the effect of redistributing this constraint so that now 2 bits of it is in internal structure and 2 bits is in external structure.

Thus the primary effect of introducing redundancy into any system of variables is to redistribute the total constraint. Redundancy decreases the amount of external structure at the same time that it increases the amount of internal structure—but *the total amount of structure remains exactly the same.*

The complete generality of these relations is apparently limited by the requirement that the selection of stimuli must not alter the uncertainties of the variables themselves. And yet this limitation is much less severe than it seems. To illustrate, let us refer to Table 5.1, in which the sixteen possible patterns of four dichotomous variables are shown. Suppose that we select the first four patterns out of the sixteen. Now these four patterns will give zero uncertainty for variables x_1 and x_2, since only the 0 value of these occurs. In this case, the external structure will still be 2 bits, but there will

Table 5.1

The sixteen possible patterns of four dichotomous variables.

Stimulus Variable

Pattern	x_1	x_2	x_3	x_4
a	0	0	0	0
b	0	0	0	1
c	0	0	1	0
d	0	0	1	1
e	0	1	0	0
f	0	1	0	1
g	0	1	1	0
h	0	1	1	1
i	1	0	0	0
j	1	0	0	1
k	1	0	1	0
l	1	0	1	1
m	1	1	0	0
n	1	1	0	1
o	1	1	1	0
p	1	1	1	1

be no internal structure since all four variables are uncorrelated. But this example shows that the effect is quite artifactual, since if two of the variables do not take different values, they are not in fact variables, and should not be included in our computations. These four stimuli are not really redundant, since we actually end up with two dichotomous variables and four stimuli. We have simply decreased the number of variables and thus have decreased the maximum possible uncertainty—which is redundancy only in a most arbitrary and artifactual sense.

Suppose, to take another example, that we select patterns a, b, c, and p. Now variables x_3 and x_4 still have an uncertainty of 1 bit each, but variables x_1 and x_2 have uncertainties of 0.81 bit, since for each of them the two possible values do not occur equally often. If we compute the total constraint, $U(y:x_1:x_2:x_3:x_4)$, using 1 bit of uncertainty for each variable, then we will again have a multiple contingent uncertainty of 2 bits and an internal constraint of 2 bits. However, the internal constraint will include 0.19 bit for each of the two variables which does not have maximum uncertainty, and this amount is not included in contingent and interaction uncertainties. In other words, we would have to redefine our total constraint term to include what we have called distributional constraint—the constraint due only to unequal probabilities within a given variable.

In order to retain a consistency of meaning of the total constraint, it would be better not to include distributional constraint. This problem is very simply avoided by computing the total constraint for the five-variable matrix with the actual uncertainties of all variables, rather than with the nominal uncertainties. Thus in Eq. 5.14 the total constraint would be 3.62 bits, rather than 4 bits, and this amount would be distributed in Eq. 5.15 as 2 bits of multiple contingent uncertainty (external constraint) and 1.62 bits of redundancy (internal constraint).

The particular selection of stimuli does not alter the generality of these equations as long as we use actual uncertainties of variables rather than nominal uncertainties, and especially if we do not include uncertainties of variables which have ceased to be variables at all by the nature of the selection of patterns.

While the particular selection of joint categories does not affect the generality of these equations, it clearly does affect the amount of internal constraint, and it is for exactly this reason that we have pointed out the nature of these relations. To define redundancy only in terms of the number of stimulus patterns used out of the number which could have been used, without reference to the effect of the particular selections on the internal structure of the variables, is to ignore an aspect of the problem which must be psychologically of primary importance. If we refer again to Table 5.1, the selection of any four of the sixteen possible patterns will reduce the multiple contingent uncertainty from 4 to 2 bits. However, the selection of patterns a, b, c, and d does not, as we saw, really produce redundancy but simply reduces the number of variables. The effect of reducing number of variables is to reduce the external structure (multiple contingent uncertainty) without at the same time increasing internal structure.

Thus any process of producing redundancy which does not actually reduce number of variables must simultaneously produce a reduction in external structure and also produce an increase in internal structure. The production of redundancy is also the production of internal structure among a set of variables—and, I am arguing, is the production of meaning within a set of variables. A decrease in meaning brought about by a reduction of the external structure carries with it a concomitant increase in meaning within the system of variables, and one cannot occur without the other.

To help clarify the significance of these statements, let us refer to a language system. If we generate a language using letters which combine into words, we can consider each position within a word as a single variable which can have all of the possible letters. The maximum number of words which we can have will be determined by the sum of the uncertainties for each letter position. Suppose we arbitrarily decide that not all of the possible words will actually be used. As soon as we have selected fewer words for use than could have been used, we have created constraint between the various letter positions within words, that is to say, we have produced meaningful relations between letters within words. This arbitrary decision not to use all possible words at the same time limits the amount of external structure possible, because we have limited the contingent uncertainty between the language and any external referent system, whether it be the real world of events or another language system.

However, suppose that we do not arbitrarily and a priori limit the size of the vocabulary, but allow all possible words to be used. If the external referent system has fewer events in it than we have words to describe, then not all of the words will be used. In other words, our external structure is not at its maximum because there are not enough referent events to use all of the words. If for this reason fewer words are used than possible, we have again produced redundancy and this redundancy produces internal constraint and meaning. Thus the actual process by which the number of words is limited is quite inconsequential, since any process which limits the amount of external structure also increases the amount of internal structure; and conversely, any process which increases the amount of internal structure at the same time decreases the amount of external structure. One cannot occur without the other, and we can almost argue that we are dealing with a single phenomenon. That phenomenon is structure, which I have identified with meaning, and the amount of structure or constraint in any system can be a fixed quantity, but the particular nature of the system will determine how much of this structure is external and how much is internal.

An example from psychological testing

A concrete illustration from the field of psychological testing may help clarify some of these relations, and the extent to which the amount of internal structure is critically related to the amount of external structure. Let us suppose that we have a test with one hundred dichotomous items, and that we have selected these items all to be of equal difficulty and of such difficulty that on the average each item will be right half the time and wrong half the time. In other words, each item has an uncertainty of 1 bit, and the maximum uncertainty of the test is 100 bits.

Let us give this test to sixty-four people. Since there are 2^{100} possible outcomes on the test, it is very unlikely that any two of the sixty-four people will have exactly the same test pattern, and we can safely assume that only sixty-four (and no fewer) of the possible patterns actually occur. We thus have a considerable amount of redundancy.

From Eq. 5.14 we know that the total constraint in the system of test items and people is 100 bits. Since only sixty-four people took the test, and assuming that each person has a different pattern of results, we know that the multiple contingent uncertainty for predicting people from the test is 6 bits. Therefore the external constraint of the test is 6 bits, and the remaining 94 bits is all internal constraint within the test. In other words, the fact that we gave the test to only sixty-four people guarantees that the test items themselves will be highly correlated, and in uncertainty terms the total constraint is very large. Thus the limiting of external structure guarantees a high internal structure. In a sense the total amount of structure was fixed by our original choice of one hundred dichotomous items; amount of external structure was fixed by the choice of number of people to administer the test to; and the amount of internal structure is the simple result of these two prior decisions.

THE FORM OF THE CONSTRAINT

To know how much structure exists in a given situation, and how much of the total structure is internal or external, is not to know the exact form of it. The same total amount of constraint can occur in many different forms, and *the form of the structure is not determined by how many patterns are used out of the total possible, but rather by which particular patterns are used.* Thus, in our illustration involving tests, we know that the total amount of internal constraint is 94 bits, but we do not know whether this amount of constraint occurs in the form of simple contingent uncertainties or as interaction uncertainties. In correlational terms, we do not know whether the constraint occurs as inter-item correlations or as partial correlations.

In many, if not most, psychological problems, the form of the structure is as important as the amount, although this factor as an experimental variable has seldom been used. In order to obtain some understanding of the potential importance of the form of the structure, an examination of the ways in which it can differ is worthwhile.

The form of internal constraint

We can analyze the uncertainty components involved in the total constraint, in the internal constraint, or in the external constraint. These terms, for any given problem and selection of patterns, are all interrelated, and for ease of presentation we shall first look at the uncertainty terms involved in internal constraint.

In Table 5.2, I have listed all of the uncertainty terms which are involved in the internal constraint of a system of four predictor (x) variables. And I have also computed actual values for each of these terms for four different sets of patterns taken from Table 5.1. In each case I have selected four out of the sixteen patterns. There are, of course, 1820 ways of selecting four out of sixteen categories, but many of the selections are either not pertinent (for example, those which eliminate one or more variables), or are equivalent in terms of the resultant uncertainty terms (such as any reversal of variables or rearrangement of the labels of the variables). Other ways in which these selections are equivalent have been discussed by Prokhovnik (1959). The four different sets of patterns I have selected will serve to illustrate some of the problems and principles. These terms can differ in a number of ways:

1. The uncertainty of each variable can be less than its maximum possible value by selection of patterns so that the two values of each

Table 5.2

Uncertainty terms and amounts involved in four different selections of four patterns each from Table 5.1. These calculations assume that each pattern selected is used equally often in each set.

Uncertainty Term	Set of Patterns Selected							
	A		B		C		D	
	a*	0000	d	0011	a	0000	h	0111
	g	0110	f	0101	h	0111	l	1011
	l	1011	k	1010	i	1000	n	1101
	n	1101	m	1100	p	1111	o	1110
x_1	1.00		1.00		1.00		0.81	
x_2	1.00		1.00		1.00		0.81	
x_3	1.00		1.00		1.00		0.81	
x_4	1.00		1.00		1.00		0.81	
$x_1 : x_2$	0		0		0		0.12	
$x_1 : x_3$	0		0		0		0.12	
$x_1 : x_4$	1.00		1.00		0		0.12	
$x_2 : x_3$	0		1.00		1.00		0.12	
$x_2 : x_4$	0		0		1.00		0.12	
$x_3 : x_4$	0		0		1.00		0.12	
$\overline{x_1 x_2 x_3}$	1.00		0		0		0.07	
$\overline{x_1 x_2 x_4}$	0		0		0		0.07	
$\overline{x_1 x_3 x_4}$	0		0		0		0.07	
$\overline{x_2 x_3 x_4}$	1.00		0		-1.00		0.07	
$\overline{x_1 x_2 x_3 x_4}$	-1.00		0		0		0.24	
$x_1 : x_2 : x_3 : x_4$	2.00		2.00		2.00		1.24	
$y : x_1, x_2, x_3, x_4$	2.00		2.00		2.00		2.00	

* These lower-case letters refer to the patterns as listed in Table 5.1 The numbers following the letters are the coded values for the four x variables as listed in Table 5.1.

variable do not occur equally often. In our illustration, set D, using patterns h, l, n, and o from Table 5.1, has less than maximum uncertainty per variable, and thus also has less total constraint than do the other sets.

2. The simple contingent uncertainties cannot be negative, but they may be zero or positive, and the number of them which is zero provides an important difference between different sets of patterns. Thus set A has just one positive contingency, set B has two of them, set C has

three of them, and set D has all six of them positive, but with small values.

3. The interactions can be either negative, positive, or zero, and here again we have differences. Set A has two positive three-term interactions, set B has only zero interactions, set C has one negative interaction, and set D again has all interactions positive but of small magnitude. In similar fashion the higher order interactions can vary.

The analysis presented in Table 5.2 is for the uncertainty terms involved in the internal constraint, and the value of the internal constraint is determined by summing all of the contingent and interaction uncertainties. These sums are all the same except for set D, which has an internal constraint of only 1.24 bits, due to the lower uncertainty per variable.

The form of external constraint

An analysis of the uncertainty terms involved in the external constraint would exactly parallel the terms in Table 5.2, a fact which can most easily be seen by spelling out the complete set of terms for the multiple contingent uncertainty in which y is predicted from the four x variables:

$$
\begin{aligned}
U(y:x_1, x_2, x_3, x_4) = \; & U(y:x_1) + U(y:x_2) + U(y:x_3) + U(y:x_4) \\
& + U(\overline{yx_1x_2}) + U(\overline{yx_1x_3}) + U(\overline{yx_1x_4}) \\
& + U(\overline{yx_2x_3}) + U(\overline{yx_2x_4}) + U(\overline{yx_3x_4}) \\
& + U(\overline{yx_1x_2x_3}) + U(\overline{yx_1x_2x_4}) + U(\overline{yx_1x_3x_4}) \\
& + U(\overline{yx_2x_3x_4}) + U(\overline{yx_1x_2x_3x_4}).
\end{aligned} \tag{5.16}
$$

For each x term there is a parallel term involving variable y, and we end up with the same total number of terms. However, the uncertainty of each x variable now becomes a contingent uncertainty between that x variable and y, and has exactly the same numerical value, because we are assuming a one-to-one relation between y and each combination of x (that is, we are assuming no equivocation). Similarly, each contingent uncertainty between pairs of x variables becomes an interaction variable involving the same two terms plus the y term. In this case, the equivalent term again has the same numerical value, but its sign is changed. Thus a positive (and all contingencies must be positive) contingency between x_1 and x_2 becomes a negative interaction, $U(\overline{yx_1x_2})$. The reason for this reversal of sign can easily be seen if we write the interaction in the form

$$
U(\overline{yx_1x_2}) = U_y(x_1:x_2) - U(x_1:x_2). \tag{5.17}
$$

The partial contingent uncertainty has a value of zero, because for any single value of y there is a unique combination of the two x variables. Therefore the interaction uncertainty simply becomes the negative of the contingency between the two x variables. In a similar fashion, each other term involving y has the same numerical value as its corresponding term involving just x variables, but with a reversal of signs. A negative three-variable interaction involving just x variables becomes a positive four-variable interaction involving the three x variables and the y variable. Note that it is impossible to have a positive three-variable interaction involving y.

The external constraint can be computed by summing all of the terms for each set of patterns in Table 5.2, but remembering to reverse the signs on the terms involving contingencies and interactions of the x variables. These sums, which are the same for each set of patterns, are given at the bottom of the table.

The important aspect of this discussion on the form of the constraint is this interlocking between the uncertainty terms of the internal constraint and the terms of the external constraint. It is important because in any real problem we cannot introduce redundancy (internal constraint) in a particular form without at the same time completely determining the form of the external constraint. Now this would create no problem if the form of the constraint were not an important psychological variable, but we shall see that it is an important variable. In addition, insofar as there is an optimum form of redundancy, we cannot have an optimum form in both the internal and the external constraints simultaneously.

Limits of independence of variables

It has probably occurred to many to ask why we did not use an example in Table 5.2 in which all contingent uncertainties were zero. The answer is simply that with our particular example it is impossible. It is not possible to have four dichotomous variables all be orthogonal with this much redundancy. Set A was the best that could be achieved, since it had five of the six possible pairs of variables orthogonal. There are some general relations involved here which put limits on the selection of patterns which we will discuss only briefly. A complete discussion of these limitations is a rather formidable task in itself.

The limitations are affected by the total number of variables, the number of categories per variable, and the amount of redundancy introduced. McGill (1955) has briefly touched on some of these relations, particularly the relation between informational analysis and experimental design. The basic limitation concerning both number of variables and number of categories per variable is the same as that which limits the use of confounded experimental designs such as latin squares and graeco-latin squares. In a latin square, n^2 out of n^3 possible joint categories are used, where n is the number of categories on each of three variables. The redundancy in a latin-square pattern is $\frac{1}{3}$, since the total used uncertainty is $\frac{2}{3}$ of the maximum possible. Now in a latin square, the particular joint categories actually used are chosen so that each variable is orthogonal to each other variable. No situation exists in which we use n^2 out of n^3 possible categories in which we cannot ensure that all simple contingent uncertainties are zero, since a latin square can be formed with three variables regardless of the number of categories per variable. Thus if we had selected, with three dichotomous variables, four out of the eight possible patterns, we could have selected them in such a way that all variables are uncorrelated.

A graeco-latin square is one in which n^2 out of n^4 possible categories are selected, and it is formed so that all six possible pairs of variables are orthogonal. In a graeco-latin square, redundancy is $\frac{1}{2}$, since the actual uncertainty will be only half of the maximum possible uncertainty. However, a graeco-latin square cannot be formed from four dichotomous variables. If each variable had three categories it would have been possible to generate a graeco-latin square, and thus have all contingent uncertainties between x variables be zero. We saw that with four dichotomous variables we could have all but one of the six pairs of variables be orthogonal. With five dichotomous variables all but two of the ten pairs can be orthogonal, and with six dichotomous variables, all but three of the fifteen pairs of variables can be orthogonal. The limits become more complicated with larger numbers of variables, and obviously depend on the number of values per variable.

Restriction of structure by grouping

We have been discussing situations where internal structure is produced by redundancy. When we have a system of variables and do not use all of the possible combinations of the variables, then we have redundancy, and this redundancy not only reduces the amount of external structure which can be used (that is, reduces the amount of correlation possible with an external system), but it also produces internal structure, in most cases in exactly the same amount by which the external structure is reduced. In this situation, we are assuming a one-to-one relation between the internal categories actually used and the external categories. In other words, we are assuming no noise or equivocation.

There is another type of problem which at first glance seems quite similar, but is in fact quite different—a problem we will discuss somewhat more in the chapter on concept formation. A brief mention of it now will help, however, to clarify the nature of the relations we have been discussing. Suppose that we have a system of x variables, again four dichotomous variables. We, however, decide to group the sixteen combinations so that sets of four of them are each given a common external designation. In other words, we will have only 2 bits of external constraint, and thus a maximum of 2 bits of multiple contingent uncertainty. Now it might seem, since we are using less uncertainty than is possible, that we are again creating redundancy, but such is actually not the case. The process of grouping events is a process of producing equivocation, not a process of producing redundancy, and this grouping, while it does reduce the external structure, does not at the same time produce internal structure.

In our actual example, the uncertainty of each x variable is 1 bit, and the uncertainty of the y variable is 2 bits. Thus the maximum uncertainty of the five-variable matrix is 6 bits. The actual uncertainty of the matrix is 4 bits, since sixteen different joint events occur. The difference between these is 2 bits, all of which is the multiple contingent uncertainty. Thus the total constraint is the same as the multiple contingent uncertainty, and there is no remaining internal constraint.

With such problems we can still be concerned experimentally about the best form of the multiple contingent uncertainty, since there is considerable freedom in the process of grouping to have the multiple contingent uncertainty occur primarily in the simple contingent uncertainties or in interaction uncertainties. There can be, however, no concern about the best form of the internal constraint, since there is none.

Thus selection of stimuli produces redundancy and internal constraint, but reduction of the external constraint by any arbitrary grouping process does not produce internal constraint.

EQUIVALENT PSYCHOLOGICAL PROCESSES

We have, in this chapter, shown that total constraint in a system of internal and external variables can be partitioned into an internal and an external constraint, and that when a single response is appropriate to each stimulus the total can remain constant while the amounts which are in internal or external constraint vary inversely. In addition, the form of the constraint can vary, and once again there are reciprocal relations involved in the form of the internal constraint and the form of the external constraint.

The most important point about these distinctions lies in this very lack of independence of the kinds and forms of constraint. If the total constraint is held constant, and if we then increase the internal constraint, we simultaneously decrease the external constraint, and one cannot occur without the other. If we decide to make the internal constraint be of a particular form, then we are again completely determining the form of the external constraint, although the form will be different from that of the internal constraint. Thus in applying these concepts to psychological research problems, our concern must be with whether the effects we obtain are due to the direct changes in, say, the internal constraint or to the necessarily concomitant changes in the external constraint.

Various psychological processes, or performance criteria, certainly will respond differentially to these different kinds and forms of constraint. Ideally, in order to make use of these concepts, we would like to have performance criteria which are prototypical counterparts of these informational concepts. We would like to be able to say that if we increase external constraint it will have such and such an effect on performance A, but will not have any effect on performance B. Or, alternatively, we would like to say that this particular form of redundancy will be advantageous in terms of performance A, but disadvantageous in terms of performance B.

Almost certainly no realistic performance criterion which can be used in an experiment is a pure counterpart of just one or another of these concepts. On the other hand, it is equally certain that some performance criteria are more nearly counterparts of one type of constraint than the other, and in these cases we certainly can make differential predictions concerning experimental results which should be obtained with changes in the amounts and forms of the constraints. As a brief summary, we will discuss three types of psychological performance in terms of these information concepts—a summary which can serve as an introduction to the more detailed discussion of psychological problems in the ensuing chapters.

Discrimination and external constraint

The psychological process most closely associated with external constraint is that of perceptual discrimination. The ability to distinguish one stimulus from another, to unambiguously use one response for one stimulus and another response for another stimulus, is certainly related to external constraint. The multiple contingent uncertainty which is the measure of amount of external constraint is a measure of the extent to which variability *between* stimuli can be correlated with an external referent system. In other words, the critical factor concerns the amount of uncertainty between stimuli, not the relations within stimuli, and interstimulus uncertainty is basically a problem of discrimination.

The previous chapters have, of course, been primarily concerned with external constraint—the amount of uncertainty between stimuli. The absolute judgment experiment is directly concerned with discrimination, and the amount of information transmitted is itself a measure of amount of discrimination, or the amount of external constraint which is used. Insofar as reaction time is a measure of discrimination, it too will be responsive to changes in the amount of external constraint. We have the evidence that increases in amount of external constraint lead to increases in amount of discrimination until a channel capacity is reached. Beyond that point, the relative amount of external constraint which is actually transmitted becomes less.

Most of the experiments discussed so far have dealt primarily with situations where the amount of redundancy or internal constraint is zero. Under these circumstances the amount of discrimination can only vary with the amount of external constraint.

The introduction of internal constraint, or redundancy, into a set of stimuli can affect discrimination performance in two important respects. First, internal constraint may have a direct effect on discrimination; and, second, once internal constraint has been introduced there arises the problem of the form of the external constraint. Without internal constraint, there can be no variation in the form of external constraint, but once internal constraint has been introduced, then the form of the external constraint will be directly affected by the particular selection of stimuli, and can itself be an important experimental factor.

We will not discuss the direct effect of redundancy on discrimination at any length here. It is sufficient to point out that under conditions in which discrimination is less than perfect, redundancy can improve discrimination. We have already seen, for example, in the Eriksen and Hake experiment discussed in Chapter Four, that when the amount of external constraint is held constant, but redundancy is introduced into the stimuli by the use of correlated stimulus dimensions, the amount of discrimination increases. Thus redundancy can be directly helpful in a discrimination task.

The form of the external constraint is of considerable interest for discrimination problems. If stimuli are presented under circumstances where discrimination is less than perfect, then redundancy can aid discrimination; but what is the ideal form of the redundancy? There are two clear requirements:

1. Each stimulus dimension should provide as much discrimination as possible. This requirement means that we want each stimulus, or x, variable to have maximum uncertainty, because these values become contingent uncertainties when referred to the response, or y, variable.

2. Each of the stimulus variables should provide its maximum discrimination in as independent a form as possible, so that the discrimination provided by one x variable does not duplicate that provided by another x variable.

Translated into the terms in Table 5.2, this latter requirement means that simple contingencies between pairs of x variables should be as small as possible, and that the resultant negative interactions (when the y variable is included) be avoided. A contingency between stimulus variables becomes a negative interaction when related to y, and a negative interaction does just what it sounds like it does—it subtracts predictability or discriminability. To illustrate, if two x variables each has an uncertainty of 1 bit, then the contingency between each of them and the y variable is also 1 bit. The multiple contingent uncertainty in which y is predicted from both of them is the sum of these two contingencies plus the interaction. In this illustration, it is 2 bits plus the interaction. This interaction will be -1 bit if the two x variables are themselves correlated. Thus if the two x variables are correlated, the multiple contingent uncertainty will be 1 bit. But if they are uncorrelated, then the multiple contingent uncertainty will be 2 bits. It is therefore obvious why contingencies between the x variables should be avoided if stimulus discrimination and identification are involved.

One way of showing the importance of this factor is to determine the average multiple contingent uncertainty for predicting y from single x variables, from pairs of x variables, from triplets of x variables, and from all four x variables. We are, in essence, asking to what extent the y variable can be predicted from randomly sampled pairs of x variables, triplets of x variables, etc.

These average contingent uncertainties for the four sets of patterns in Table 5.2 have been computed and are shown graphically in Fig. 5.1. A concrete illustration may help clarify this graph. With set A, of the six possible pairs of x variables which can be used to predict y, five of them provide the maximum possible value of 2 bits of con-

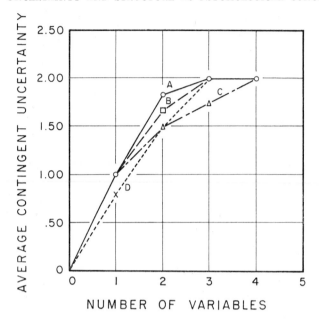

Fig. 5.1. The average amount of prediction of the criterion variable, y, as a function of the number of x variables used. Each function is for a different set of patterns from Table 5.2.

tingent uncertainty. One pair, x_1, x_4, provides only 1 bit of contingent uncertainty because these two variables are correlated. The average for these six pairs of predictors is then 1.83 bits, the value plotted in Fig. 5.1.

With just a single predictor variable, all sets give 1 bit of information except set D, which gives just 0.83 bit. Thus, selecting sets of patterns which provide less than maximum uncertainty per variable not only decreases the amount of internal structure but also decreases the value of the external structure, even though its total amount remains the same, at 2 bits. That is to say, selection of such a set of patterns decreases the amount of internal structure without affecting the amount of external structure; but it also has an effect on external structure in that it prevents obtaining maximum prediction from a few variables at a time.

With two predictor variables used, sets A, B, and C now all become different, even though the totals for these three sets, and the averages per single variable, are the same. Set A maintains the maximum prediction, set B has less, and set C has the least. This relation is directly the result of the number and magnitudes of the contingent uncertainties between pairs of x variables, and it becomes clear that if maximum prediction from two variables is desired, then the contingencies between variables should be as small as possible.

With three predictor variables, all sets except C achieve the full prediction of 2 bits. With set C we still cannot be sure which referent category is called for even when three of the four variables (randomly selected) are known. It is interesting to note that set D has, with three variables, achieved full prediction, even though with fewer variables it was inferior to set C, and even though it has less total internal constraint. It is evident that the form of the constraint can be just as important as the amount of it. Set C, in our illustration, is still suffering the effects of having too many contingent uncertainties between pairs of predictors.

This aspect of the problem can be summarized rather simply. When we have redundancy due to the fact that fewer categories are used than is possible, then we want to select the categories in such a way as to maintain high internal constraint, but we also want to select categories so that the amount of prediction of the referent variable is as high as possible for each individual variable or any combination of variables. In other words, we want the prediction from the several variables to be as independent as possible, which is simply to say that we want the predictor variables to be uncorrelated.

Free recall and internal constraint

The psychological performance criterion which is most closely related to internal constraint or redundancy is free-recall learning. The subject is given a list of stimuli and is required to reproduce them, in any possible order. In other words, the subject does not have to align the stimuli with any external referent system, not even an ordering of the stimuli.

That free recall is most directly related to the amount of redundancy can be seen if we consider the task given to the subject in such an experiment. Suppose, first, that the subject is shown a list of stimuli which are created from three dichotomous dimensions, and that all of the eight possible stimuli are actually used (that is, there is no redundancy). Now in free recall the subject really has no problem, because all he has to do is to reconstruct all of the possible stimuli, and since he is not required to do so in any particular order, he can, with a little time, construct all possible stimuli. So, in a sense, when there is no redundancy, the subject actually has nothing to learn.

But suppose now that we give him only four of the eight possible stimuli, and ask him to reconstruct these by free recall. Now his task has been made more difficult because not all of the stimuli have been given, and he has to learn which ones have and which ones have not been given. In other words, the introduction of redundancy has produced something for the subject to learn—the redundancy itself.

At first glance, the expectation that a subject will take longer to learn by free recall a set of four stimuli than a set of eight seems like a contradiction, since ordinarily we expect that learning will be more difficult the longer the list of items to be learned. However, we can see here that if the longer list is non-redundant, there is in fact little if anything to learn, and free recall will be very easy.

This discussion is not meant to imply that free-recall learning is unaffected by the length of list, or amount of external constraint. Certainly if the amount of redundancy is the same in two cases, but the amount of external constraint is different, learning will be slower with the longer list. For example, eight stimuli out of a possible sixteen stimuli will almost certainly take longer to learn than four out of a possible eight, although the amount of redundancy in each case is the same—1 bit. Thus free recall is no more a perfect counterpart of internal constraint than is discrimination a perfect counterpart of external constraint.

In terms of the optimum form of internal constraint, we can make a very simple assumption: *Simple contingencies are easier to learn and to use than are interactions.* This assumption suggests, then, that the optimum form of internal constraint, for free-recall learning, is one which has high intervariable contingencies within the set of stimuli to be learned.

Note that in our discussion of discrimination I suggested that redundancy could aid discrimination, and that the optimum form was such that minimum contingent uncertainties should exist in the internal constraint, in order to have maximum independent contingencies with the external variable. Yet for free recall, I suggest that the introduction of redundancy should make learning more difficult, and that the optimum form of redundancy is to have high contingencies in the internal constraint. For these two performance criteria, then, we would expect the amount and the form of redundancy to have exactly opposite effects. *Thus redundancy is not just good or just bad in general, but will be good or bad depending on the particular performance criterion.* It can hardly be overemphasized that in dealing with these informational concepts experimentally, we should be most careful to distinguish different performance criteria.

Paired-associates tasks

A common form of psychological task is that in which one of a set of items is presented as a stimulus and the subject must use, or learn to use, an item from another set as the response. The two sets may be nonsense syllables, or they may be tone intensities as stimuli and numbers as responses. In other words, the experimental paradigm for paired associates learning and for absolute judgments is actually the same. The differences lie in how much of the learning has been acquired before the experiment, how much the pairing of stimuli and responses is self-evident, and how much the pairing must be learned in the experiment itself.

Such experiments invariably involve considerable mixtures of internal and external constraint requirements, and thus to understand the expected effects of amount and form of redundancy is often difficult. When the absolute judgment experiment is used, we assume the experiment to be primarily one on discrimination because the stimuli are ordered on a simple continuum, the responses are overlearned, and the pairings are by simple orderings of the stimuli and responses. Thus in such an experiment we would expect the effects of redundancy to go with the expected effects for discrimination.

But when nonsense syllables must be learned, there is certainly a considerable effect with respect to internal constraint, since the actual stimuli and responses must be learned as well as the pairing relations. The particular nature of such an experiment could make a great difference in the role of amount and form of redundancy. Suppose, for example, that we present thoroughly familiar objects as stimuli and require a subject to respond to each with a separate nonsense syllable which is part of a redundant set. Now the internal constraint in the responses must be learned as well as the pairings. However, if the nonsense syllables are the stimuli, and the familiar objects (perhaps real words) are the responses, the subject will not have to remember the redundant stimuli, and his task will be made easier with respect to the internal constraint.

These different factors can be experimentally separated, and Horowitz (1961) has not only done this, but has shown that different experimental results are obtained with regard to these redundancy relations when the different factors are experimentally separated. Horowitz used two different lists of twelve nonsense words, which differed in amount of intralist similarity. While intralist similarity does not correspond in any exact way with amount or form of redundancy, Horowitz' method of constructing the lists was such that his high-similarity list was less redundant than his low-similarity list. (We will discuss this relation in more detail in Chapter Eight.) The actual number of words was the same in both lists, so the amount of external constraint was the same. The subjects were required to learn these lists in two different ways, by free recall and by serial order. When serial order was used, the subjects always knew what the words were, since they had them on cards. Thus in that task, external constraint was primarily involved, while with free recall, internal constraint was primarily involved.

With free recall, learning was best for the high-similarity (low-redundancy) list; however, when serial-order learning was required, performance was best with the low-similarity list. Thus it is clear that the experimental effects which will be obtained as a function of redundancy relations will depend on the particular performance criterion used. We cannot state that redundancy is good or bad in general, or simply that a particular form of redundancy is good. We must specify the exact performance with which we are concerned; and what is good for one performance may be bad for another.

In most paired-associates tasks there are mixtures of free recall and discrimination, the relative amounts of each depending on the particular nature of the stimuli and responses. Thus in most such tasks it is difficult if not impossible to predict accurately what the effects of redundancy should be. If the discrimination and free-recall aspects of tasks are separated, however, such predictions should be quite feasible.

COMMENTARY

Perhaps this entire chapter should have been labeled as commentary, since to a large extent it is just that. I have been discussing a set of mathematical relations and trying to suggest psychological counterparts of these relations. Sometimes the mathematical relations can be quite directly translated into psychological equivalences, and sometimes the relations have more tenuous equivalences. If all the equivalences were exact, of course, we would have no further problem nor even need for research; but they are not exact, and only considerable research can establish the usefulness of the concepts I have been discussing.

The crux of this chapter lies in the demonstration that

Total Constraint = External Constraint + Internal Constraint.

While constraints are identified in uncertainty terms, they are clearly equivalent to psychological structure, and to meaning insofar as meaning itself derives from perceived structure.

The distinction between these two types of structure has been understood in psychology for some time, although not in this strict form. For example, the difference between reliability and validity is essentially the difference between internal and external constraint, and the conflict between having maximum reliability and maximum validity has long been understood. It has generally been accepted that the optimum test is one which compromises between maximum validity and maximum reliability.

To me, the really important aspect of this relation is the demonstration of the complete exchangeability between internal and external constraint, a demonstration made possible by the generality of the uncertainty measure. This exchangeability has two important implications.

First, it suggests very strongly that the commodity of internal constraint or meaning and that of external constraint are one and the same, that somehow there is no essential difference between meaning as the structure within a system of variables and meaning as the structure between two different systems of variables. Thus in one sense the kinds of problems involved with one type of constraint need not be essentially different from those involved in the other type of constraint.

Second, this relation also shows how impossible it is to change one form of constraint or structure without simultaneously changing the other form. There are three terms in this relation, and only two degrees of freedom. If total constraint is held constant, then increases in internal constraint are accompanied by equivalent decreases in external constraint. Or if external constraint is held constant, then changes in internal constraint are accompanied by changes in total constraint. Thus we cannot deal with all three of these terms as independent.

The importance of this limitation lies in the fact that different psychological processes do not correspond equally to the internal and external constraints. Some processes are more affected by one kind of constraint and others by the other kind of constraint. Thus the extent to which changes in either internal or external constraint will affect the results of an actual psychological experiment will depend crucially on the particular performance criterion used.

In a real world these various processes are thoroughly intermixed. Almost every real task involves mixtures of free recall (learning and using the internal structure) plus pure discrimination. Insofar as such "realistic" tasks are used in experiments, the results we obtain with changes in the amounts of constraint will at best be confusing, and on occasion downright contradictory. In order properly to understand the role of these constraints in psychological processes, we must use the same discretion in separating the psychological processes as we do in separating the mathematical concepts and quantities. In other words, we must be as analytic in our research as we are in our mathematical derivations.

If we ask what is the optimum distribution of internal and external constraint in a real world, there can be no single answer. Various media have different requirements concerning the amounts of external and internal structure. A real language system must satisfy the needs of the actual communication process and must, therefore, have enough external constraint to provide the needed communication. In this case, internal constraint is added to the language by increasing its capacity for communication so that some uncertainty is left over for internal meaning. On the other hand, the arts have not been bound by the need for an amount of communication, and thus have been much freer to use high degrees of internal constraint. Modern visual art, for example, has tended more and more to keep external structure to a minimum in favor of internal meaning. Music has had the greatest freedom in this respect—a freedom so great as to produce a problem of the possible overuse of internal structure.

As long as any medium has some need to relate to an external referent system, then there must be some division between internal and external structure. Language, and even a painting, cannot be entirely devoid of external meaning and therefore cannot be completely structured internally, but music could be. A set of sounds used in music has little need to relate to anything externally. Yet if, because of this freedom, a sequence of notes was made entirely predictable, the music would hardly seem meaningful. Pinkerton (1956) uses the term *banal* to refer to the type of melody generated in nursery tunes, because the internal structure is so very great.

I would like to make just one last comment on the material discussed in this chapter, and that concerns the problem of the form of the internal and external constraint, not just its amount. This problem is tremendously complicated and I have only attempted to explain the nature of it, with some illustrations of a fairly restricted sort. The complications arise primarily because the nature of the variables used in a system greatly influences the nature of the internal constraint which is possible. And there are conflicting requirements concerning the optimum form of the constraint, even if we designate a particular performance criterion.

Consider discrimination tasks, for example. I have suggested that the optimum form of redundancy is that in which the internal contingencies are at a minimum but also is that in which each variable has maximum uncertainty. Now often both of these requirements cannot be satisfied simultaneously. In the discussion of the Eriksen and Hake experiment, I mentioned that their twenty stimuli in which size, color, and brightness were perfectly correlated were probably the best twenty stimuli which could have been selected from the possible eight thousand stimuli which could have been generated from orthogonal combinations of these three stimulus dimensions. However, with this selection, these dimensions are all perfectly correlated, and correlated stimulus dimensions should be poor for discrimination. The problem is simply that the use of correlated dimensions is the only possible way in which each dimension can have maximum variability; and this limitation will be true whenever redundancy is so great that we use only n stimuli out of n^2, n^3, etc., possibilities, where n is the number of steps on each stimulus dimension.

It seems reasonable that the requirement of maximum uncertainty per dimension take precedence over the requirement of independent dimensions. However, there are so many ways in which we can generate multivariate stimuli, each one of which will produce some limitations on our freedom to manipulate independently both the amount and the form of constraint, that it is very unsafe to proclaim any universal rules.

SUMMARY

In this chapter, I have introduced essentially just one additional uncertainty term, *constraint* of a system of variables,

$$U(w{:}x{:}y) = U_{\max}(w, x, y) - U(w, x, y),$$

where $U(w{:}x{:}y)$ is the total constraint in this system of three variables, and the other two terms are the maximum (based on marginal uncertainties) and the actual uncertainties of the system of variables.

Meaning may be signification or it may be structure, and it may be internal to a system of variables or external (referential). Meaning as structure may be quantified, and can be identified with constraint in a system of variables. If we consider two kinds of variables, those making up the set of stimuli (the internal variables), and the external variable (the referent for the symbols), then it can be shown that

Total Constraint = External Constraint + Internal Constraint.

Total constraint is that involved in the entire system of internal and external variables, external constraint is the multiple contingent uncertainty between the system of internal variables and the external referent variable, and internal constraint is the total constraint within the system of internal variables alone. External constraint is clearly identifiable with external structure, and internal constraint is clearly identified with internal structure.

The above relation shows that if total constraint is held constant, then internal and external constraint are interchangeable, such that one increases by exactly the same amount as the other decreases. This fact prevents independent manipulation of internal and external constraint.

It would be nice if there were perfect psychological performance counterparts of internal and external constraints, but there probably are not. However, it is quite clear that external constraint is primarily identifiable with perceptual discrimination, and internal constraint is primarily identifiable with free recall type of learning. Thus increases in external constraint will mainly affect discrimination performance, while increases in internal constraint will mainly affect free recall. In both cases, however, there should also be some effects due to the other kind of constraint.

When there is no internal constraint in a system of variables (that is, when all variables are orthogonal), then the form of the external constraint cannot be varied. However, once internal constraint has been introduced, then the form of both the internal constraint and the external constraint can be varied by the particular selection of combinations of variables (ordinarily by which particular stimuli are selected for use). This selection, and the resultant effects on form of redundancy will affect performance also, and almost certainly will differentially affect discrimination and free recall. In other words, the form of redundancy which is best for free recall will be poorest for discrimination and conversely. However, the form of internal and external constraint cannot be manipulated independently, since a given selection of stimuli completely determines the form of both types of constraint. Thus it is impossible to have forms of constraint which are optimum for both discrimination and free recall simultaneously.

CHAPTER SIX

Pattern Perception

THE PSYCHOLOGICAL STUDY OF pattern perception has been confined almost exclusively to the study of visual pattern perception, and has been a sufficiently important topic for entire books to be devoted to it. Almost since the introduction of information concepts into the psychological literature various psychologists have attempted to apply these concepts to the problems of pattern perception. The success of these ventures cannot at the present be considered overwhelming, and for a variety of reasons. The psychological problems themselves have not been satisfactorily reduced to analytic concepts. For example, we are still not entirely sure what is meant by such Gestalt terms as goodness and good continuation, and we need to point to specific illustrations to clarify the meaning of the terms. Furthermore, the meaning of various informational terms as related to patterns and pattern perception has not been entirely clear. In applying some of the informational concepts, most researchers have had the experience of finding, for example, that what intuitively seems like redundancy cannot be described in a manner which is congruent with the informational meaning of that term.

The appeal of information concepts in this area lies in their ability to deal with things such as organization and structure in a quantitative manner, the very things which have seemed to be the essence of the nature of pattern perception. Both the need for quantification and the appeal of the concepts are so great that the attempt to use information concepts in this area will undoubtedly continue. It seems likely, however, that considerable clarification of the information concepts within the context of pattern perception is necessary. Here we shall attempt a better understanding of these problems in the light of the concepts and ideas developed in the last chapter.

The experimental literature in this area easily divides itself into two major approaches. First we have the more traditional psychophysical approach to problems of pattern perception—an approach which emhasizes discrimination, recognition, and even learning of patterns. While this approach is primarily concerned with discrimination problems, that is not the essential characteristic for our purposes. Rather, the distinguishing characteristic of this approach is that the experiments always deal with sets of stimuli rather than with single stimuli. Whether the subject is required simply to discriminate, to learn to reproduce, or to learn identifying labels, he is always required to distinguish between stimuli of a given set, or to reproduce a fixed number of stimuli, etc.

The second major approach to problems of pattern perception has been emphasized by the Gestalt psychologists, who have been concerned about such things as goodness of figure, simplicity, etc. Here again, the critical factor for our purposes does not lie in the types of experimental procedures used, but rather lies in the fact that the concern is with the characteristics of unique patterns. When a Gestalt psychologist talks about "goodness of figure," he is not referring to a characteristic of a set of stimuli; rather, he is talking about a characteristic of a single pattern. Such an approach does not, of course, easily suggest experiments on interstimulus discrimination, because it is not concerned about interstimulus differences, but rather about intrastimulus characteristics.

The Gestalt approach has always posed considerable difficulty in the past, and we shall see that it still does. This difficulty is fundamentally inherent in the process of trying to describe unique events with general characteristics. There is a certain incompatibility between concepts of uniqueness and concepts of generality, an incompatibility which does not disappear when we try to deal with pattern perception.

In the last chapter I distinguished between external and internal constraints, the former having to do with interstimulus characteristics, and the latter having to do with intrastimulus characteristics. It is tempting to provide a proper balance to this topic by aligning the difference between external and internal constraints with the difference between these two approaches to pattern perception, but to do so provides a precarious balance indeed. There is some relation between them, but the relation is most tenuous. It is true that problems of stimulus discrimination are primarily problems of external constraint, but concerns with the characteristics of unique stimuli is not in any simple fashion related to internal constraint. Internal constraint is indeed concerned with intrastimulus characteristics, but still with characteristics of sets of stimuli, not with characteristics of the single stimulus.

Our organization in this chapter will be in line with these two approaches to pattern perception problems. First we will discuss experiments and problems associated with sets of stimuli; then we will discuss experiments and problems associated with single stimuli. While an organization along the lines of the distinctions made in the last chapter would be very satisfying, it is not at present feasible, largely because the experiments which have been done simply do not easily fit these distinctions. Thus while we shall be dealing with the concepts developed in the last chapter, our organization must to some extent follow the nature of the experiments in the field.

PATTERN DISCRIMINATION AND EXTERNAL CONSTRAINT

The importance of external constraint in simple pattern discrimination has already been established to a considerable extent. The relations between speed and accuracy of perceptual discrimination and stimulus uncertainty (that is, the amount of external constraint required with perfect discrimination) are as relevant to discrimination of patterns as to discrimination of anything else, and indeed we have used some examples of pattern discrimination in showing the nature of these relations.

Several experiments have shown that discrimination (measured by some kind of accuracy criterion) becomes poorer as the number of stimuli to be discriminated increases. Krulee, Podell, and Ronco (1954), for example, measured the longest distance at which numerals could be visually discriminated as a function of the number of possible numerals, and found that the distance threshold decreased (that is, perception became poorer) as stimulus uncertainty was increased. In addition, in one part of their experiment they informed the subjects that a larger number of numerals was possible than was in fact so, and found that the distance threshold was a function of the number expected rather than the number actually used. Reasonably enough the subject's expectancy is the critical factor, not the experimenter's knowledge.

In another experiment, Krulee and Weisz (1955) used three-digit displays, and demonstrated that the distance threshold was determined primarily by the most complex of the three positions, when complexity is determined by stimulus uncertainty.

Discrimination of patterns is not a phenomenon in any essential way different from other discrimination phenomena, and it depends to a great extent on actual stimulus uncertainty—that is, on the number of stimuli which could occur but do not occur on any given presentation. Klemmer and Loftus (1958) have further demonstrated that the unique characteristics of any given pattern are less important in determining accuracy of perceptual discrimination than are the characteristics of the entire set. They used as stimuli all of the 128 patterns that can be generated from a seven-bar figure which forms the figure 8 when all seven bars are used. Each of the seven segments was illuminated from behind, and subjects were required to copy, after a short time, the actual figure presented. This particular stimulus arrangement was used because with it all of the common Arabic numerals can be generated to a degree of accuracy such that the numerals are easily identified correctly.

These authors found that, when they ran their tests with all 128 figures, those ten figures which constitute the Arabic numerals were correctly reproduced with no greater accuracy than were the other figures. When, however, tests were run with only the Arabic numerals, accuracy was considerably greater. Thus we have confirmation that accuracy is a function of number of alternatives, although these results also showed that when information transmission is used as the measure of discrimination, then the larger set of figures gave greater information transmission—a relation conforming completely to results discussed here in earlier chapters. Discrimination is clearly related to the characteristics of the entire set of stimuli, not to the characteristics of the particular stimulus.

Patterns as multivariate stimuli

These experiments have been mentioned here only to establish the fact that pattern discrimination shows the same general relations to stimulus uncertainty that we have discussed before. We have also seen that information transmission on any perceptual discrimination task is greatest when the stimuli vary in more than one dimension; and a pattern is clearly such a multivariate stimulus.

This relation between information transmission and the number of independent dimensions on which the stimuli vary has been emphasized by Pollack and Klemmer (1954a,b), who use the term *coordinality* to refer to this characteristic of a stimulus. The experiment they report demonstrates the role of dimensionality in pattern perception.

When is a visual stimulus a pattern? Certainly there is no simple answer to this question, and almost any visual stimulus can be considered to be a pattern if it has spatial characteristics. We all would agree that two dots on a plane surface constitute at least an elementary pattern. Pollack and Klemmer have shown that when information transmission measures are used, the critical factor is not whether the dots appear on a line or on a plane, or whether there is one dot or two. Rather, the critical factor is simply the number of dimensions which must be used to specify the positions.

These authors carried out an experiment in which subjects were required to reproduce linear dot patterns. The stimuli consisted of a set of eight dot positions, any number of which could be filled. For some of their experiments, subjects were presented with stimuli in which just one position was filled; in other experiments, two, three, or a larger fixed number of dots was used. From the reproduction data, the authors computed information transmissions which would have been obtained if the number of dots varied from 1 to 2, 1 to 3, and 1 to 4.

These estimated information transmissions as a function of number of possible dots are shown in Fig. 6.1, which indicates that information transmission increases as the number of possible dots increases, going

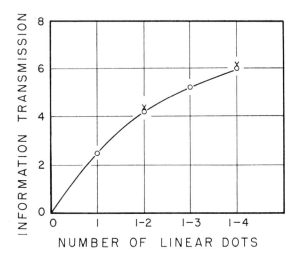

Fig. 6.1. Information transmission with linear dot patterns. Each open circle represents the information transmitted when the number of dots in the pattern may vary as indicated on the abscissa. The two x's are data for one and two dots on a plane, taken from Fig. 4.2. (After Pollack and Klemmer, 1954a,b.)

to a value of about 6 bits when there can be as many as 4 dots at a time. (Numbers of dots beyond this would show a decrease, since the complementary situation would exist—that is, six out of eight dot positions filled is the same as two out of eight filled.) The critical parts of Fig. 6.1, however, are the two x's, which show information transmission for one and for two dots on a plane. Notice that the information transmission for one dot on a plane is the same as it is for one to two dots on a line, and, likewise, that for two dots on a plane it is the same as that for one to four dots on a line. Now it takes two dimensions to specify the position of a single dot on a plane, just as it takes two numbers to specify the positions of two dots on a line. Similarly, four numbers are required to specify the positions of two dots on a plane or four dots on a line. The evidence could not be much clearer that the critical factor for information transmission is the number of dimensions required to specify the position of the stimulus. It is also clear that the perceptual discrimination problem is not fundamentally different if we have dots on lines or dots on planes. Pattern perception is simply the perception of spatial relations, at any level of complexity.

Various other writers have emphasized the multidimensional aspect of perception. Krulee (1958), for example, devised a set of stimuli which had four binary dimensions, and he found, using distance thresholds, that the threshold depended primarily on the least discriminable single dimension. Thus in this particular case multidimensional discrimination reduced to unidimensional discrimination when one dimension was substantially more difficult to discriminate than the others.

In a somewhat different type of experiment, Archer (1954), measured the time required to identify thirty-two visual patterns, when these patterns required 1 to 4 bits of information for their correct identification. He found that response time increased directly as a function of the information load—and in this case each bit of information was obtained from an independent dimension. However, in some experimental conditions there were also some irrelevant dimensions (that is, dimensions which varied but were not relevant to the response). The number of irrelevant dimensions had no effect on the total response time, and were apparently effectively ignored.

Deliberate experimentation on multivariate aspects of perceptual recognition and discrimination has not been carried very far, and much of the research along these general lines has been done more within the framework of concept formation than within the framework of pattern perception. Binder (1955), however, has developed a schema for describing the process of visual recognition which emphasizes the perception of separate attributes or dimensions. Even though little work has been done in which multiple dimensions are deliberately used as experimental variables, still there is considerable value in recognizing the essentially multivariate nature of pattern perception. Certainly at a first level of description we can think of any pattern as being formed of a series of defined spaces which are filled or unfilled. Thus the cells of a two-dimensional matrix can be considered each to be a single variable which can have two values—filled or unfilled. Each cell is then a single dimension, or logon, and we can attempt to describe patterns in terms of the relations between these variables or logons.

PATTERN PERCEPTION AND REDUNDANCY

The information concept which has had the most teasing appeal to psychologists interested in pattern perception is that of redundancy. It seems intuitively clear that somehow a structured pattern is one which is redundant, and a meaningless pattern is one which is random, or non-redundant. However, ways of determining, describing, or producing known amounts of redundancy have not been as easy as it seems reasonable they should be. There have been performed quite a few experiments in which redundancy has been an experimental variable, either within or outside the framework of information concepts per se. These experiments have met with varying success, and at times it would seem that the most general result which has come from these experiments is that there is no general result.

However, redundancy has been a most elusive concept in this area, and at times an experimental manipulation which was designed to increase redundancy has actually decreased it. Therefore, before discussing the experimental literature, it might be well if we looked at this problem of redundancy from the point of view outlined in the last chapter. We should be very clear on exactly what redundancy is and does in a set of patterns. In particular, we should be careful to distinguish *amount* and *form* of redundancy. We should be even more careful to distinguish redundancy as a concept which might be applied to a single or unique pattern, and redundancy as a concept concerning sets of patterns.

Amount of redundancy
The concept of redundancy can be dealt with in an exact manner only when we are dealing with sets of stimuli, not with single stimuli,

since redundancy is a measure (in uncertainty terms) of the extent to which an actual number of stimuli is smaller than the maximum number which could exist given the same number of variables with a given uncertainty. In other words, redundancy must relate to amount of stimulus uncertainty, and stimulus uncertainty cannot be specified for a single stimulus. Uncertainty measurement deals with sets of stimuli, and probability distributions of these sets.

There are three basic information variables which can be used in any experiment on pattern perception: multiple contingent uncertainty (external constraint), amount of redundancy (internal constraint), and the form of redundancy (the particular uncertainty terms involved in the internal or external constraint). Each of these factors can be expected to have some effect on pattern perception, although the particular effect which each might have will certainly depend on the nature of the performance criterion used. Let us discuss each of these factors in turn.

To make our discussion a bit more concrete, let us suppose that we have a square matrix of nine cells and that each cell can be either black or white. We shall consider that we are dealing with nine dichotomous variables, each cell being one variable. The maximum possible uncertainty (total constraint) which we could use would be 9 bits, corresponding to 512 possible patterns. Our problem is to decide how many and which of these 512 patterns we will use in an experiment. The number we use will determine the maximum information transmission (external constraint), and the number we don't use will determine the redundancy. In addition, our decision as to which particular ones to use will determine the pattern of the relations between the variables, and, thus, the form of the redundancy. This selection may also affect the amount of redundancy, since if we select our stimuli such that some cells are never or always black, then we have simply reduced the number of variables.

Suppose we decide to use sixteen of the patterns out of the total of 512 possible patterns. We have, by this decision, limited external constraint (amount available for discrimination) to 4 bits. This decision will affect the identification accuracy, reaction time, and information transmission.

Our decision to use only sixteen patterns also fixed the amount and percent of redundancy, since we are working with a fixed total constraint, or maximum uncertainty. Clearly, we have only two degrees of freedom available to us, and if we fix the maximum uncertainty and the maximum information transmission, we have also fixed the redundancy. This fact has real implications for experiments on pattern perception. Suppose, for example, that we keep our maximum uncertainty fixed at 9 bits but vary the number of stimuli used in an experiment. With such a procedure we ensure that as actual stimulus uncertainty (external constraint) is increased stimulus redundancy is decreased. Thus if we work with a fixed total constraint, then actual stimulus uncertainty and redundancy cannot vary independently, and as one goes up the other must go down. .

If we want to study the effects of redundancy on pattern perception it would be better if we held actual stimulus uncertainty constant and increased the maximum possible uncertainty, thus increasing redundancy. In our illustration, for example, redundancy might better be increased by increasing the number of cells in the original matrix. Then we could hold constant the external constraint required while increasing the redundancy (and necessarily the maximum stimulus uncertainty).

We have discussed the interrelations between stimulus uncertainty, maximum stimulus uncertainty, and redundancy in this manner to be able to emphasize a point which has led to considerable confusion. That point is this: If we hold constant the number of stimuli and increase redundancy by increasing the maximum stimulus uncertainty, then we are automatically increasing the number of ways in which the stimuli used can differ. Thus, *to add redundancy to any fixed number of stimuli is to add discriminability to the stimuli by making them more complex.*

This is a characteristic result and necessary concomitant of the addition of redundancy. The process of adding redundancy to a set of visual patterns is not a process of simplifying the patterns. On the contrary, it is a process of complicating the patterns—complicating them so that there are more ways in which the stimuli within a used set can differ. Thus, as long as the number of stimuli actually used is held constant, *redundancy is not identifiable with simplicity of figure or pattern, but rather is identifiable with complexity.* Conversely, if we have, say, eight figures which we want to use in a discrimination experiment, and if two sets of these figures differ in complexity, then the more complex figures are the more redundant figures, not vice versa.

Perhaps this statement seems intuitively in conflict with the relation shown in Chapter Five that the process of introducing redundancy is also a process of providing internal struture within the set of figures. Internal structure is indeed provided, but *internal structure is a set of relations between the variables making up the total set of figures, not a set of relations between elements within a particular figure.* The correlations which are introduced when redundancy is introduced are correlations between variables across the different selected patterns. In fact, for a single figure in the type of situation we are describing, there can be no correlations between its elements. In each figure the cell is either black or white, and there is no variability. Without variability, however, there can be no correlation.

Thus redundancy produces correlation between variables, and structure within an entire set of variables. But it also produces greater discriminability between particular patterns, because the patterns differ in more ways. This is the essence and the purpose of redundancy—to increase the number of variables on which two or more events in a set can be discriminated, so that if discrimination is lost for some of the variables, other variables will still be able to provide the discrimination required.

Form of redundancy

So far we have been discussing the determination of the amount of redundancy, and the effect of redundancy on sets of patterns. Amount of redundancy is determined primarily by the number of stimuli actually used in an experiment compared to the number which could have been used with the same number and uncertainty of variables. Form of redundancy, on the other hand, is determined by which particular stimuli are selected from the larger initial set. In some experiments there has been confusion between form of redundancy and amount of redundancy. With a fixed total constraint, *amount of redundancy is determined by how many stimuli are selected, and form of redundancy is determined by which particular ones are selected.*

To detail this distinction, suppose that in our illustration of the square matrix with nine cells, we select eight stimuli in two different ways. In the first case, we select them randomly from all 512 possible patterns; in the second case we select according to the rule that in any one column we can have only bars extending from the bottom. (That is, once a given cell in a column is white or empty, no cell above it may be filled. Thus each column can have black bars with heights of 0, 1, 2, or 3 units.) In the former case, our redundancy is clearly 6 bits, since we use 3 bits of uncertainty out of 9 bits possible. However, in the latter case our redundancy is also 6 bits, since once again we use 3 bits out of 9 bits. Thus the process of specifying a rule by which we select the stimuli is not a process which produces redundancy; it is simply a process which states in what form the redundancy will come. Any experimental question based on such selection procedures is a question concerning the nature of the redundancy not its amount.

The confusion between amount and form of redundancy comes about primarily because of the confusion between redundancy as a concept pertinent to sets of stimuli and redundancy as a concept which describes the single stimulus. We often choose a particular rule for selecting stimuli on grounds related to the characteristics of the individual stimuli, but regardless of the reasons for choosing a particular selection rule, the fact still remains that such a procedure does not affect amount of redundancy, but only its form.

The importance of the particular selection of stimuli (because it determines the form of redundancy) cannot be overemphasized. That the selection rule determines the form rather than the amount of the redundancy does not mean that the form of the redundancy is an unimportant or trivial variable. As I pointed out in the last chapter, the form of the redundancy will certainly affect both discrimination between stimuli as well as free recall of stimuli. The problem is that the expected nature of the effects sometimes look quite different when we realize that we are changing the form of the redundancy rather than its amount. With the selection rule mentioned above, which allows only bars of varying heights, the redundancy produced will have high contingencies between variables. As we saw in the last chapter, this form of redundancy should be good for free recall, but poor for discrimination. Now if an increased amount of redundancy improves discrimination, but the particular form of redundancy produced is poor for discrimination, we will have a very confusing state of affairs, to say the least.

What is a variable?

The selection rule just described raises a very interesting question, the answer to which suggests that a particular selection rule may actually decrease redundancy rather than produce or increase it. That question has to do with what really constitutes a variable in a psychological experiment, and it seems to me that only that which varies over the range of stimuli actually used can be considered a variable. Let us see how this works out in our example.

We have two different selection rules to use. With one rule we randomly select eight stimuli, and with the other rule we also select eight stimuli but from a subset which includes only vertical bars of varying heights. In both cases our actual stimulus uncertainty (that is, external constraint) is 3 bits, but in the former case we randomly select from 512 patterns, or 9 bits, while in the latter case we randomly select from 64 patterns, or 6 bits. (That is, with the restricted sampling we have three bars each with four different heights, giving 64 possible combinations of heights.) Therefore our redundancy would be 6 bits in the former case, and only 3 bits in the latter case, since in the latter case maximum stimulus uncertainty is lower.

This line of reasoning has considerable merit, for it is based on the assumption that for the subject what constitutes a variable is only that which varies; and in this case all he ever sees are bars of differing heights. Thus the effective total constraint for him is considerably less than for the subject who sees the random selection of filled cells. In other words, with the random selection, the subject sees each cell as a variable, while with the restricted sampling he sees only vertical bars as variables.

There are many experiments in which a proper analysis of the amount and form of redundancy requires careful consideration of the variables as the subject sees them. For example, suppose that we still have our nine-cell matrix, but now generate patterns all of which have just two black cells. In this case we should no longer consider the cell to be the variable, with two values to each variable; rather, we should consider the two black cells as the variables, each of which can take nine possible values. We do so, because a variable is that which exists for every stimulus, but with values which change from one stimulus to another. Since the existence of two filled cells is stable, but their positions are not, then it would seem more reasonable to consider that we are dealing with a two-variable problem with 3.17 bits per variable. Thus the total constraint would be 6.34 bits, not 9 bits. If the total constraint for the subject is lower due to his seeing fewer variables, then, clearly, the redundancy which we would assume to be operating for any fixed number of selected stimuli would also be lower.

It is necessary, in other words, to use a considerable amount of good judgment in applying these principles and concepts to an actual experimental problem.

The performance criterion

In a similar vein, some further comment needs to be made about the different kinds of performance criteria which can be and are used experimentally. It would be simple if a given amount or form of redundancy had the same effect on all possible performance criteria, but such is not the case. On logical grounds alone it is obviously necessary to distinguish between criteria which primarily require discrimination and those which require free recall. Even the many types of discrimination performance which can be used might well lead to different effects. Hake (1957) presents an excellent summary and discussion of various performance criteria in relation to pattern discrimination, and we need not go into these in detail here.

These factors, real or artifactual, complicate our ability to clarify the role of redundancy in pattern perception. Many different performance criteria have been used in the experiments reported, and these different performance criteria can easily lead to apparently contradictory results. As we noted in the last chapter, changes in informational terms should lead to changes in performance, but the nature of the change is directly related to the nature of the performance and the nature of the uncertainty change. Tasks which deal exclusively with discrimination, and not learning of internal structure, will show some kinds of change. Tasks which emphasize or include learning of internal structure will show other kinds of change. We cannot alter the way experiments have been done, but we can keep a note of caution in their interpretation.

SOME EXPERIMENTAL RESULTS CONCERNING REDUNDANCY

One of the most straightforward experiments on the effect of redundancy on pattern perception was carried out by Bricker (1955a), who used the stimuli schematically shown in Fig. 6.2. These stimuli were patterns of lights, arranged in a row of five pairs, and either the top or bottom light of each pair could be lighted. Thus when three pairs of lights were used, the maximum stimulus uncertainty was 3 bits, but when five pairs were used the maximum stimulus uncertainty increased to 5 bits, although only 3 bits of uncertainty were ever used. In his experiment, Bricker used either the last three pairs of lights, variables c, d, and e, or the last four pairs (1 bit of redundancy), or all five pairs (2 bits of redundancy). His subjects were required to learn a verbal response to each of the eight patterns, and accuracy and response time were measured. The stimulus was flashed on for 0.7 sec.

The results of the experiment show unambiguously that redundancy had a deleterious effect on both rate of learning and speed of responding. The two redundant sets of stimuli were learned more slowly, and even after many trials, were responded to more slowly. Thus redundancy only made the perceptual discrimination more difficult.

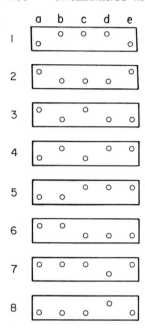

Fig. 6.2. The eight stimulus patterns used by Bricker (1955a). Each circle represents a light. When non-redundant stimuli were used, only the three right-hand lights (c, d, and e) were used.

This result is not entirely unreasonable if we consider the nature of the stimulus situation and also the nature of the relations between the variables which made up the stimuli. As we noted above, the stimulus was flashed on for a relatively brief period of time. This fact means that the subject had to be very alert to see all of the elements or variables in the display, and if the number of elements in the display increased, his total perceptual load was appreciably increased without an appropriate increase in time. Suppose that with all five variables the subject was able to perceive correctly only three of the variables. If he always made sure to perceive the three right-hand pairs of lights, then he still could have discriminated perfectly. But if he saw, for example, variables (lights) a, b, and d, he could not determine whether the total pattern was the second or the third. In fact, for these three variables, patterns 1 and 4 are identical, as also are patterns 2 and 3, 5 and 8, and 6 and 7. Thus if only these three pairs of lights were seen, the subject could only narrow the choice down to two possible patterns. Other sets of three variables also prevent perfect discrimination.

We discussed in the last chapter the fact that it is often impossible to select redundant patterns in such a way that any subset of variables will lead to perfect discrimination. This is what has happened here. The net result of this fact is that the addition of redundancy may lead to poorer discrimination unless we can be sure that the additional discriminating variables can be perfectly perceived. In other words, redundancy increases the discriminability of the stimuli actually used, but this increased discriminability can be of value only if it is perceived. Under some conditions, as we have seen, the increased discriminability can lead to poorer performance unless we control which variables are seen—in which case we no longer really have redundancy.

In another experiment on pattern discrimination, Deese (1956) generated a series of patterns which are illustrated in Fig. 6.3. The patterns were solid black figures which differed in terms of two variables: the number of changes in contour, and the angular change in contour. His regular figures changed contour only with right angles, while his irregular figures could change contour with varying angles. His simple figures had few changes in contour, while his complex figures had many changes in contour.

In Deese's discrimination task, the subject was shown a figure for 10 sec, and then either immediately or after a delay he was shown a set of five figures of the same general kind, and was required to identify out of these five the one he had previously been shown. (As we noted before, since the set of stimuli to be discriminated was held constant at five, then the more complex or irregular forms are

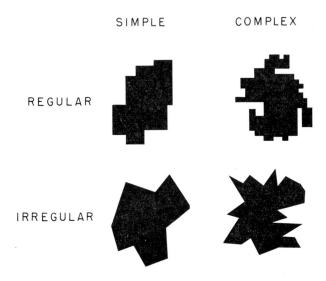

FIG. 6.3. Examples of figures used by Deese (1956).

the more redundant, since they are generated from a larger initial class of stimuli.) Deese measured both response time required for discrimination and accuracy of discrimination. His results for speed of discrimination for complex and simple figures (regular figures in both cases) are shown in Fig. 6.4, which shows that identification time was greater for the complex figures, thus confirming Bricker's results that the more redundant figures require greater response time. Deese's results for accuracy of identification are shown in Fig. 6.5, and here we have an opposite result: The complex figures are more accurately identified.

In this regard, the results appear to contradict those of Bricker, since his subjects learned to identify the redundant figures more

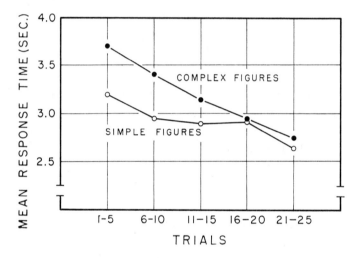

Fig. 6.4. Mean discrimination time as a function of trials. These data are for regular figures only, as in Fig. 6.3. (After Deese, 1956.)

slowly. The difference may be due to the experimental procedure used, since Deese required a direct discrimination judgment, while Bricker required a learned response. It seems more likely, however, that the difference is due to time of exposure of the stimulus. Deese exposed the critical stimulus for 10 seconds, and the set of figures from which the correct one was to be chosen was exposed as long as necessary. Thus there should have been none of the effect that probably existed in Bricker's experiment; that is, there was no need for sampling of variables which could lead to insufficient discriminatory cues.

At any rate, Deese's results make a certain amount of good sense. They indicate that the more complex (more redundant) figures are

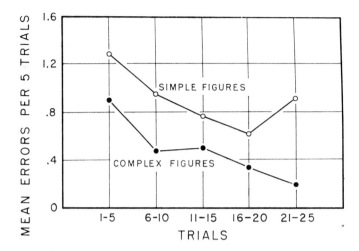

Fig. 6.5. Mean number of discrimination errors as a function of trials. These data are for regular figures only, as in Fig. 6.3. (After Deese, 1956.)

discriminated more accurately, but with a loss in speed of discrimination. In other words, the extra discriminability which comes with redundancy is used, given sufficient time, to produce greater accuracy of discrimination, but more time is required to make use of the inherently greater discriminability.

Still another attack was made on the role of redundancy in pattern discrimination by Attneave (1955). He generated a series of patterns by placing dots in the cells of a two-dimensional matrix. He used matrices of 3 x 4, 4 x 5, or 5 x 7 cells. In the twelve-cell matrix the dots were always placed randomly, but in the others they were placed randomly or symmetrically by mirroring the smaller random matrix. His subjects, in different phases of the experiment, were required either to reproduce the patterns or to identify them with a learned label. His results for identification learning are presented in Fig. 6.6. With both of his methods, the symmetrical patterns were identified slightly more accurately than were the random patterns, when the number of cells was the same.

If the symmetrical patterns are considered as more redundant than the random patterns, then this result appears to contradict that found by Bricker for a similar learning task. However, the symmetrical patterns are not really more redundant. In both cases, symmetrical and random, twelve actual stimulus patterns were used, and since the total number of possible patterns was the same in both cases,

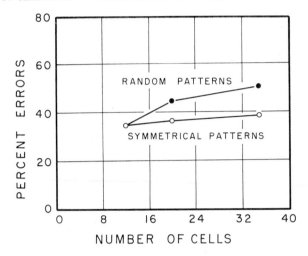

F𝐈𝐆. 6.6. Errors of identification of patterns of dots as a function of the number of cells. Either random or symmetrical patterns were used. (After Attneave, 1955.)

so also was the redundancy the same. Actually, these results show the effect of a particular form of redundancy, not the effect of an amount of redundancy. The symmetrical patterns are selected by a particular rule—a rule which affects the terms in the internal constraint. The selection of symmetrical patterns will have the general effect of maximizing and equalizing the contingent uncertainties between variables, since if the lower left cell is always the same as the lower right cell, for example, then correlation involving the lower right cell and any other cell will be high and the same as those involving the lower left cell and any other cell.

In many respects, the important fact shown by this experiment of Attneave's is the increase in number of errors as the number of cells is increased. Since twelve patterns were used in each case, then the increase in number of cells directly produces an increase in redundancy, because of the increase in maximum stimulus uncertainty. In this case, the increased number of errors with increased redundancy shows the same effect as Bricker obtained, that is, an increased difficulty of identification with increased redundancy. Thus once again it would appear that the increased complexity and discriminability which accompanies increased redundancy does not necessarily aid accuracy of identification.

Another means of generating redundant stimulus figures has been developed by Fitts et al. (1956, 1957), and some of the types of figures they used are illustrated in Fig. 6.7. They start with a square matrix of any given size, and our illustrations are for a 6 x 6 matrix. Then they generate columns or bars within the matrix as the first step. A set of figures generated with no more restriction than this is called random, as illustrated in the upper left figure. From this basic scheme, other figures can be generated. One additional restriction which they have used is illustrated in the upper right figure. These figures, which they call constrained, are the same as the random except that no two columns may have the same height. Thus the set of all possible figures from which this type can be selected is considerably smaller than is the set of all possible random figures. (As we have seen, constraining figures in this manner affects only the form of redundancy.)

Beyond this restriction, two other changes are made. One change is simply to take a basic pattern and double it in a mirrored fashion. Thus a symmetrical figure is produced, and the symmetrical figure can be generated from either random or constrained figures. A last change is to duplicate the pattern by simply repeating the same basic pattern. Either random or constrained figures can be repeated, and the mirrored figures can also be repeated. Figure 6.7 shows two figures which have been both mirrored and repeated.

Sets of figures are generated with these various procedures, and then samples are taken from these sets. Fitts et al. (1956) used samples of eight from various sets of figures. They then required their subjects to select from the entire sample of eight a particular one which was shown at the top of the total sample. The time required

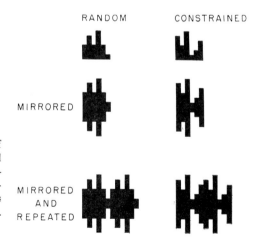

RANDOM   CONSTRAINED

MIRRORED

MIRRORED
AND
REPEATED

Fig. 6.7. Various methods of constructing redundant visual patterns. Mirroring and repeating patterns produces extra redundancy. Constraining affects the form of the redundancy. (After Fitts et al., 1956.)

to identify the correct one from the entire sample was used as the dependent variable. These authors found that the random figures were discriminated more rapidly than the constrained figures. While there were some differences due to mirroring and repeating, these differences were small.

Anderson and Leonard (1958) compared samples of random and constrained figures, using three different experimental techniques. Using samples of twelve figures, in one technique they required subjects to sort a deck of stimulus cards into twelve different boxes, one for each figure. In another technique, subjects were required to learn, by a paired-associates procedure, a letter to correspond to each figure. With both of these techniques the previous finding was duplicated, namely, that the random figures were more easily discriminated than were the constrained figures. In still another experiment, subjects were required to reconstruct the figures, and with this procedure the constrained figures were more accurately reproduced. These authors argued that in the latter case only were the subjects required to attend and respond to all detail in the figures, and that in the former cases they were able to deal more rapidly with the random figures because the subjects attended to only as much detail as required.

Actually, as I pointed out above, these results with constrained versus random figures are not really pertinent to the question of the effect of amount of redundancy, but rather are pertinent to the question of the form of redundancy. Since in all comparisons made the actual sample size was the same, then the amount of redundancy was the same, and sampling by a different rule only affects the form of the redundancy, not its amount. Furthermore, I showed in the last chapter that for discrimination purposes the optimum form of redundancy is that which minimizes the contingent uncertainties between pairs of stimulus variables. The sampling restriction that no two columns may have the same height is a rule which produces such contingencies. We cannot know the exact amount of it without knowing the precise sample of stimuli used, but with patterns formed from eight bars it is at least 5.32 bits.

Thus, we have every reason to expect that this particular method of sampling should have led to poorer discrimination performance. It is interesting to note that the one experimental procedure which showed better performance with the constrained figures was when Anderson and Leonard required reproduction of figures. With this method, no discrimination between figures was required, but only identification of the characteristics of each particular figure. In other words, with this method the subjects are in fact dealing more with internal constraint; thus this form of redundancy should have been good for that purpose.

When figures are created by mirroring or by repetition, redundancy is indeed made greater. With a fixed sample size, for example, the mirroring procedure creates additional redundancy because the maximum stimulus uncertainty has been increased. If in mirroring we double the number of cells, then we have a larger original matrix from which a larger number of figures could have been generated. Rappaport (1957) used mirrored and repeated figures with the same experimental technique as that used by Fitts et al., that is, subjects were required to identify one out of the eight figures in the sample as the one shown at the top of the sample.

With this technique, mean recognition time increased as redundancy increased. However, Rappaport had made all of his figures to be of the same total size, a procedure which means that the more redundant (repeated) figures had smaller detail. When he ran a control for this factor by making the detail the same size, he found very little difference in recognition time as a function of redundancy.

Some conclusions

These various experimental results do not appear to leave us with a clear picture of the effects of redundancy on pattern perception. And yet there may be more consistency here than it seems at first glance.

Increasing redundancy should improve pattern discrimination: It has the effect of increasing complexity and discriminability between the patterns in a particular set of stimuli, because the redundancy provides more distinctive cues than are actually required for the discrimination. However, we should note that redundancy, while producing more discriminability, does so by increasing the amount of difference between the stimuli. Therefore, we might well expect that while maximum accuracy should improve, a longer discrimination time will be required for the subject to make use of the additional discriminative cues. In other words, discrimination will improve with increased redundancy, but at a cost in time.

Deese's results clearly suggest this possibility, since his complex figures were discriminated more accurately, but more slowly. In his experiment the subjects were allowed considerable time to look at the figures, so they should have been able to make almost full use of the discriminability inherent in the figures. That they did so is indicated by the very low error scores.

In both Bricker's and Attneave's experiments, where exposure times were limited, we actually find that error scores are greater for the redundant figures. Thus with limited time, not only were the subjects unable to improve their discrimination performance, but the greater discriminability of the redundant figures produced a deleterious result. It seems likely that we have the same effect operating here as we do with timed tests: If a test is not time limited, then the time to complete it is the critical score, and differences between subjects will show up as time differences. If the test is time limited, however, these same differences will show up as errors.

Thus we can conclude that redundancy will aid discrimination, but only if sufficient time is allowed for the subject to make full use of the additional discriminative cues.

Increasing redundancy should make free recall of stimulus patterns more difficult. Here we have no direct data, since no experiments have been done involving free recall of redundant patterns, but it seems highly unlikely that any other result could occur. This effect, however, may have entered into the results of some of these experiments on discrimination. In both Bricker's and Attneave's experiments, identification learning was the performance criterion used. As we noted in the last chapter, such performance must to some extent require learning of internal constraint. Thus the fact that *more* errors are made to the redundant stimulus patterns may be an artifact of that particular method.

As regards the form of the redundancy, here the evidence is fairly favorable. In the various experiments comparing constrained versus random figures, the constrained figures were poorer for discrimination purposes, just as they should be, since such figures provide fewer independent discriminable cues. Yet when a reproduction task was used, the constrained figures were better. Insofar as reproduction is more concerned with optimum internal constraint, this is the result that should have been expected.

Thus, while no single experiment clearly establishes the effect of either amount or form of redundancy on either pure discrimination or free recall, the results are, on the whole, not out of line with what we might reasonably expect.

REDUNDANCY AND DISCRIMINATION IN NOISE

In discussing the problem of pattern discrimination and redundancy, there is one question which should be raised: What function can redundancy have in discrimination? We have discussed the fact that redundancy increases discriminability of a set of stimuli, but clearly whether such extra discriminability is an advantage depends on whether or not it is needed. Many factors other than redundancy or stimulus uncertainty affect discriminability of patterns—things such as duration of exposure, figure detail, and condition of the eye. Now if all of these factors are optimum, we might well ask of what possible use is redundancy, since if a set of patterns is clearly discriminable without redundancy, then redundancy at best will have no effect on discrimination and at worst may have a deleterious effect. While we have discussed some possible effects of redundancy on pattern perception, it is clear that the magnitudes of the effects found experimentally are relatively small compared to the amount of redundancy used, and it is possible that these experiments suffer under the handicap of using redundancy in situations where it is not needed.

Redundancy has a real purpose. Its purpose is primarily to ensure against error—error which might be the result of poor perceptual conditions, or might be the result of some form of stimulus distortion. There are two major forms of stimulus distortion in which redundancy can be helpful. Both of these can come under the general category of noise, as that term is used in communication engineering (noise being any random distortion of the signal). Perceptually, however, these two forms are probably quite different.

Stimulus impoverishment

By stimulus impoverishment I mean any loss of the actual stimulus presented. For example, if part of the stimulus pattern is omitted, or if all of it is not seen because the duration of exposure is too short, then we have stimulus impoverishment.

Now it is clear from our discussion in the last chapter that redundancy must be helpful under conditions of stimulus impoverishment. If three binary variables are used to form eight stimulus patterns, then the loss of any one of them will prevent accurate identification of the pattern. If, however, eight stimulus patterns are used from a possible sixteen, then the loss of one variable will not prevent perfectly accurate identification. While redundancy cannot guarantee that any three will produce accurate identification (because of the orthogonality restrictions we discussed), identification will always be more accurate with any random deletion of variables with redundant patterns than it will be with non-redundant patterns.

We have one experimental check on the effectiveness of redundancy when there is stimulus impoverishment. Bricker (1955a) used one condition in which one of the three, four, or five elements of the pattern was deleted in 10 percent of the trials. If we look only at those trials on which the deletion occurred, we find that 20 percent of the incomplete stimuli were correctly identified for non-redundant stimuli, while for the two redundant sets, an average of 45 percent of the incomplete stimuli were correctly identified. Thus here we have a straightforward and sizeable effect of redundancy: It can and does aid in stimulus identification under conditions of stimulus impoverishment.

Pattern distortion

The other form of noise is pattern distortion: One or more elements of the pattern will have different values than they should. With Bricker's stimuli, for example, the top light might be incorrectly lit instead of the bottom one. In the Fitts-type patterns, a particular column might be higher or lower than it should be, or the white spaces might be randomly filled with black cells which are not part of the original pattern. In any of these forms of noise, the net result is that the actual pattern presented is different from what it should have been. With stimulus impoverishment, part of the stimulus is simply not presented or perceived; with pattern distortion, all of the stimulus is presented, but some of the elements are incorrect.

Rappaport (1957), using mirrored and repeated stimulus patterns to produce redundancy, introduced pattern distortion by randomly filling in spaces (with a $\frac{1}{6}$ probability) which had not been filled in the original figures. Under these conditions, his mean recognition times decreased with increased redundancy, as shown in Fig. 6.8. His stimuli for this experiment were matched in overall size (not size of detail), and we may recall that under these conditions mean sorting time without pattern distortion was greater for the redundant figures. Thus the use of noise in this case shows an advantage of redundancy, while under noise-free conditions redundancy has been disadvantageous. It would appear that redundancy is useful when it is needed, but may be harmful when it is not needed.

Using a vertical series of dots arranged on an 8 x 8 cell matrix, Pollack and Klemmer (1954a) showed that randomly placed dots in addition to the linear pattern caused poorer identification of location. In addition, however, the loss in identification accuracy was much greater when the linear dot patterns were formed from a small number (say, two or three) of dots than when the dot pattern was formed from a larger number of dots (eight, for example). The use of the larger number of dots, of course, reduced total information transmission because fewer positions were possible, and the stimuli

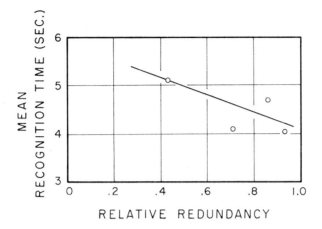

Fig. 6.8. Mean recognition time for discrimination of redundant figures that have been distorted by noise. (After Rappaport. 1957.)

were more redundant. But the redundancy had exactly the effect it should have had in maintaining accurate response under conditions of pattern distortion.

French (1954a) had shown that in the recognition of dot patterns from memory approximately seven dots gave optimum performance. That is, the increased complexity of a larger number of dots gave poorer recognition performance. In a later experiment, French (1954b) also showed that, when extra dots are randomly added to the pattern, recognition performance improved as the ratio of number of target dots to number of noise dots increased to a value of about 3:1. In other words, the more noise there was, the greater the advantage of a larger number of signal dots.

These results concerning the effects of redundancy under conditions of stimulus depletion or stimulus distortion are unequivocal: Increased redundancy leads to better discrimination. Our results with respect to simple discrimination certainly leave a large question mark concerning the benefits of redundancy. However, when there is a real need for the redundancy, there is no longer any doubt that redundancy aids discrimination. This is perhaps as it should be. Redundancy should aid discrimination only when in fact it is impossible to obtain completely accurate discrimination without it. If enough discriminable cues are available to account for all of the external constraint needed, there can be little advantage in adding more cues. If for any reason, however, more external constraint is needed than the stimuli (or the perceptual system) can provide, then redundancy should aid discrimination.

REDUNDANCY OF THE UNIQUE PATTERN

I mentioned earlier that the problem of describing properties of a unique pattern is somewhat more complicated. We all recognize, or have been informed by the Gestalt psychologists, that a circle, or a square, for example, have different properties than do highly irregular figures. Somehow these differences are related to such factors as regularity of the contour, or degree of predictability of the contour. However, degree or amount of regularity is certainly a concept which rings a bell to us, and it seems that we should be able to deal with some of these problems in information terms.

Various attempts to specify and quantify those characteristics of a figure which make it a "good" figure have been made. Attneave (1954), for example, has suggested that the major function of the perceptual process is to describe or encode any stimulus in as economical a form as possible, and that basically the problem of describing a figure is the problem of determining the minimum number of parameters which is needed to specify the figure. Attneave discusses several ways in which the various characteristics of a figure can be described. For example, we can specify boundaries, gradients, loci of principal points, differences between adjacent patterns, minimum degrees of systematic distortion, etc.

Hake (1957) also has emphasized that the visual system perceives in such a way as to maximize the coherence of the entire pattern, and that perception is selective in striving for maximum coherence. Those aspects of the perceptual pattern are selected which lead to the greatest apparent consistency of stimulation, consistency both of the parts of the total pattern with respect to each other, and consistency with respect to past experience and expected future experience. Both Hake and Attneave are stating that in pattern perception the visual system seeks out and selects regularities and consistencies in the total pattern, and that that pattern is most complex which has the fewest consistencies.

Attneave and Arnoult (1956) describe various ways of generating forms, particularly contour forms, which have different degrees of randomness and Attneave alone (1957) had subjects make direct judgments of the complexity of seventy-two different shapes. He found that judgments of complexity were most highly correlated with number of independent turns in the contour, with the variability of the angular changes, and with the symmetry of the contour. Symmetry was judged more complex if the symmetry was produced by doubling (mirroring) a figure but less complex in comparison to another figure with the same total number of turns.

Hochberg and McAlister (1953) had approached this problem with concepts quite like those later reported by Attneave, but with an entirely different and unique experimental approach. These authors used four reversible figures (Kopfermann cubes, as illustrated in Fig. 6.9), which can be seen as two- or three-dimensional figures. They determined the number of line segments, number of angles, and number of points of intersection necessary to specify the two-dimensional figure, and found that the proportion of time in which each of the different figures was seen as bidimensional was directly related to the simplicity of the bidimensional figure, if by simplicity we mean minimum number of lines, angles, and intersections.

In a later, much more thorough, set of experiments Hochberg and Brooks (1960) used direct ratings of three-dimensionality of many different reversible perspective drawings—drawings which could be seen as either three- or two-dimensional. Then eighteen different measured characteristics of the two-dimensional figures were determined, and correlations between these stimulus characteristics and direct ratings were computed. A complete factor analysis was carried out, and three major factors resulted. These factors were identified as: (1) number of angles, which is a general measure of complexity; (2) number of continuous line segments, which the authors identify with continuation; and (3) ratio of number of different angles to total angles, that is, angular variability, or symmetry. The relations between these factors and the ratings are such that the less the complexity, the greater the symmetry, and the greater the continuity of the two-dimensional figures, the more two-dimensional will the reversible figure be judged.

Fig. 6.9. Two Kopfermann cubes of the type used by Hochberg and McAlister (1953). The figure on the left, when seen as two-dimensional, has 16 line segments, 25 angles, and 10 points of intersection. The figure on the right, when seen as two-dimensional, has 13 line segments, 19 angles, and 8 points of intersection.

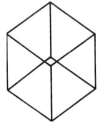
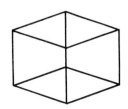

We seem to have quite clear evidence that some of the Gestalt concepts for describing characteristics of the unique pattern can be quantified, and that these quantifications can be shown to be experimentally meaningful. These measured characteristics are certainly related to the information concepts of constraint or redundancy, but how can we fit measurements of the unique figure into a paradigm which deals with sets of events and their probabilities?

Psychological redundancy as an inferred subset

Let us look a little more closely at exactly what is required to talk about the redundancy of a single or unique stimulus, and how we might specify in meaningful informational terms how redundant one pattern is compared to another. Suppose we have two different patterns of x's and o's like this:

$$\text{O X O X O X O X O X}$$
$$\text{X O O O X O X X O X}$$

Each of these patterns has exactly five x's and five o's, but they occur in different orders. Suppose that these two patterns had been generated in such a way that at each position there was a probability of .50 of obtaining x or o. The maximum uncertainty of such stimulus patterns would then be 10 bits, since 1024 such patterns could be generated. We now ask how redundant is each of these single stimulus patterns, and the answer is that each has 10 bits of redundancy, since each is just one pattern out of a possible 1024 patterns. Furthermore, the probability that each of these patterns would have been generated on a chance basis is exactly the same—each pattern is unique from the total set that could have been generated, and one would not occur more often by chance than the other. Nor do we have any way of demonstrating that one would occur more often other than by chance.

In other words, as we have noted before, there is no exact and directly meaningful way in which we can say that one unique pattern is more redundant than another. Yet any but the most perverse subject would say, if asked, that the first pattern was more regular, more meaningful, and even more redundant, than the second. How can we express this psychological opinion in terms which do not violate the true meaning of redundancy? Certainly one way to handle the problem, at least as a start, is to deal with it in exactly the same way that we deal with any other situation in which we want to provide a statistical description of a finite sample of events. Suppose we have a sequence of 100 responses from an experiment, and we want to ask whether the subject's responses are sequentially independent, that is, whether the subject generated this sequence randomly. Notice that we do not ask whether this particular unique sequence *could* have been generated randomly, because the answer most certainly is yes. Any particular sequence could have been generated randomly. Rather, we are asking whether the subject, in generating this actual sequence, was acting randomly or not. If we answer that he was not, we do not mean that on another occasion we would expect him to generate exactly the same sequence of responses. We would only expect that all sequences generated by the subject would have certain similarities.

We can put this another way. We are, in assuming the sequence not to be random, assuming that the subject would, in repeated trials, produce many different sequences of responses—but that all of the sequences he would produce would provide a smaller total number than would be provided on the assumption of randomness. In other words, we are saying that this particular sequence was one of a subset of possible sequences which is smaller than the set of all such sequences which could be generated on a random basis. If we can determine the size of this smaller subset, then we can specify the amount of redundancy by comparing it to the entire set possible. However, it is not the particular unique sequence of responses we are saying is redundant; rather, it is this subset of possible sequences which we are presuming to exist and to be smaller than the maximum possible set.

What we do to estimate the size of this smaller subset is to determine certain statistical characteristics of the finite sequence which we presume to exist for all possible sequences in the subset, and which we use to define the subset of possible sequences. We can determine the correlation between adjacent elements—and in a time series there is no ambiguity about which elements are adjacent. Or we can carry out a more complete autocorrelation, in which we determine the correlation between adjacent pairs of elements, pairs displaced one step, pairs displaced two steps, etc. This autocorrelation function, based entirely on measurements from the unique sequence of responses, is then presumed to be true for the entire subset of sequences, and we can use the autocorrelation function to determine the size of this subset, and thus its redundancy.

What I am trying to make clear here is that this process for determining the redundancy of a unique sequence or pattern is not at variance with the specific meaning of the term redundancy as we have used it. Redundancy means that fewer patterns exist than could exist, and when we say that a particular finite sequence is redundant we are simply saying that this sequence is one of many which could occur, but that the number which could occur is far less than the total number of such sequences which could occur if there were no redundancy.

To make this idea more concrete, let us consider the constrained figures generated by Fitts et al., which, it will be remembered, consist of adjacent bars of varying heights, but selected by the rule that no two bars in any figure may have the same height. Now any single constrained figure can be considered redundant only in the sense that there is an implied sampling set from which this one figure was drawn, and that this implied sampling set is smaller than the total set which could be generated if no restricted sampling rule were imposed. In other words, the redundancy exists only because of the implied restricted sampling of figures. We pointed out above that such a sampling rule does not really generate redundancy when we are dealing with a discrimination problem in which a fixed number of patterns must be discriminated. It seems quite possible, however, that direct perceptual judgments of such figures may be that they are more regular, more patterned, etc. In an information sense, however, such judgments can be meaningful only if they imply that such figures were generated by a restricted sampling rule. It is this entire set of assumed figures which is redundant, not the particular figure itself.

This is the implied aspect of judgments of redundancy of unique patterns. If a subject looks at a circle, for example, he will judge it to be more regular, a better figure, etc., than an irregular star. Probably he is using the characteristics of the particular figure or pattern to infer a subset of patterns which he can consider to form an equivalent set, and the smaller the size of this inferred set (with respect to the size of the set which could be generated), the greater the redundancy. Thus a unique pattern is judged to be redundant because it seems to be one of a smaller class of patterns than does the figure judged non-redundant, irregular, complex, etc. A vertical line within a confined space would be judged more redundant than a slanting line, because there is a smaller number of vertical lines possible than there is of slanted lines, assuming some finite resolution of the lines. And a square contour would be judged more redundant than a trapezoid because there are more ways to make trapezoids than there are to make squares.

What I am suggesting, in summary, is that a judgment of the redundancy of a unique figure (or judgments of other characteristics presumably related to redundancy) is not really a judgment of the redundancy of the figure itself (which is a meaningless judgment) but is, rather, a judgment of the redundancy of the particular subset of figures from which the unique figure is presumed to have come. Such a subset of figures, of course, can be inferred only from the characteristics of the unique figure, just as a subset of sequences of events is inferred from the statistical properties of the unique sample sequence. Our psychological problem then becomes the determination of those characteristics of figures which lead to small inferred subsets of figures. In essence, it is an attempt to find such characteristics that has engaged the attention of Attneave, Hochberg, and their co-workers.

The problem of finding physical characteristics which lead to inferred small subsets of figures is far more difficult than is the problem of determining statistical characteristics of sequences or series of events, where the time factor provides such an obviously meaningful criterion for relating events. With two-dimensional geometric patterns, the problem is more complex because of the several directions of movement possible on the plane surface. With a time sequence of stimuli, for example, there is no doubt about which stimulus comes after any given stimulus; but with filled cells on a matrix, each stimulus has eight adjacent stimuli, if each cell is considered a stimulus. Perhaps this fact suggests the possibility that as a first order analysis, we could use a multivariate analysis of patterns of cells on a matrix, in which each cell is predicted from the eight adjacent cells. Attneave (1954) has suggested a more restricted procedure of this sort, by having subjects guess along horizontal rows whether the next cell will be black or white. Thus Attneave converted the two-dimensional problem into a unidimensional problem so that it could be handled more easily.

Another problem in measuring physical characteristics which lead to small inferred subsets of patterns is that psychologically the meaningful units can be many different types of things. For example, in a contour the perceived critical characteristics may be the line segments, angles, etc. With lines, the angle of orientation may be critical. Thus the psychological problem is not easily solved even if we can relate the informational concept of redundancy to the Gestalt concept of good figure. The nature of the perceptual process will still be critical in working out meaningful ways of applying the informational concepts to the problem of form perception.

COMMENTARY

In my opinion, the concepts and analytic procedures developed in this book, particularly in the last chapter, are more applicable to problems of pattern perception than to any other problem area in psychology. Nor need the applications be confined to visual pattern perception. In recent years there has been some increased interest shown in auditory pattern perception, and even in tactual pattern perception. Perhaps these research areas will yet come into their own.

While it is most profitable to apply these ideas to problems of pattern perception, it is eminently clear that very careful and critical analysis of the nature of the problem in relation to concepts of amount and form of internal constraint or redundancy is necessary. In addition, careful attention to experimental procedure must be used, since it is so clear that different performance criteria must lead to different conclusions concerning the effects of redundancy. Certainly, careful distinction between problems of sets of stimuli and problems of single stimuli is most necessary. I feel that the concepts can indeed be used with regard to characteristics of the single stimulus, but the application and the expectations will be quite different in the two cases.

The evidence we have concerning the effects of redundancy on pattern perception is unfortunately skimpy. Yet some reasonable conclusions can be drawn, particularly concerning the effects of redundancy on pattern discrimination. One of these conclusions, from one point of view, seems eminently reasonable, yet I have a certain reluctance to accept it as it stands. That is the conclusion concerning the effects of redundancy on pattern discrimination with limited exposure times. My difficulty is this:

The clearest conclusion from the various experiments on the effects of redundancy on pattern discrimination is that it aids discrimination when there is stimulus noise—either stimulus impoverishment or stimulus distortion. This result by itself seems reasonable enough. Yet by a very simple extension we could suggest that presentation of a visual stimulus pattern for a very brief period of time should result in stimulus impoverishment, since if the stimulus appears for too brief a time the subject should not see all of it. Thus he ends up not seeing all of the stimulus in the same sense that Bricker's experiment prevented his seeing it all by deliberate omission of part of the stimulus. We would conclude, therefore, that with brief exposures, accuracy should be better with redundant stimuli than with non-redundant stimuli.

The data we have, however, suggest no such effect. Rather, they suggest that the redundancy is of value only if extra time is allowed for its use; and if extra time is not allowed, then we get either no effect of redundancy, or an actual increase in identification errors.

This result can be understood if we recognize that the redundant elements in the stimulus pattern are also impoverished when short exposure durations are used. Thus their value is also diminished. Even so, the redundancy should be of some value as long as more elements are added, and the added elements each provide some information. The fact that there appears to be no improvement must mean that as more elements are added to the patterns to make them redundant, the probability of correct perception of each element decreases such that the total information perceived remains approximately constant. In fact, if we assume that the information *perceived* remains constant, regardless of the number of elements, then we have an explanation for the decreased discrimination with the redundant stimuli.

If we think of each element in the pattern as providing some information, and the total *potential information* provided by all of the elements is constant regardless of the number of elements, then discrimination should be poorer with the redundant stimuli because with them some of the information is being duplicated from one element to another. That is, in so far as the elements (variables, or dimensions) are correlated, then the total information received from several elements will on the average be less useful than if the elements are uncorrelated. In other words, perceived information may be constant, but the amount of it which is useful for discrimination will decrease in direct proportion to the amount (and form) of redundancy.

Wayne Lee and I have done some preliminary work on pattern discrimination with simple redundant patterns, and our early results definitely suggest that at very brief exposures the redundancy is not helpful. Rather, as a first approximation, the subjects seem to get the same amount of information at a given duration regardless of the amount of redundancy. Such a conclusion seems too simple to be true, but it may be that the amount of information which can be perceived in a brief exposure is limited by the exposure itself, and cannot be improved with redundancy.

Time and dimension limits in discrimination

Time as an experimental variable keeps cropping up as a very critical factor in these discussions, yet it has rarely been used in this type of experiment. When a fixed exposure duration is used, then reaction time may be critical. However, a more obviously critical factor is the exposure duration itself. If I may be permitted to carry through a little more logical analysis (or conjecture), there is a way of looking at this whole set of relations between time, information transmission, discrimination, and redundancy which makes a considerable amount of sense. It also leads to some implications about material discussed earlier in relation to channel capacity which does not check with available data, but which may help explain some problems there as well.

Let us suppose that we use a very short duration of stimulus exposure, and that at this short duration there is a fixed channel capacity. In other words, if we use non-redundant stimuli and increase the stimulus uncertainty by increasing the number of stimulus elements (or dimensions), there is a value of stimulus uncertainty beyond which no increase in information transmission will occur. To use a concrete illustration let us suppose a channel capacity of 2 bits. This value means that if we increase the number of stimuli beyond four, information transmission will still be just 2 bits. Accuracy, on the other hand, will decrease, since we have more total stimuli, and the probability of being correct will decrease with a fixed information transmission—a relation we discussed somewhat earlier.

Let us suppose now that we are using eight stimuli. Information transmission will be only 2 bits, and there will be a moderate number of errors. Since we are not obtaining complete information transmission, we decide to add redundancy. So we increase the total constraint, just as before, but this time we add it in the form of redundancy rather than in the form of external constraint. In other words, we increase the number of possible stimuli without increasing the number of stimuli actually used. Such a procedure should have no effect on information transmission, since if the channel capacity concept is real, then we already know that more information cannot be transmitted by increasing stimulus uncertainty. Furthermore, the number of errors should not improve, since we still have the same number of stimuli. Thus adding redundancy should improve neither information transmission nor accuracy if the channel capacity concept is valid. The data on pattern discrimination suggest that this is a reasonable way of looking at the problem, since there is little evidence of improvement in either accuracy or information transmission with added redundancy.

If, on the other hand, information transmission improves with increased number of dimensions, then the addition of redundancy should improve accuracy and information transmission, since we now know that the subject is capable of greater discrimination with increased stimulus uncertainty. The difficulty here lies in the fact that in Chapter Four we discussed evidence that the channel capacity concept is not valid when stimulus uncertainty is increased by increasing the dimensionality of the stimulus. Rather, information transmission increases when stimulus uncertainty is increased by increasing the dimensionality, even though the increase in information transmission is less than the increase in stimulus uncertainty. Thus the assumption above of a fixed channel capacity seems not to be valid.

This fact has been responsible for my reluctance to accept the result that redundancy leads to no improvement in either information transmission or accuracy. If we accept the result that increased dimensionality leads to increased information transmission, then there is a very clear implication that redundancy produced by such means should improve both information transmission and accuracy of discrimination. (It should be remembered that accuracy and information transmission should be equivalent when dealing with a fixed number of stimuli, but will not be when the number of stimuli varies.)

This conflict is resolved if we assume that information transmission increases with increased dimensionality only when perceptual discrimination is not time limited. In other words, we assume that the channel capacity concept is valid for any method of increasing stimulus uncertainty if discrimination is time limited. Thus if the previously discussed research had been done with very brief stimulus durations, the channel capacity concept would have been valid, and furthermore there would have been no advantage to redundant stimuli, as in the Eriksen and Hake (1955b) experiment.

In summary, I am assuming that perceptual discrimination can be either time limited or dimension limited. If it is limited in either way, then the channel capacity concept will be valid for any increase in stimulus uncertainty produced by the other. To illustrate, if perceptual discrimination is limited to 2 bits of information transmission by the shortness of the exposure duration, then no increase in dimensionality will produce greater information transmission or any advantage to redundancy. If, however, duration is increased, then information transmission will be increased and redundancy which uses more time will also improve discrimination. Similarly, perceptual discrimination may be dimension limited, since we know that there is a low maximum value of information transmission which can be obtained with any single dimension regardless of the time. If discrimination is dimension limited, no increase in time will improve discrimination, but an increase in dimensionality will. Likewise, redundancy produced with increased dimensionality, as in the Eriksen and Hake experiment, will also improve accuracy and information transmission.

Thus if we have a long time but few dimensions, then increasing dimensions will improve discrimination. However, if we have many dimensions but little time, then increasing time will improve discrimination. And in parallel fashion, redundancy can lead to increased accuracy.

To return more directly to our problem here, redundancy produced by increased dimensionality can lead to improved accuracy of discrimination only if the exposure duration is fairly long. If duration is so short that accuracy is time limited, then the redundancy should improve accuracy only if time is increased sufficiently to allow the subject to make use of the greater discriminability produced by the greater number of dimensions.

All of this sounds reasonable enough, and ends up with the conclusion drawn earlier in this chapter: Redundancy can lead to improved discrimination accuracy, but only at some cost in time. We have no direct evidence, however, on two points involved: (1) the channel capacity concept is valid even when stimulus uncertainty is increased by increased dimensionality with short exposure durations; and (2) redundancy will not improve discrimination accuracy with very short durations (that is, when discrimination is time limited), but will do so with longer durations.

Unique patterns

One last comment concerns the problem of redundancy of unique patterns. If my suggestion is right that when we judge one pattern to be more redundant than another we are in reality saying that it came from a smaller subset of possible patterns, there are certain experimental implications which should be testable. It might be possible, for example, to have subjects produce all figures which they feel are of the same kind as a test figure, and they should produce more of them for the less "redundant" figures. On the other hand, it might be possible to have subjects sort large sets of stimuli into equivalent groups, and we would expect that the larger groups would contain those figures judged less redundant. This problem area is a difficult one, and perhaps by its concern with the characteristics of the single stimulus is really not suitable to the present type of analysis. I am, however, unconvinced that it is not suitable. Some advances have been made, notably by Attneave and by Hochberg, and it is to be hoped that the future will show real improvement.

SUMMARY

Discrimination of patterns is essentially the same as discrimination of any other class of stimuli with regard to the amount of stimulus uncertainty, or required external constraint. Errors of identification increase with increased stimulus uncertainty, although information transmission measures show improved discrimination, at least within limits. And the number of independent dimensions is the critical factor in determining the amount of discrimination.

The concept of redundancy has caused some difficulty in pattern perception work, primarily because of the confusion between the characterisetics of sets of stimuli and characteristics of unique stimuli. When the concept is applied to sets of stimuli (as it properly should be), then the effect of redundancy on the nature of the patterns in a set can be seen by remembering:

1. For any fixed number of stimuli, increase in redundancy leads to an increase in total constraint. That is, if external constraint is held constant, then total constraint varies directly with redundancy.

2. An increase in total constraint means that the stimuli differ in more ways. Either the number of variables or dimensions has been increased, or the uncertainty of each dimension has been increased.

3. Therefore, an increase in redundancy leads to an increase in the number of ways in which the fixed number of stimuli differ. A redundant set of patterns or figures is thus more complex than a non-redundant set of figures.

This increased complexity of redundant patterns leads to improved discrimination of stimulus patterns if part of the pattern is deleted or if the pattern is distorted. In other words, redundancy aids discrimination under conditions of stimulus noise.

Redundancy does not aid discrimination or identification learning under conditions of relatively brief stimulus exposure, however. When time measures are used as the criterion variable, then increased redundancy leads to higher time scores. The conclusion seems inevitable that redundancy aids pattern discrimination only when it is actually needed, and only if sufficient time is allowed for the subject to make use of the added information. Thus redundancy is useful for discrimination, but it carries a cost in time.

With regard to redundancy of unique patterns, various attempts have been made, with some degree of success, to specify the characteristics of single figures which give them good Gestalt. I have suggested that a direct judgment can be made of the "redundancy" of single patterns, and that this judgment is related to the size of an inferred subset of patterns—a subset which is smaller than the total set which could be generated. Thus a judgment about the redundancy of a single stimulus pattern is in reality a judgment about the redundancy of a subset of patterns from which the particular pattern was drawn. This approach allows a definition of redundancy which is in keeping with the true meaning of the term.

CHAPTER SEVEN

The Redundancy of Language

LANGUAGE IS, WITHOUT DOUBT, the most important communication system used by humans. As such it is of rather special interest to psychologists to understand something of the statistical and informational structure of language. We know that the language we use is not an efficient one in the informational sense, since there is considerable statistical constraint, or redundancy, in the sequences of symbols which compose the language. Although the determination of the redundancy of the English language poses several difficulties, there have been many attempts to determine its amount as well as its nature.

Our interest in the redundancy of our language has two different, although not unrelated, facets. In the first place, language is a communication device used by all adult humans, and it is of considerable psychological interest to know the extent to which humans are aware of and can use the redundancy inherent in the language. Before we can determine the extent to which redundancy is used, however, we must know how much of it there is to be used. In other words, we need to know something about the characteristics of language both as a stimulus and as a response system for humans.

In the second place, language has a rather special interest to psychologists because most languages, and certainly English, have developed rather naturally. That is, language has not come to its present state by any application of highly arbitrary rules to its use; rather, it has developed spontaneously in the course of centuries of usage by humans. Many of the more specialized communication systems have been devised and set up with known a priori characteristics. For example, a coding system for aircraft locations is not a communication system which evolved primarily by the process of its being used, but rather is set up with arbitrary characteristics to which the human operators must adjust. However, languages evolve only by usage. To learn something of the structural characteristics which have evolved in this natural manner may give us some insights into the optimum characteristics of a language—if we assume that the changes have come about in the development of the language because of some real utility to the users of the language.

It should be clear that we are talking now only about the amount of structure in language, not about signification. The distinction which we discussed between signification and structure in Chapter Five is equally appropriate here, since the problem of redundancy of language is simply the problem of the determination of the amount of internal constraint. In internal constraint, as well as in external constraint, the amount of structure is one problem, but the particular relational rules which determine signification is another. Thus, our problem in this chapter is, in a broad sense, the determination of the amount of internal structure. In the language context internal structure is sensibly interpretable as redundancy, since it is a measure of the extent to which more symbols are used in the language than are needed.

THE REDUNDANCY OF SEQUENCES

Language consists of a sequence of symbols, and the study of the redundancy of language is concerned with the measurement of the extent to which these sequences of events are non-random. The actual units used in such studies are somewhat arbitrary. We can, for instance, study the language as spoken, in which case our primary concern would be with the sound unit, or phoneme. Black (1954), for example, analyzed pairs of phonemes in words of different lengths, and determined that on the basis of pair (digram) restrictions alone the redundancy is on the order of 30 percent. Harris (1955) also did an analysis of the possible phoneme combinations, without regard to probability of occurrence, and used these data to argue for the meaningfulness of larger sound units, morphemes, on the grounds of the limited possible combinations of phonemes.

We could, on the other hand, do analyses with words, and a few such analyses have been done. Since words, however, can themselves be degenerated into sequences of letters and spaces, we generally gain little by using words as our unit of analysis. Certainly the most easily accessible language unit is the printed letter. There is little ambiguity about the letter units, and higher-order groups of letters such as words and phrases can always be dealt with as combinations of letters.

Thus, most studies of the redundancy of language have dealt with the printed letter as the unit of analysis, and the problem of measuring redundancy has become, in large part, the problem of determining the statistical constraints involved in sequences of printed letters.

When we have discussed the problem of redundancy before, we have dealt with situations in which there is a known number of variables which occur simultaneously, and in these cases the specification of redundancy is relatively simple. If, for example, we have four variables, with a total of 10 bits of uncertainty in the variables (the variables need not have the same uncertainties) but use only enough combinations of these variables to account for 4 bits, then we have 6 bits of redundancy. Redundancy is, in other words, simply the amount of possible uncertainty in a set of variables which is not used.

In dealing with any sequence of events, however, it is much more difficult to specify exactly the number of variables. The basic method of dealing with this problem is to use letter positions as variables, and the different letters as the values which each variable can take. Then if we want to determine the redundancy of, say, groups of five letters, our problem is relatively simple again, because now we have five specified variables. We determine the total possible uncertainty of these five variables, and the uncertainty of the actual distributions of letter combinations. The difference between these is the redundancy. The difficulty is that we cannot be sure that all statistical constraints extend over no more than five letters, so we must consider the necessity of dealing with even longer groups of letters.

Distributional redundancy or constraint

Total redundancy is rather simply defined. It is simply the difference between the total possible uncertainty of a set of variables and the actual uncertainty. It is convenient, however, as we have noted before, to distinguish between *distributional constraint* and constraint between variables, and in the present context this latter form will be called *sequential constraint*. The distinction between these two types of redundancy is particularly useful in dealing with the sequential problem, as Garner and Carson (1960) have pointed out. In the sequential case, the amount of distributional constraint is independent of the nature of the prediction problem, while the amount of sequential constraint is definitely not. Thus distributional constraint is always easily interpreted in redundancy terms, but only certain types of sequential constraint are directly interpretable as redundancy.

Distributional redundancy is the difference between the nominal and the actual uncertainty for any variable or group of variables. In the case of printed English, for example, the nominal uncertainty of a 27-letter alphabet (26 letters plus space) is log 27, or 4.75 bits. The actual uncertainty of letters and space is approximately 4.10 bits. This difference, 0.65 bits, is then the amount of distributional redundancy for single letter distributions.

If we want to determine the amount of distributional redundancy for groups of n letters, then we consider each letter position within the sequence as a single variable. The total nominal uncertainty of this sequence of letters will be n times the nominal uncertainty of single letters. Similarly, the actual uncertainty (without regard to sequential constraints) will be n times the uncertainty of single letter distributions. Thus the total distributional redundancy for sequences of n letters is simply n times the distributional uncertainty for single letters.

Sequential constraint

The second form of redundancy or constraint is the form involving constraints between the variables within a given set of variables. In any sequence of events, these constraints operate in a sequential fashion, and thus we use here the term *sequential constraint*.

The total constraint in any system of variables is the difference between the maximum uncertainty (the uncertainty based on actual uncertainties of variables, not nominal uncertainties) and the obtained uncertainty. In dealing with the sequential case, we select sequences of letters of a given length, and then consider each letter position to be a single variable. Our problem, then, is to determine the maximum uncertainty and the obtained uncertainty, since the difference between them will be the total constraint. In addition, however, we must consider different lengths of sequence, since longer sequences may involve different relative amounts of constraint than shorter sequences, and we will want some estimate of the total constraint for very long sequences.

This problem can be approached by first noting that the actual uncertainty of each letter position (each variable) is the same, since the distribution of letters in positions of sequences selected at random will not be a function of the actual position of the letter in the sequence. Suppose we label each letter position in the sequence with a number, conceptualizing the sequence of letter positions as[1]

$$n \cdots, 5, 4, 3, 2, 1.$$

Now with these variables,

$$U(1) = U(2) = U(3) \cdots = U(n). \tag{7.1}$$

Since the uncertainties of all variables are equal, the maximum uncertainty of the set of n variables is

$$U_{\max}(1, 2, 3, \ldots n) = U(1) + U(2) + U(3) + \ldots U(n)$$
$$= n\,U(n), \quad \text{or} \quad n\,U(1). \tag{7.2}$$

In words, the maximum uncertainty of a sequence n letters long is simply n times the uncertainty of single-letter distributions.

The obtained uncertainty of sequences of exactly five letters can be written in the following form, after Eq. 5.2a:

$$U(1, 2, 3, 4, 5) = U(5) + U_5(4) + U_{45}(3) + U_{345}(2) + U_{2345}(1).$$

(Sequences of exactly five letters have been used momentarily to simplify the notation.) Each of these terms can be written in many alternative ways because of the particular restrictive properties of sequences. For example, we have already noted that $U(5)$ is the same as $U(1)$. In addition, the conditional uncertainty, $U_5(4)$, is simply the conditional uncertainty for letter distributions when the preceding letter has been held constant. Thus $U_5(4)$ is the same as $U_4(3)$, or $U_2(1)$. Furthermore, the multiple conditional uncertainty, $U_{45}(3)$, is simply the conditional uncertainty for letter distributions when two preceding letters have been held constant; it could just as easily be written as $U_{23}(1)$. Thus each term can have 1 as the variable whose uncertainty is under consideration, and we can rewrite this equation in the much more general form,

$$U(1, 2, 3, \ldots n) = U(1) + U_2(1) + U_{23}(1) + \ldots U_{23\ldots n}(1). \tag{7.3}$$

Thus, the total uncertainty in a sequence of n letters is the sum of a series of terms, starting with the uncertainty of single letters, adding

[1] The reason for writing the numbers in reverse order is that we ordinarily think of predicting the last letter in a sequence from the preceding ones, and thus it is convenient always to have the same designation for the variable being predicted. As we add more predictor variables, we will have the same form of the multiple contingent uncertainty, since 1 will always be the criterion variable, and the higher numbers, up to n, will be the predictor variables. This notation in no way affects any of the relations involved, since we could deal with the whole problem as a backwards prediction with the same results.

the conditional uncertainty of letters with the preceding one held constant, then with two preceding letters held constant, until all letters in the sequence but the last one have been held constant.

We can now obtain the total constraint by subtracting this obtained uncertainty from the maximum uncertainty, and if we subtract each term in Eq. 7.3 from the uncertainty of single letters, $U(1)$, we obtain a series of contingent uncertainties.

$$U(1{:}2{:}3{:}\ldots n) = U(1{:}2) + U(1{:}2, 3) + U(1{:}2,3,\ldots n). \quad (7.4)$$

Thus the total constraint is a series of contingency terms, each successive term involving prediction from one more preceding letter. This term for total constraint is what we actually want as a measure of sequential redundancy, since it is the measure of total constraint due to constraints between the various letter positions.

It is clear, from this equation, that total sequential constraint will be different for different lengths of sequence, but that it must always increase as sequence length increases. Ultimately, however, the additional constraint which comes from the addition of one more predictor letter will become a constant, when the length of the sequence is great enough that no further prediction length will improve prediction of the last letter. Notice that total constraint does not become a constant, but only the amount added per letter.

This situation is illustrated graphically in Fig. 7.1, where maximum uncertainty, actual uncertainty, and total constraint are all shown as a function of sequence length, for a completely hypothetical example. All three terms increase, as they should, since the greater the length the larger the number of variables considered. Notice that at first total constraint does not increase linearly with length of sequence, but that (in our illustration) it does at length 10. The ratio of total constraint to maximum uncertainty is not a constant, and will not become one until the curves are extrapolated to infinity, where the intercept constant of the linear portion of the curve becomes trivial.

In our example relative redundancy is 12.5 percent at length 5, 22 percent at length 10, 31 percent at length 15, 38 percent at length 20, and 40 percent at length 25. It is, in fact, approaching an asymptotic value of 50 percent, which is the value we would obtain if we analyzed sequences of infinite length. Its value can be obtained, however, without analyzing infinite length sequences, by simply comparing the slopes of the linear portions of the curves, that is, by comparing slopes with sequences long enough to provide no further prediction of the last letter by the addition of another predictor letter. The appropriate

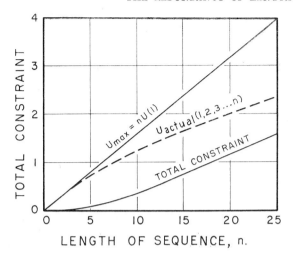

Fɪɢ. 7.1. An illustration of how total constraint is a function of the length of the sequence analyzed. All units are arbitrary. Total constraint for each length is the difference between maximum and actual uncertainty.

slopes are the actual uncertainty of single letters for the maximum uncertainty and the largest obtained multiple contingent uncertainty for the total constraint (the multiple contingent uncertainty obtained when prediction is made from very long sequences).

In less graphical form, we can define redundancy in IRE terms as an average, and if we use SR to mean sequential redundancy, then

$$\text{avg SR} = U(1{:}2{:}3{:}\ldots n)/n \approx U(1{:}2, 3, \ldots n), \qquad (7.5)$$

when n is very large. Likewise, the percent redundancy can be written as

$$\% \text{SR} = U(1{:}2, 3, \ldots n)/U(1). \qquad (7.6)$$

Thus the problem of determining the total constraint or redundancy of sequences of letters reduces to the problem of determining the uncertainty of single letters after very long sequences of letters, or its converse, of determining the predictability of letters from very long sequences of letters. If we can determine the multiple contingent uncertainty from sequences long enough that no further increase in sequence length will improve prediction, then we have a measure of redundancy. Our problem, then, is to determine how long the sequence must be for there to be no further improvement, and also the value of the actual multiple contingent uncertainty for sequences that long.

LOWER-BOUND ESTIMATES OF REDUNDANCY

The direct measurement of redundancy of printed English is, of course, essentially impossible. The number of possible different letter sequences, even as short as ten letters, is prohibitively large for any direct count of them. It has therefore been necessary to use indirect techniques for estimating redundancy of language.

All of the indirect techniques have used the assumption, in some form, that intelligent adults can and do use the statistical properties of printed English, and that therefore performance measures can be used to estimate the redundancy of the language. The particular nature and importance of the assumptions have, however, varied with the technique.

Shannon (1951) described and used a procedure which can establish, within sampling restrictions, a lower bound for the multiple contingent uncertainty in which the last letter of a sequence is predicted from preceding letters. The essence of this procedure, which is usually called the "guessing-game" technique, is this: One or more subjects are given samples of printed English and are required to guess the next letter of the sample. If their first guess is wrong, they are required to continue guessing until they are correct. They are given many samples of a given length, and from the successive guesses of these different samples a distribution of the correct guesses is formed.

To illustrate, a single subject may have been given one hundred samples of length 10. He then guesses the eleventh letter until he is correct in each case. His correct guesses for the hundred samples may have been sixty on the first guess, thirty on the second, six on the third, and one each on four other positions. The uncertainty of this distribution of guesses is computed, which is 1.47 bits in this illustration. This then is taken as the upper bound for the uncertainty of eleventh letters, and if this value is subtracted from the uncertainty of single letters (approximately 4.10 bits) we obtain a lower bound for the multiple contingent uncertainty of 2.63 bits.

The rationale for using the uncertainty of the distribution of guesses to obtain a lower bound for redundancy is this: If we have an intelligent human who makes use of the statistical constraints in the language to guess next letters more correctly than he would by chance, then the distribution of guesses itself could be transmitted rather than the actual letters. If we make the assumption that the distribution of guesses is decoded at the receiving end by a decoder who uses the same guessing system as the original guesser, the original language can be reconstructed with the uncertainty of the distribution of guesses.

This last assumption, known as the identical-twin assumption, is simply that the same system of decoding can be used as was used to encode.

Such a procedure clearly leads to a lower bound for redundancy, since the distribution of correct guesses can become more restricted only if there is in fact more consistency to the language itself. If the guesser fully uses all of the properties of the language, his distribution of correct guesses will be limited by the redundancy of the language itself. If he does not use all of the redundancy available, his distribution of guesses may be greater but cannot become smaller, except by pure luck. In other words, the distribution of correct guesses is limited by the redundancy of the language. Even if the subject uses all of the redundancy in the language, this procedure still gives a lower-bound estimate because it takes into account only the order of guessing, not the actual probability of each letter in the language itself.

There are three factors which enter into the adequacy of this technique. First, how close the lower-bound estimate comes to the true redundancy of the language is obviously a function of the skill of the guesser in using the redundancy of the language. The subject must be aware of the statistical restrictions and must use these restrictions in some systematic way. For example, he may always guess the most-likely letter first, the next-most-likely letter second, etc. Actually, of course, the subject may use other methods of guessing which will be equally adequate. He may, for example, guess completely in reverse, guessing the least-likely letter first, the next-least-likely second, etc. Such a procedure will result in a distribution of guesses with the same uncertainty as the first guessing procedure. The critical factor is not whether the subject uses one particular guessing procedure or another, but rather that the procedure be consistent and systematically related to the actual probabilities of letters in the language. Regardless of the procedure, however, the subject must be skilled in his knowledge and use of the statistical properties of the language for the lower bound estimate to be near the true value of redundancy.

Second, it is necessary to ensure that the subject have no prior knowledge of the language samples being used. If the subject is making guesses from language samples he is familiar with, then his guesses will be more accurate than they could have been on the basis of knowledge of the prior letters alone, and the lower bound for redundancy will be estimated too high (and thus not truly be a lower bound). Suppose, for example, that a subject is given the letter sequence "Now is the time for all go—," and is required to guess the next letter. The guess is almost certainly going to be an "o" because of our great familiarity with this phrase. In an extreme form, if a passage has been memorized, then guesses on samples from the passage will all be correct, and we would not have a meaningful lower-bound estimate.

Thus we need skill with the language in order to have an adequately high lower-bound estimate; but we also need to be sure of no prior familiarity in order to be sure that the estimate is not too high, and therefore that it is in fact a lower-bound estimate.

The third factor relates to the problem of sampling. With the guessing-game technique, sampling of subjects is not necessary. Since we are trying to determine the redundancy of the language itself, we can use a single skillful subject—a subject who knows as much as possible about the statistical properties of the language. We can even give our subject all possible help and training in the use of the language, as long as no familiarization with the actual language samples is given. A reasonable procedure would even be to test several subjects on sample material and to use the best of these subjects in further tests. Obviously, we cannot select the best single subject and use the guesses from the sample material itself, because then we would be capitalizing on sampling variations. However, we can use this best subject on all tests given after his selection is made. Sampling of the language, however, is required. While a single subject may be used, we must use many different language samples to obtain an adequate estimate of the average constraints operating in the language. Not only should many different passages be used, but they should come from many different sources.

Fig. 7.2 shows the results of two different experiments in which the guessing-game technique was used to obtain lower-bound estimates of redundancy. Shannon's data were obtained from a single subject, who guessed at successive lengths of one hundred different passages from a single source. In other words, the subject guessed the second letter of a passage, then the third letter of the same passage, etc., after learning the correct previous letters. Burton and Licklider (1955) used ten different subjects on material from ten paper-backed novels. From each novel, ten different passages were selected for each of the different lengths used. Thus there was much broader sampling of language and of subjects in the latter experiment.

Nevertheless, the results from these two experiments are in quite reasonable agreement, and the Burton and Licklider results always seem to be within the sampling range of the Shannon results. Shannon's

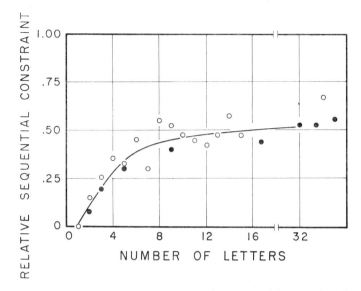

Fig. 7.2. Estimated lower bounds for the relative sequential constraint of printed English. These estimates were obtained with the Shannon guessing-game technique. The open circles represent data from Shannon (1951). The filled-in circles represent data from Burton and Licklider (1955). Shannon's last point was obtained with 100 letters. The last three filled circles are with 33, 65, and 10,000 letters.

single point obtained for hundred-letter sequences indicates a relatively high sequential redundancy (about 65 percent), but we cannot take this single value too seriously considering the general sampling fluctuations in his data. The Burton and Licklider data suggest little if any improvement in prediction after thirty-two letters, and both sets of data suggest only slight improvement after about twelve letters. Similar results have been obtained by Black (1959) for flight phrases and newspaper material.

The single curve drawn through these data suggests that the sequential constraint in printed English reaches a maximum of a little more than 50 percent, and that this maximum is reached at about twelve to sixteen letters. If we recall that this technique leads primarily to a lower-bound estimate, then we can say that sequential constraint is at least 50 percent for printed English. However, remembering also that sampling problems can lead to sample values greater than the true redundancy, not just to over-estimation of a lower bound, we can feel that this technique also gives us a reasonable best estimate. Thus our best estimate from these data is that sequential redundancy of printed English is on the order of 50 percent.

THE MULTIVARIATE APPROACH

The guessing-game technique, with its lower-bound estimate, has been one attempt to obtain an estimate of the total redundancy by directly obtaining lower-bound estimates of constraint after long sequences of letters. Another approach which has been used goes about the problem in a somewhat different way by first analyzing the total redundancy into a series of components, and then attempting to obtain measures of the various components separately. Some of the component terms have been measured directly, while experimental estimates have been required for other components. A solution for total redundancy is then obtained by summing the various components.

Multivariate analysis of sequences: unilateral prediction

First, to understand the nature of this approach, and the extent to which it can be useful in determining redundancy, we should look at

Table 7.1

Uncertainty terms involved in prediction of the end of a sequence of letters. Each column includes simple contingency terms (C) and interaction terms (I) involving different numbers of letter positions. Each row includes all of the additional prediction terms involved when the total prediction sequence (including letter being predicted) is increased one letter to the length indicated.

Length of Sequence	Class of Uncertainty Terms				
	C	I_3	I_4	I_5	I_6
2	1:2				
3	1:3	$\overline{123}$			
4	1:4	$\overline{124}$	$\overline{1234}$		
		$\overline{134}$			
5	1:5	$\overline{145}$	$\overline{1345}$	$\overline{12345}$	
		$\overline{135}$	$\overline{1245}$		
		$\overline{125}$	$\overline{1235}$		
6	1:6	$\overline{156}$	$\overline{1456}$	$\overline{13456}$	$\overline{123456}$
		$\overline{146}$	$\overline{1356}$	$\overline{12456}$	
		$\overline{136}$	$\overline{1256}$	$\overline{12356}$	
		$\overline{126}$	$\overline{1346}$	$\overline{12346}$	
			$\overline{1246}$		
			$\overline{1236}$		

a multivariate analysis of sequences of events. Garner (1957, 1958) and Garner and Carson (1960) have shown the general nature of these analyses, but we shall go into somewhat more detail here. We, of course, are interested in sequences of letters, but the nature of the analysis is indifferent to the particular type of communication used, and applies equally to any statistical sequence.

First, we shall consider unilateral prediction, where we are interested in prediction of a single letter from all of the letters on one side of it. The prediction of the last letter (or the first) of a very long sequence of letters is written as a multiple contingent uncertainty, as in Eq. 7.5. This multiple contingent uncertainty can be broken into all of its component parts, including simple contingencies and interaction terms.

Table 7.1 lists these various components out to a sequence length of 6, which is sufficient to show the pattern of the analysis, and one meaningful way of grouping the various terms. The notation used implies that variable 1 is the last letter of a sequence, which is being predicted from preceding letters, which are variables 2, 3, 4, etc. Thus a contingency of 1:5 is the simple contingent uncertainty between letters and letters four steps behind. An interaction, $\overline{1234}$, is the interaction involving the letter being predicted and the preceding three letters. Actually, of course, we can just as well think of the variable 1 as being the first letter of a long sequence which is being predicted from subsequent letters, since predictability in any sequence such as this is completely symmetrical.[2] I have used 1 as the variable to be predicted simply to be able to add other predictor variables without changing

---

[2] This symmetry of prediction in the sequential case may be intuitively obvious. Its proof may be most easily seen by first considering a three-letter sequence, 1, 2, 3. The amount of constraint or predictability is the same for the first and the third letters, since

$$U(1{:}2,3) = U(1{:}2{:}3) - U(2{:}3),$$

and

$$U(3{:}1,2) = U(1{:}2{:}3) - U(1{:}2),$$

and $U(2:3)$ is the same as $U(1:2)$. Predictability of the middle letter is greater, since $U(1:3)$ is subtracted from the total constraint, and that value is normally less than $U(1:2)$. In like manner, the two end letters of four-letter sequences involve the same predictability, since

$$U(1{:}2,3,4) = U(1{:}2{:}3{:}4) - U(2{:}3{:}4),$$

and

$$U(4{:}1,2,3) = U(1{:}2{:}3{:}4) - U(1{:}2{:}3),$$

and $U(2:3:4)$ is the same as $U(1:2:3)$. In similar fashion, it can be shown that any two letter positions which are symmetrically placed in a sequence will have the same predictability or constraint.

the notation for the letter being predicted. And numbers are used as the variables to help in perceiving the sequential relations of the variables.

In Table 7.1, the columns are arranged according to the number of variables involved in the various terms. A simple contingency, C, always involves just two variables, and these terms are listed first. The interaction terms may involve three or more variables, and all interactions involving just three variables (regardless of length of sequence from which they come) are listed as I_3. Interactions involving four variables are listed as I_4, etc.

The rows are arranged according to the length of sequence from which the prediction is being made, and each row includes all of the terms which are involved in prediction from a given length which were not involved in prediction from any shorter length sequence. For example, when the sequence is two letters long, including the letter to be predicted, there is only one prediction term, the simple contingency. When the prediction sequence is increased to three terms, another contingency is added plus the interaction term involving three successive letters. When the prediction sequence is increased to four, then one more contingency is added, plus two more three-variable interactions, plus an interaction involving four successive letters. Thus the total number of terms involved in predicting the end letter from any length sequence is the sum of all the terms in a particular row and all rows above. The total redundancy for an infinitely long sequence of letters is the sum of such a matrix which includes an infinite number of rows and columns, but the practical problem would be to determine at what point the addition of another row adds no more predictability. In other words, at some length all of the terms involved in the increase in length of one step will sum to zero.

Bilateral prediction of middle letters

One advantage of the multivariate approach to this problem is that there is no need to restrict our analysis or experiments to prediction at the end of sequences. Just as we can predict the end letter of a nine-letter sequence, so also can we predict the middle letter of a nine-letter sequence or any other letter within the sequence. In these cases we have a bilateral context of letters from which prediction can be made. The pattern of uncertainty terms involved in these different prediction cases will be different, but the identities of the separate terms themselves are still the same. Furthermore, there are systematic differences in the patterns of the uncertainty terms which may be of some assistance in determining the magnitudes of the terms.

In Table 7.2 are listed the uncertainty terms involved in bilateral

Table 7.2

Uncertainty terms involved in predicting the middle letter of a long sequence of letters. Columns and rows are as in Table 7.1. The subscript of the C terms indicates the total length of the sequence from which the most remote contingency is used. The subscript of the I terms indicates first the number of variables involved in the interaction and second the length of the prediction sequence. The cells correspond to the appropriate groups of terms from Table 7.1. The coefficient in each cell is the number of such uncertainty terms which occur for middle prediction.

Length of Sequence	C	I_3	I_4	I_5	I_6
		Class of Uncertainty Terms			
2	$2C_2$				
3	$2C_3$	$3I_{33}$			
4	$2C_4$	$3I_{34}$	$4I_{44}$		
5	$2C_5$	$3I_{35}$	$4I_{45}$	$5I_{55}$	
6	$2C_6$	$3I_{36}$	$4I_{46}$	$5I_{56}$	$6I_{66}$

prediction of a single letter in the middle of a very long sequence of letters. In order to allow direct comparison of the terms involved in unilateral prediction with those involved in bilateral prediction, the terms are grouped in Table 7.2 according to the classification of terms in Table 7.1, but the interpretation of the table is slightly different. Each group of terms in a given row and column in Table 7.1 has been given a single designation. The term C stands for a contingency term, and the subscript denotes the length of sequence from which the term has been computed, and is a single contingency term in all cases. Thus C_2 is the contingency between two adjacent letter positions; C_3 is the contingency between the two end positions of a three-letter sequence; and likewise, C_6 is the contingency between the two end positions of a six-letter sequence.

The term I stands for a group of interaction terms, and two subscripts are involved. The first subscript designates the column in Table 7.1 from which the terms are taken, thus indicating the number of variables in the interactions. The second subscript designates the row in Table 7.1, thus indicating the length of sequence necessary to produce these particular interactions. For example, I_{34} includes two interactions, $\overline{124}$ and $\overline{134}$, the two interactions which have three terms in them and which come from a four-letter sequence, but could not have been obtained from a sequence of any shorter length.

In Table 7.1, each successive row contained the additional terms which occur as the sequence length is increased by one unit. While the rows are labelled in similar fashion in Table 7.2, they cannot be interpreted in the same way, since this table shows all of the terms involved in bilateral prediction of the middle letter of a very long sequence. Thus the two tables can be compared as entire tables, but cannot be compared row by row. This method of arranging the terms has been used simply to facilitate certain comparisons.

It can be seen that the matrix of Table 7.2 is identical to that of Table 7.1 except that each column is multiplied by an integer which is the same as the number of variables involved in terms in that column. Thus each column is multiplied by a progressively larger number, the C column being multiplied by two, the I_3 column being multiplied by three, etc. With this arrangement, it is clear that if we knew the sum of the terms for any column in one table we would also know the sum in the other table.

The relation between these two matrices can be seen a little better by considering prediction in the middle of a long sequence in the following way. Consider that we have a three-variable problem, in which y is predicted from x and z, and also consider that y is a single letter position which is to be predicted in the middle of a very long sequence of letters, that x is all of the context preceding the letter to be predicted, and that z is all of the context following the letter to be predicted. Now we know that

$$U(y{:}x, z) = U(y{:}x) + U(y{:}z) + U(\overline{xyz}). \tag{7.7}$$

However, the terms $U(y{:}x)$ and $U(y{:}z)$ are simply the unidirectional multiple contingent uncertainties whose values we have been concerned with, and furthermore they are identical, since forward prediction is the same as backward prediction. We can then write

$$U(y{:}x, z) = 2[U(y{:}x)] + U(\overline{xyz}), \tag{7.8a}$$

or

$$U(y{:}x) = \tfrac{1}{2}[U(y{:}x, z) - U(\overline{xyz})]. \tag{7.8b}$$

Thus the extent to which total predictability for the middle letter of a very long sequence of letters is greater or less than twice the prediction at either end is entirely a matter of the interaction term $U(\overline{xyz})$.

The more exact identification of this term can be seen in Table 7.3, which spells out with the classification of Table 7.2 the detailed nature of the uncertainty terms involved in this total interaction. This table is obtained simply by subtracting two of each of the terms in Table 7.1 from Table 7.2; that is, Table 7.1 gives the terms for $U(y{:}x)$, and

Table 7.3

Uncertainty terms involved in the total interaction between the middle letter of a very long sequence and both the prior and subsequent context. The meaning of the terms is the same as in Table 7.2.

Length of Sequence	Class of Uncertainty Terms			
	I_3	I_4	I_5	I_6
3	I_{33}			
4	I_{34}	$2I_{44}$		
5	I_{35}	$2I_{45}$	$3I_{55}$	
6	I_{36}	$2I_{46}$	$3I_{56}$	$4I_{66}$

Table 7.2 gives the terms for $U(y\!:\!x, z)$, and as Eq. 7.8a shows, the interaction is $U(y\!:\!x, z)$ minus two of $U(y\!:\!x)$. It should be noted that no contingent uncertainties are included in Table 7.3, so that the relation between end and middle prediction does not depend on the contingency terms, but only on the interaction terms. If the sum of all these interactions in Table 7.3 is zero, then prediction at the end is exactly half of prediction in the middle. If we can determine the amount of prediction in the middle we have a good first step toward determining the amount of prediction at the end.

To carry this sort of analysis one step further, Table 7.4 shows the uncertainty terms involved in the total constraint of different length sequences, where by total constraint we mean that specified in Eq. 7.4. In other words, we are now concerned with the total constraint in a sequence of letters, not just the constraint for predicting one letter in the sequence. For example, suppose we want to know all of the

Table 7.4

Uncertainty terms involved in the total constraint of a sequence of letters of different length, n. Each row is for a different length of prediction sequence, as before.

Length of Sequence	Class of Uncertainty Terms				
	C	I_3	I_4	I_5	I_6
2	$(n-1)C_2$				
3	$(n-2)C_3$	$(n-2)I_{33}$			
4	$(n-3)C_4$	$(n-3)I_{34}$	$(n-3)I_{44}$		
5	$(n-4)C_5$	$(n-4)I_{35}$	$(n-4)I_{45}$	$(n-4)I_{55}$	
6	$(n-5)C_6$	$(n-5)I_{36}$	$(n-5)I_{46}$	$(n-5)I_{56}$	$(n-5)I_{66}$

terms involved in the total constraint of five-letter sequences. Table 7.4 shows that we would have four C_2 contingency terms, three C_3 terms, one I_{55} term, etc. (If the length of the sequence as indicated by the row is greater than the length analyzed, then all terms in that row are zero. In other words, no negative multipliers of rows are used.)

The total pattern of these terms compared to Table 7.1 is that each row is now multiplied by an integer which decreases by 1 for each row, and its initial value is 1 less than the length sequence for which the total constraint is desired. Since, as we saw in Eq. 7.5, the total constraint for very long sequences divided by the number of letters is approximately the same as the multiple contingent uncertainty for predicting the last letter of a very long sequence, then when n is very large, the sum of the matrix in Table 7.4 should be n times the sum of the matrix in Table 7.1.

Clearly, each of these matrices of uncertainty terms has so many terms in it that if we needed to determine empirically the value of each of them we would have a hopeless task. Actually, however, there are many restrictions on the matrices which make them quite meaningful as a frame of reference from which to work. The restrictions are in some cases exact, so that we can know some definite limits. In other cases, however, the restrictions can merely serve as general guides for types of solutions.

We know that all contingency terms must be zero or positive, but that the interaction terms may be negative. Therefore the number of possible patterns of actual numerical values for the terms in Table 7.1 is very great. However, we also know that the sum of all terms in any row of that table must be zero or positive, because each row shows the additional prediction which comes as a result of adding one more predictor term, and we can never get a decrease in prediction by increasing the number of terms from which prediction comes. Now since each row contains one contingent uncertainty which must be positive, and also some interaction terms, we know that the sum of just the interaction terms alone may be positive or negative but that this sum, for any row, may not be more negative than the contingency is positive.

We also know that in each of these matrices there is a correlation between rows and columns, because only cells on and below the diagonal are filled. In addition, it is almost certain that the values of the terms are smaller near the lower left corner, because these are terms involving more remote variables than the other terms. This fact will tend to increase the degree of correlation between rows and columns.

This correlation becomes important when we look at Tables 7.2 and 7.3, which contain terms involved in prediction of middle letters of very long sequences. For example, notice that Eq. 7.8a shows that the sequential redundancy can exceed 50 percent only if the total interaction in that equation is negative. In other words, the sum of the terms in Table 7.3 must be negative if sequential redundancy is greater than 50 percent. This table includes only interaction terms, and we saw that each row of these terms in Table 7.1 may be no more negative than the contingency term in the row is positive, so that the sum for the row is not negative. Now if the rows and columns were perfectly correlated, then the sum for each column would also need to be negative by no more than a small amount, and since each column in Tables 7.2 and 7.3 is multiplied by a constant, there would obviously be severe restrictions on how negative the sum of the interactions could be.

Since both Table 7.2 and Table 7.3 involve multiplication by columns, even if the rows and columns were perfectly correlated in Table 7.1 it would be possible to obtain a sum which is negative. This would happen, for example, if the higher order terms were small and negative, but by being multiplied by a larger number, they produce a sum which is negative.

As I pointed out above, there are still too many degrees of freedom in these matrices to pin down the relations between the various matrices exactly. Nevertheless, the restrictions that do operate are sufficient to allow us to check our estimates of terms; also, these restrictions indicate when a pattern of results seems unlikely.

Experimental extimates of redundancy

One of the simplest assumptions to make in estimating the redundancy of printed English is that the interaction terms involved in the multiple contingent uncertainty are not important, and that the contingent uncertainties of Table 7.1 are the only important terms. Newman and Gerstman (1952) obtained direct measurements of several of these contingency terms, using part of the King James Version of the Bible as their material. Their values for the contingency terms are shown in Table 7.5. If these values are summed and converted into relative values of constraint (for unilateral prediction), we obtain the upper curve of Fig. 7.3. A comparison of this curve with the curve obtained with the guessing game technique of

Table 7.5

Contingent uncertainties computed by Newman and
Gerstman (1952). The starred values are interpolated.

C_2	0.91
C_3	0.42
C_4	0.26
C_5	0.16
C_6	0.11
C_7	0.08*
C_8	0.06*
C_9	0.05*
C_{10}	0.04
C_{11}	0.03*
Σ	2.12

Shannon suggests that simply summing the contingent uncertainties,
while ignoring the interaction terms, gives reasonably good agreement
with the lower-bound estimates.

The sum of the Newman-Gerstman values up to eleven-letter sequences is 2.12 bits. The Newman-Gerstman value for the uncertainty
of single letter distributions is 4.08 bits, so that relative redundancy
on the basis of the contingency terms is 52 percent. This value agrees
quite well with the lower-bound estimates at the longer lengths of
letter sequence. At four letters, the Newman-Gerstman value is
slightly higher than the lower-bound estimates, but the difference
cannot be considered serious when we take into account the sampling
fluctuations of the lower-bound estimates.

It does not, of course, seem entirely reasonable that the interaction

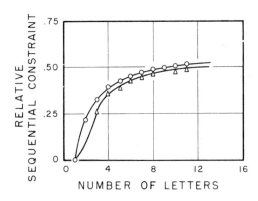

FIG. 7.3. Relative sequential
constraint for unilateral prediction of printed English
estimated from multivariate
components. The open circles
are data for simple contingent
uncertainties, from **Newman
and Gerstman (1952)**. The triangles are the same data plus
two interaction terms, from
Garner and Carson (1960).

terms should all be trivial. Garner and Carson (1960) attempted to deal with this problem by again resorting to the use of human subjects to obtain estimates of some of the interaction terms. These authors deleted single letters at all possible positions in randomly selected passages of different lengths. Letter sequences were used with lengths of 3, 5, 7, 9, and 11 letters. Since each position in each length sequence was deleted, a total of 35 deletion conditions was used. For each of these conditions, 25 randomly selected passages were prepared, and these passages were presented to subjects who were required to fill in the missing letter.

Altogether, 160 subjects filled in the missing letters for each of the 25 samples of each of the 35 deletion positions. Then the distributions of the responses for each deleted letter were determined, and the uncertainties of these distributions calculated. The averages of the 25 uncertainties for each deletion condition were then obtained. This value was subtracted from 4.08 bits (the uncertainty of single letter distributions from the Newman-Gerstman data) to obtain an estimated constraint for each of the letter positions—that is, an estimate of the multiple contingent uncertainty in which a given letter position is predicted from all of the others.

The assumptions involved in this procedure are quite different from those involved in the guessing-game procedure. Here we are assuming that a large number of individual letter responses will reasonably accurately reflect the actual distribution of possible letters in the real language. Such an assumption, of course, is common in psychological work, and has often proved to be valid. It is the basic assumption involved in most of the discriminative-scaling procedures, where distributions of responses are used to obtain estimates of scale values. In the probability-guessing experiments, most of the research has been aimed at determining why subjects match the probabilities of the stimuli even when best game theory suggests that they should not do so. More pertinently, Attneave (1953) has shown that subjects can match the probabilities of printed English letters in several experimentally determined ways.

At first glance it seems that the assumption made here is in direct contradiction to the assumption made in the guessing-game technique, but it actually is not. With that technique it must be assumed that a given subject uses a consistent scheme for making his guesses, and a scheme which is related to the actual probabilities of the letters as they occur in English. However, it is not necessary to assume that all subjects use the same scheme, and it is quite possible for two different subjects to have the same uncertainty of the distribution of guesses, but actually to have guessed according to a quite different rule. In the simplest case, one subject can simply guess in reverse order to the other. Thus it is quite possible for each subject's successive guesses to be related to the true probabilities of letters, and at the same time for a large number of subjects to have a distribution of initial guesses which reflect the overall distribution of letters.

Actually, of course, if it were necessary to assume that the uncertainties of such distributions of first guesses reflected the true uncertainty in an absolute sense, we would be on somewhat tenuous grounds. It is quite possible, for example, that distributions of guesses are similar to the true distributions, but unless they are identical (not just related) the absolute values of the computed uncertainties will not correspond to the actual uncertainties.

It is, however, possible to use this technique with a much weaker assumption, namely, that differences in estimated uncertainties from one situation to another will parallel differences in uncertainties of real letter distributions. For example, uncertainties computed after a five-letter sequence and after a ten-letter sequence may both be larger than the true uncertainties, and yet the difference between the two uncertainties could be the same as the true difference, within reasonable sampling limits. This is the assumption Garner and Carson made.

As a first step in checking the validity of this assumption, the estimated constraints were compared with constraints predicted on the assumption that the Newman-Gerstman contingency terms were the only important terms in the prediction. For each prediction case the sum of the appropriate contingencies was determined. For example, with the second letter deleted in a five-letter sequence, there are two C_2 terms, one C_3, and one C_4. The sum of these terms from Table 7.5 is 2.50. The same value would hold if the fourth letter were deleted. The data obtained are plotted against these predicted values in Fig. 7.4, and all symmetrical values are averaged (that is, the first and last positions for each length have been averaged, the second positions from each end, etc.).

It is clear from Fig. 7.4 that distributions of first guesses certainly, in general, follow expected patterns of differences. While we know that the contingent uncertainties do not contain all of the constraint, still they establish the general pattern of the constraints. This general pattern is followed quite accurately by the constraints obtained from distributions of first guesses.

In a sense, these two sets of data are mutually supporting. We would like to know how important terms other than contingencies are,

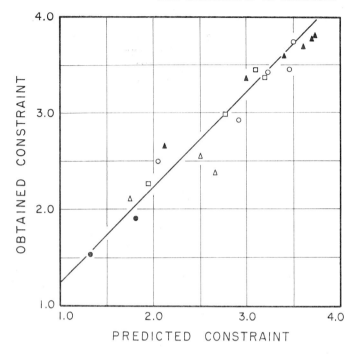

Fig. 7.4. Relation between predicted and obtained constraints for single letter deletions. The predicted constraints are based entirely on the contingency terms from Table 7.5. Each symbol is for a different length sequence. (After Garner and Carson, 1960.)

and would also like to know the extent to which we can use distributions of guesses to estimate the importance of the other terms. Since the relation between these two sets of values is so close, it seems reasonable to assume that the method is all right and also that the contingency terms are of primary importance.

Estimates of interactions

Garner and Carson carried their analysis a step further. While it seems clear that the contingencies are of primary importance, it is not clear that the interactions are zero; and in fact the data suggested certain systematic deviations which seemed to be correlated with the number of interaction terms of different types. If we assume that the interactions involving successive letter positions are the most important, then we can carry out a further analysis by determining the number of these interactions at different prediction positions, and correlating this number with residual scores—that is, the scores which represent the difference between obtained constraints and constraints predicted on the basis of contingencies alone. If these differences are systematically related to the number of different kinds of interactions, then we can use the regression equations to estimate the magnitudes of the interactions. Once again, this procedure is only making use of the assumption that the pattern of obtained constraints is systematically related to the pattern of the true constraints—not that the absolute values are reliable.

Table 7.6

Number of interaction terms involved at different positions in a nine-letter sequence. The composition of the interaction terms is the same as that in Table 7.2.

Position	I_{33}	I_{44}	I_{55}
1	1	1	1
2	2	2	2
3	3	3	3
4	3	4	4
5	3	4	5
6	3	4	4
7	3	3	3
8	2	2	2
9	1	1	1

Table 7.6 shows the number of interaction terms of three different types which are involved in the nine-letter sequences. These three interactions are those involving three, four, and five successive letters. It can be seen that the number of these terms is correlated, but not perfectly. Therefore it is possible to obtain estimates of the magnitudes of the different terms by computing the multiple regres-

Table 7.7

Solutions for various interaction uncertainties. Each column gives solutions for different numbers of interaction terms used in the regression equations. Data from Garner and Carson (1960).

I_{33}	-0.10	-0.23	-0.20	-0.21
I_{44}		0.09	0.01	-0.02
I_{55}			0.06	0.16
I_{66}				-0.17

sion equation of the differences mentioned above and the number of these different terms for all of the different conditions. Table 7.7 shows solutions for these interaction terms when different numbers of interaction terms were used in the regression equations. Using I_{55} and larger terms showed no significant improvement in correlation; therefore it was decided initially to use only I_{33} and I_{44} terms in further computations. Sequential constraint as a function of length, with these terms added to the contingencies, is shown in Fig. 7.3.

Sequential and total redundancy

It is possible to check the adequacy of these values in the total picture by recalling the relations which must exist between prediction of the end of a long sequence and prediction of the middle of such sequences. Of considerable importance is the fact that prediction in the middle of very long sequences is essentially perfect. In fact, it is very difficult to find cases where a single letter can be deleted in the middle of a long sequence and in which any letter other than the one deleted can possibly make sense. Thus we know that the multiple contingent uncertainty, $U(y{:}x, z)$ from Eq. 7.7, for predicting the middle letter of a long sequence is 4.08 bits. Now in the middle of a very long sequence, we have two of every contingency term (C_i), three I_{33} terms, and four I_{44} terms. Therefore,

$$2 \sum_{}^{\infty} C_i + 3I_{33} + 4I_{44} = 4.08$$
$$2 \sum_{}^{\infty} C_i - 0.69 + 0.36 = 4.08$$
$$\sum_{}^{\infty} C_i = 2.20 \tag{7.9}$$

In other words, if these values of the interactions are correct, then the sum of all contingency terms out to infinity must be 2.20 bits. This figure, of course, checks well with the sum of the Newman-Gerstman data, which sum to 2.12 bits out to eleven steps.

We can now compute the sequential redundancy by determining the value of the multiple contingent uncertainty for prediction at the end of long sequences.

$$\begin{aligned}
\text{SR} &= \sum_{}^{\infty} C_i + 1I_{33} + 1I_{44} \\
&= 2.20 - 0.23 + 0.09 \\
&= 2.06 \\
\% \text{ SR} &= 2.06/4.08 = 50.5\% \tag{7.10}
\end{aligned}$$

Thus we see that with this method the relative sequential redundancy is slightly more than 50 percent, a value which agrees very well with that obtained from the lower-bound estimates with the guessing-game technique.

If we use the value of 4.08 bits for the uncertainty of single letter distributions, then the amount of distributional redundancy is 0.67 bit with the commonly used 27-letter alphabet. If this amount is added to the 2.06 bits of sequential redundancy, then total redundancy is 2.73 bits, which is 57 percent of the nominal uncertainty.

A word of caution should be inserted here. It is clear that solutions for the redundancy of printed English from a complete multivariate analysis are as impossible as are actual counts of long sequences of letters. In order to make use of the approach at all, we must make simplifying assumptions. Most important of all, however, we must make use of the patterns of these terms as they vary from one situation to another.

We cannot take too seriously the actual values for I_{33} and I_{44} calculated by Garner and Carson. Table 7.7 shows, for example, that other solutions are possible, and that the actual numerical values obtained depend on the number of terms used. The pattern of these various solutions is such that the final answer concerning the redundancy of printed English is relatively unaffected by which of these solutions is used. Thus if we used the fourth solution, we would assume a negative I_{44} term, while in the second solution this term is positive. The particular values computed cannot therefore be considered exact. However, the pattern of the solutions and the end result seem to have considerable validity. A great deal of cross-checking is possible, and agreement with other results is excellent.

Also, while Garner and Carson used only I_{33}, I_{44}, etc. terms, the terms as computed are not really as simple as that. Comparison of Tables 7.1 and 7.2 shows that the number of I_{33} terms is correlated with the number of I_{34} and I_{35} terms, and that other interactions are correlated as well. Thus we must recognize that the terms as computed are actually composite terms and that even the composite terms do not have fixed values in our solutions.

More recent work by Newman and Waugh (1960) has shown further how complicated the problem really is. They determined contingencies for several different languages, and the contingencies for printed English do not correspond to those obtained from the King James Version of the Bible obtained by Newman and Gerstman; they are somewhat smaller. And Newman and Waugh[3] have even more recently done actual counts of four-letter sequences of printed Eng-

[3] Personal communication.

lish letters. Again, these contingencies are smaller than the earlier ones, and their direct calculations show a positive I_{33} term, not a negative one as calculated by Garner and Carson. With smaller contingency terms, however, it is clear that the interaction terms must be more positive in order to account for the redundancy. Thus we again have to accept the fact that there is probably not a single set of values which will be true for English in general. Some kinds of English may have large contingencies and small interactions, and other kinds may have quite a different pattern.

LETTER REDUNDANCY AND WORDS

While we have no perfect solution to the redundancy of printed English, the best available data suggest that sequential redundancy is a bit over 50 percent and that total redundancy is nearly 60 percent. These values are of considerable interest, since they show the extent to which the language can be recoded into a more efficient form. These measures, however, have one difficulty which is particularly meaningful psychologically, namely, that they treat sequences of letters and spaces as ergodic series, assuming that the statistical properties are uniform throughout a long series. Any recoding which is done to achieve the efficiency which is indicated must also deal with long sequences of letters in order to recode effectively.

Yet language is not, to users of it, simply a long series of letters and spaces, with equal value to all symbols. Letters are grouped into words and words into phrases and sentences, and these groupings are psychologically very meaningful. That these meaningful groupings affect the uncertainties of the series of symbols is clearly shown by the Newman and Gerstman data. For all symbols on the average, as we saw, the contingent uncertainty between adjacent pairs of letters was 0.91 bit. Yet, if we look only at the distributions of letters following spaces (that is, the distribution of first letters of words), we find that there is very little reduction in uncertainty.

The particular importance of the word unit in determining overall redundancy has been experimentally investigated by Carson (1961), who had subjects fill in letters after different numbers of letters were given in the beginning of a word. He used the distribution of guesses to obtain estimates of constraint, and then determined the unilateral constraint as a function of the position of a letter within a word. Some of his average results are shown in Fig. 7.5. For these data, all preceding letters in the word were given, but no later letters. For the lower curve, there was no additional context prior to the word

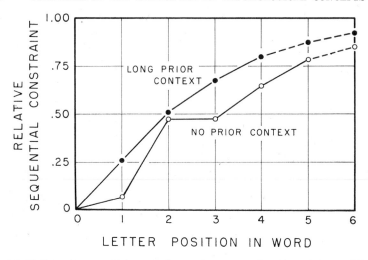

F_IG. 7.5. Unilateral sequential constraint on letters as a function of the position of the letter within a word. Subjects were required to guess the next letter in the word when all previous letters and the space were given. For the upper curve, thirty-one letters of additional prior context were given. Dashed portions of curves are extrapolated. (After Carson, 1961.)

itself while, for the upper curve, thirty-one additional letters and spaces were given.

If we look first at the lower curve, where no prior context is given, we can see that the first letter of a word is constrained very little, but when the first letter is given, the second letter is constrained nearly 50 percent. Knowing the first two letters is little better than knowing just the first letter (partly because of the vowel-consonant alternation), but, by the time the first four letters are known, the fifth is highly constrained. Now this amount of constraint, after five symbols (space plus four letters) is considerably higher than the amount of constraint for five symbols randomly selected in the language, and strongly suggests that by far the most important constraints are those which operate entirely within words themselves.

The upper curve makes this fact even clearer, since the difference between it and the lower curve shows the total effect of the long preceding context on the constraint. The average difference between these two curves is less than .15, which shows that less than 15 percent of the total constraint is due to influences which extend across word boundaries. Thus the really important constraints in printed English are those which exist within words, and not constraints which operate across words.

Carson used these data to obtain an estimate of the total redundancy in printed English. Using actual probabilities for different lengths of words, and assuming equal probability of occurrence for any letter position within a given length word, he computed the average constraint expected after random selection of letter positions. These computations showed slightly better than 50 percent sequential redundancy, and consequently approximately 60 percent total redundancy. Once again the figures check very well with other methods of calculation.

The reasons why so much of the redundancy in printed English is due to intraword constraints are varied. Certainly phonetic considerations have a great deal to do with it. For example, Newman (1951) showed that approximately 20 percent of the sequential constraint in printed English is due to the vowel-consonant alternation tendency by doing an analysis of English using only vowel and consonant classifications. This constraint is even greater in Italian and other Latin languages. The vowel-consonant alternation is to a large extent a matter of phonetics, in that words without vowels are generally not pronounceable. Likewise, some sequences of consonants are not pronounceable.

Sheer inability to pronounce certain sequences of sounds, however, is not the only factor involved in the high degree of intraword constraint. Each language has some combinations of consonants which are actually quite pronounceable but which simply never occur in the language, at least at certain positions within words. In English, for example, words never begin with "dl," "vl," or "vr"; yet the "dr" beginning is fairly common, as well as the "fl" and "fr" beginnings. A beginning "dl" is just as pronounceable as a beginning "dr" or "bl," but it simply does not occur. Similarly, the only difference between an "f" and a "v" is simply that the "v" is vocalized. Thus if we start words with "fl," there is no reason not to start them with "vl." English-speaking people find it awkward to pronounce "Vladimir" and "Vladivostok," although they are really quite easy to pronounce. We simply are not accustomed to the initial "vl" sound.

These restrictions within words account for much of the intraword constraint, and yet it is clear that the restrictions for any given language are to a large extent quite arbitrary, and are not due entirely to simple inability to pronounce certain combinations of letters. These arbitrary differences between languages are also what give the languages their flavor.

The fact that less than 15 percent of the sequential redundancy of printed English is due to constraints operating across words means that considerable efficiency in the language could be obtained by recoding entirely within word units. In other words, since so much of the total redundancy is due to intraword constraints, then a recoding schema which maintained the word unit but shortened the length of words could accomplish a good deal. There would not be a great deal lost by not recoding with long sequences of letters and spaces in random combinations.

COMMENTARY

It seems unfortunate that a problem of such importance as determination of the redundancy of language should not be capable, with existing techniques, of an exact solution. It does seem inevitable that no direct solution of the problem is possible, since even with high-speed computers the language sample necessary to determine directly the probabilities of ten-letter sequences is prohibitively large. As a matter of fact, even direct counts of various sequences are not without their problems, since the sample size is necessarily small compared to the number of possible sequences, and we then are faced with the problem of determining the best estimate of an unbiased uncertainty, and we unfortunately do not have available an exact solution to this problem for intermediate amounts of constraint. Whatever technique we use has its own shortcomings, and at best we seem to be able to establish reasonable estimates of redundancy, and can feel some degree of assurance only insofar as the various types of estimate agree with each other.

In another sense, perhaps this problem is not as important as at first glance it seems, because it may be that there is no single solution to the problem. Generally, when we use language samples we attempt to use material which we intuitively consider "typical" printed English. We try to avoid too highly specialized a vocabulary, too many proper nouns of a given class, too elaborate forms of punctuation, etc. The problem of selecting such "typical" material is not easy, which fact suggests the possibility that there is no such thing as "typical" printed English.

Whenever a special communication situation exists, it is very likely that the redundancy is considerably higher than it is for general printed material. Frick and Sumby (1952), for example, have done an analysis of the special language used by aircraft control tower operators in directing the landing of aircraft. They estimate that the redundancy may be as high as 96 percent in this special case, when situational factors as well as linguistic factors are taken into account.

In a similar study, Fritz and Grier (1955) estimate that redundancy is as great as 80 percent for the same type of situation.

It seems likely that in many other restricted communication situations redundancy can run equally high. Probably the language used within a particular family setting, for example, would be equally redundant, and occasionally husbands and wives need say only a phrase or two for communication to be well understood.

The evidence we have suggests that total redundancy is on the order of 60 percent for language in general, insofar as we can establish what language in general is. This figure very likely is a lower value for redundancy in the many different situations in which language is used for communication. It is, of course, possible to use languages which have very low amounts of redundancy if we create and use somewhat artificial languages. Mathematical systems of communication tend to do just that, which is why it is often possible to communicate a great deal in a small space with the use of mathematical symbols.

Even if we can establish a reasonable single figure for the redundancy of "typical" printed English, the particular nature of the redundancy may vary considerably from one type of printed English to another, or from one author to another. As the various studies by Newman and his co-workers show, languages differ in the vowel-consonant alternation pattern, and also in the extent to which the contingency terms are important. Not only do languages differ, but also different types of material from the same language, as Newman's studies have again shown. The earlier studies with the King James Bible show considerably higher contingencies than do studies with more modern English, and these differences are far greater than can be accounted for on the basis of sampling biases.

It is clear, therefore, that a general solution to the redundancy of printed English (or any other language) is possible only in an average sort of sense. Not only will the amount of redundancy depend on the special situation in which language is used, but the particular nature of the redundancy will also vary considerably. Still in all, it is of real value to have established that a general figure of 50 percent for sequential redundancy, and a figure of 60 percent for total redundancy, is approximately correct.

Over and above the problem of obtaining an estimate of redundancy in printed English, the relations between the uncertainty terms involved in unilateral and in bilateral prediction (as well as in intermediate cases) have an intrigue in their own right, at least to me. I have an intuitive feeling that there are more restrictions operating between the uncertainties for the various situations than I have been able to show.

However, even if there are no further restrictions operating, it is of considerable interest that unilateral constraint (the term ordinarily used for redundancy) will be exactly half the value of the bilateral constraint only if a certain pattern of relations between the interactions exists. In particular, the sum of all the extra interactions (Table 7.3) which occur for the bilateral case with prediction of a middle letter must be negative in order for unilateral constraint to be more than half of bilateral constraint. In the limiting case, this fact means that unilateral sequential redundancy (omitting the distributional redundancy) can be greater than 50 percent only if these terms are negative, since bilateral constraint cannot, of course, exceed 100 percent. Since the interaction uncertainties involved in unilateral constraint are closely related to these extra terms involved in bilateral constraint, it would seem reasonable that the sum of the unilateral interactions should also be negative. If these are negative, however, the only way that unilateral constraint can be greater than 50 percent is for the contingency terms (which must be positive) to be sufficiently great that they can more than offset the effect of the negative interaction terms.

All in all, it is difficult to conceive of a pattern of uncertainty terms in which the sum of the interaction terms can be positive, since these terms are multiplied in the bilateral case, and could easily lead to apparent overprediction of the middle letter. Thus there is a strong suggestion that the values of the contingent uncertainties are the controlling factor in redundancy, and that quite possibly the amount of redundancy cannot exceed the sum of the contingent uncertainties.

The relations between prediction of letters at ends and prediction in the middle of sequences also suggest a reason for the amount of redundancy which has developed in the language. It seems reasonable to assume that redundancy does not exist in the printed language just as an accident; and it seems equally reasonable that in the course of development the amount of redundancy increased to satisfy some realistic criterion. Sequential redundancy is approximately 50 percent for a good reason, and I suggest that the reason has to do with the ability to detect and correct isolated errors in the middle of long sequences.

Since the amount of redundancy is estimated by determining the relative constraint on letters at the end of sequences, it is natural for us to think of redundancy as satisfying some criterion of accuracy with regard to prediction at the ends. However, redundancy is, in fact, used bilaterally, and the criterion which is probably being satisfied is that *bilateral* prediction be essentially perfect for the single letter. If this criterion is satisfied, then isolated errors or deletions can be corrected perfectly. In other words, the criterion being satisfied is one of 100 percent constraint for letters in the middle of reasonably long sequences, and the figure of approximately 50 percent sequential redundancy (for unilateral prediction) is probably just an accidental concomitant of the requirement of 100 percent constraint for bilateral prediction of single letters.

Thus, for purposes of understanding the nature and use of the language by humans, figures for bilateral constraint are more meaningful than figures for unilateral constraint—the measure of amount of redundancy. Any real language will develop redundancy to satisfy some criterion relevant to the users of the language, and language as used involves bilateral constraint, not just unilateral constraint. The critical criterion being satisfied is essentially complete constraint for single letters with bilateral context.

SUMMARY

Redundancy in any system of variables is the difference between the maximum uncertainty which the system of variables can have and the actual uncertainty of the variables operating jointly. If maximum uncertainty is defined in terms of nominal uncertainties of variables, then total redundancy is determined. It is convenient, however, to distinguish between distributional redundancy and sequential redundancy. Distributional redundancy is the difference between nominal and actual uncertainties, while sequential redundancy is that due to constraints operating between the variables, in this case sequential constraints.

While strictly speaking redundancy is concerned with the amount of constraint in a total system of variables, the problem of its determination reduces to that of estimating the constraint operating on single letters at the end of long sequences of letters. This figure can be considered an average redundancy, in that it is the amount of redundancy operating per variable, or per single letter position.

There have been two general methods for estimating the amount of redundancy in printed English. The first of these, based on the guessing-game technique of Shannon, leads to a lower-bound estimate of redundancy. With this technique, direct lower-bound estimates of the constraint on single letters at the end of long sequences are obtained.

The other approach is a multivariate analysis of the terms involved in prediction of letters at various positions in sequences. Some of these terms can be computed directly, particularly the contingency terms, and other terms can be estimated from experimental data. There are interrelations between the terms involved in unilateral prediction and those involved in bilateral prediction which set certain limits on numerical estimates.

Both of these methods lead to estimates of approximately 50 percent sequential redundancy. When distributional redundancy is added back in, the best estimate of total redundancy is approximately 60 percent. Most of this redundancy is due to intraword constraints, and a relatively small amount of it is due to constraints operating across words, even for long sequences.

CHAPTER EIGHT

The Use of Language Redundancy

In CHAPTER SEVEN, WE were primarily concerned with the determination of the redundancy of language, particularly of printed English. Our interest there lay in the nature of the language itself and on some methodological considerations involved in the determination of redundancy. In this chapter we shall be primarily concerned with the extent to which this redundancy is actually used by humans. The two aspects of the problem, of course, are not entirely separable, since human performance is needed to determine the redundancy of the language itself. Thus the experimental determinations of redundancy have already established that humans can and do make use of the redundancy in the language, and all we can do here is to examine some ways in which redundancy is used in greater detail.

DISTRIBUTIONAL REDUNDANCY

Just as we distinguished between distributional and sequential redundancy in the last chapter, we shall also distinguish between them in terms of the effects of redundancy on human performance. Distributional redundancy is simply due to the fact that all letters (or words, or any other language element) are not used equally often in the language. Knowledge of the language statistics by humans will affect the use of these various elements, and in some circumstances at least the elements are used in proportion to their actual occurrence in the English language.

247

Distributional letter redundancy

Single letters of the English alphabet occur with widely different frequencies in normal usage. To what extent are adult users of the language aware of these differences? Attneave (1953) attempted to answer this question with several different types of judgment on the part of airman basic trainees. In one experiment, he simply asked his subjects to indicate how many times, out of a thousand letters, each of the letters of the alphabet would occur. The correlation between such judgments and actual counts of printed English was .79, indicating a rather high degree of accuracy on the part of the subjects. While the overall correlation was quite good, his subjects did tend to underestimate the high-frequency letters somewhat and overestimate the low-frequency letters.

Attneave then used another method of determining these subjects' knowledge of letter statistics. His basic method was to have the subjects guess what letter was on a card which the experimenter turned over, one at a time. The number of times each letter was guessed was then tabulated, and these frequencies were compared with actual frequencies in printed English. He used three groups of subjects, differing only in the instructions which were given concerning the origin of the letters. One group was told nothing about the origin of the letters, and for this group the correlation of frequency of guessed letters with actual counts was .42. Another group was told that the letters were drawn at random from a hat, and for this group the correlation was .43. The third group was told that the letters were selected as every fifth letter from actual English text, and for this group, the correlation was .83.

These results indicate that the use of letters by the human subjects match actual frequencies of occurrence to a fairly high degree. The degree of matching is highest when the subjects are informed that the letters they are trying to guess come from actual English, but the degree of matching is still moderate even when there is no reason for their guesses to match actual occurrence of letters in English. Thus it would appear that the tendency to use letters in proportion to actual occurrence to some extent overrides instruction which should produce no correlation.

That such response tendencies will affect performance on other tasks has been shown by Battig (1957, 1958). He had subjects attempt to form words by guessing at letters until they had completed the words. He found a decided tendency for the guesses to follow the order of frequency of occurrence, and this tendency was stronger for the better subjects on this task than for the poorer subjects. Battig also found that this tendency could be influenced by recent experience. He gave his subjects words with uncommon letters in them, and found that on later words the subjects tended to guess the uncommon letters too frequently, with a subsequent deterioration in performance on words with more common letters in them. Thus not only do subjects respond in general according to their experience with the language, but the more recent experience has a stronger effect than the long term experience.

Distributional word redundancy

Far more research has been carried out with words than with letters, since words are, psychologically, more meaningful units than are letters.

Solomon and Howes (1951) and Howes and Solomon (1951) first showed that a visual duration threshold for words, obtained from tachistoscopic exposures of the words, is systematically related to the frequency of occurrence of the words in general English usage, such that the more frequent words have shorter thresholds. This dependence of visual duration thresholds on word frequency has been verified by many experimenters. Frequency of occurrence also affects the threshold of words heard in noise, again in a manner such that the more frequent words are heard more easily; that is, they have lower thresholds in noise. Postman and Rosenzweig (1957) discuss many of these relations and point out that number of repetitions required for correct identification will also be affected by word frequency. Pierce and Karlin (1956) have shown that reading rates are faster with more familiar words. Howes (1957) has shown that, with auditory recognition of words in noise, this relation is more exact if word length is controlled, that is, its effect is partialled out.

Solomon and Postman (1952) brought this phenomenon under better experimental control by using nonsense words whose frequency of use during a preliminary period was controlled, and once again established that prior frequency of use affected visual duration thresholds. This method, used again with success by King-Ellison and Jenkins (1954), was modified by Cohn (1954). During the preliminary training series, Cohn rewarded use of some words, punished use of others, and made neutral statements for use of still others. In the test series, in which she used several different performance criteria, she established that the nature of reward or punishment had a negligible effect on the test performance, while prior frequency of usage had a very large effect.

The fact that prior frequency of word usage affects visual and auditory thresholds, as well as related measures, is sufficiently established that there is little need to go into more detail. On the other hand, it is worth asking what the nature of the effect is, whether it is truly a perceptual effect, or as our earlier discussions of similar topics suggest, whether it is primarily a response effect. The available data certainly suggest that it is primarily a response effect in that the critical factor seems to be how likely a person is to use a particular word rather than how easy it is to perceive it.

In one quite conclusive experiment, Goldiamond and Hawkins (1958) showed that the effect could be produced without there being any stimulus actually presented, a fact which makes it eminently clear that perception is not what is being affected. In their experiment, they had subjects learn nonsense syllables in a preliminary task, and then later ran what was presumably a visual recognition test. During the visual recognition test, no words were actually flashed on the screen, but otherwise the experiment was conducted as a regular threshold experiment, with a nominally correct word for each exposure. The results of this experiment are shown in Fig. 8.1, where the "recognition" thresholds are shown as a function of training frequency for the nonsense syllables.

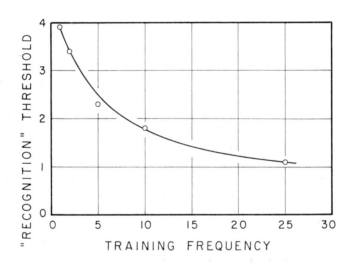

Fig. 8.1. "Recognition" thresholds for nonsense syllables as a function of frequency of use during training. Since no stimuli were actually presented on the test, the thresholds are entirely artifactual, and are the result of frequency of use of the syllables. (After Goldiamond and Hawkins, 1958.)

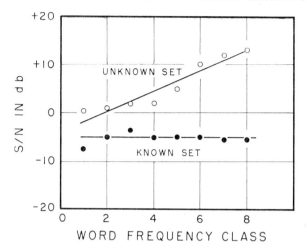

F𝐼𝐺. 8.2. The effect of word frequency on perceptual thresholds of words in noise with a known and unknown message set. The abscissa shows word frequency, with lower numbers representing higher frequency of occurrence in the language. The message set, both known and unknown, was 144 words. (After Pollack, Rubenstein, and Decker, 1959.)

That there is a relation between "recognition" and training frequency is clear, but what is equally clear is that the function results entirely from different frequency of usage of the nonsense syllables. The more frequently used words, of course, will be used correctly more often, and threshold values will be reached more quickly. In a sense, then, any perceptual effect of prior frequency of word usage must be considered artifactual. However, this result does not really destroy the phenomenon, but rather makes clear that it works because of effects on probabilities of use of words as responses, not because of direct effects on the perceptual system.

In another manner, Pollack, Rubenstein, and Decker (1959) have shown that the relation between auditory thresholds and word frequency is primarily due to probability of responding, not to a perceptual factor per se. These authors determined auditory recognition thresholds under two conditions, one where all words were known to the subject, and another where the same set of words was used but they were unknown to the subject. For the known sets of words, the subjects were simply given an alphabetical list of the words to be used in the tests. Within each list, words (all monosyllables) with different frequency of usage in general English were included. Results for 144 word sets are shown in Fig. 8.2. Here it is clear that the usual relation of a lower auditory threshold for high frequency words is confirmed for the unknown message set, but that the relation completely disappears when the message set is known. In other words, when the subject has the complete list of words before him, presumably all words have equal probability of being used by him; but when he doesn't know the message set, he accepts the probabilities from language in general. Similar results were obtained by these authors for other sizes of message sets.

To summarize this section, we have seen that the probability of a human subject's using a word or letter is a direct function of the probability of the word's or letter's occurrence in normal English usage. These probabilities can be changed with recent experience and can be created with learned nonsense syllables or words. By whatever means the probability of use of words is altered, such differential probabilities will affect threshold measurements of these words. Such threshold effects cannot be taken as indications of true perceptual changes. In fact, we have essentially no evidence that perception as such is affected by frequencies of occurrence of words, but rather that response tendencies (perhaps expectancies) are the major factors influenced.

SEQUENTIAL REDUNDANCY

Although it is clear that humans are aware of distributional probabilities of letters and words, and that these probabilities affect human responses (and possibly perception), of far greater interest is man's ability to make use of the sequential constraints inherent in language. The total amount of redundancy which is due to distributional constraints is relatively small compared to that due to sequential constraints, and thus any truly effective use of redundancy must take into account the sequential constraints.

Perception of letter patterns

We have seen that visual duration thresholds for words are affected by the probability of the words' occurrences in ordinary printed English. It is also true, as Miller, Bruner, and Postman (1954) have shown, that perception of groups of letters is affected by the extent to which the groups of letters resemble ordinary English.

These authors determined the accuracy of perception of eight-letter nonsense words as a function of duration of visual exposure, using four different kinds of words. They generated lists of words which correspond to real English in various degrees with a method

described by Shannon (1948). In this method an order of approximation to English is produced by using actual statistics of letter distributions extending over various lengths. For zero-order approximations, letters for the eight-letter words are drawn at random from the
letters of the alphabet. With this procedure words such as "yrulpzoc"
and "eapmzcen" are produced. For first-order approximations, letters
are again drawn at random, but they are restricted by the actual
distribution of letters in printed English. Thus rare letters will rarely
occur, and words like "stanugop" and "nhgttede" are generated. For
second-order approximations, pair probabilities in actual English are
used, so that no letter can follow another letter unless it does so in
actual English. With this order of approximation words like "wallylof"
and "edesener" are formed. Similarly, with fourth-order approximations, sequences of four letters in proportion to their actual occurrence
in printed English are used, and words like "ricaning" and "exprespe"
are generated. The higher the order of approximation, the more like
English the words become, although all words still technically remain
nonsense words.

These words were flashed one at a time on a screen, and the percent
correct letters for three different durations are given in Fig. 8.3. It is
clear from these data that accuracy of perception increases as the nonsense words more nearly approximate actual English, at all durations.

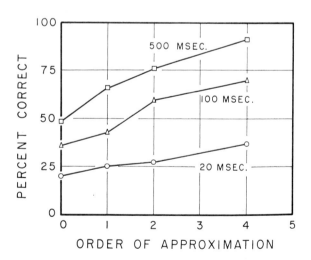

Fig. 8.3. Accuracy of perception of eight-letter sequences as a function of order of
approximation to English. Tachistoscopic exposures of durations indicated were
used. (Data from Miller, Bruner, and Postman, 1954.)

These authors corrected the obtained percentages by relative redundancy factors, and came to the conclusion that the same amount of information was perceived regardless of the order of approximation.

In a similar experiment, Augenstine et al. (1956) used first- and second-order approximations to English, as well as actual English words. They likewise found increased accuracy of perception with closer approximation to English, but concluded that total information perceived decreased with closer approximation to English, particularly when actual English words were used. The discrepancy in regard to this particular conclusion cannot, however, be considered too serious, since there were substantial differences in methodology, and also in methods of estimating information.

The conclusions which can be drawn from this type of material must be limited, particularly with regard to concepts of redundancy. It is very tempting to think of order of approximation to English as a measure of amount of redundancy; and it is further tempting to consider a recognition threshold as a measure of discrimination. Both temptations should be avoided, however, and can be avoided if we consider some of the distinctions made in Chapter Five.

If we generate a fixed number of words to use in an experiment, then the redundancy of this set of words is determined solely by the number of words which could have been generated with the same number of letters per word and the same number of different letters per letter position in the words. The particular method of selecting the set determines the form of the redundancy, not its amount. Thus the different orders of approximation determine, for a fixed set of words, only the form of the redundancy. The form of redundancy can be expected to affect both discrimination and free recall, although in different ways. However, in the experiments reported here, with the recognition task, it is questionable that this task is appropriate to a clear measure of either discrimination or free recall. It is much more related to familiarity of the particular letter patterns to the subjects. Thus it leads to a legitimate measure of the extent to which people know the particular sequential rules in English, but does not lead to a measure of the value of redundancy per se for either discrimination or free recall.

In the Miller et al. experiment, for example, all of the words generated were presented in a random order; that is, words of different orders of approximation were intermixed. Suppose, however, that each set of words of different orders of approximation had been used alone and that the subject in the experiment knew the total response set for each of these sets when it was being used. In this case, it is much clearer that the amount of redundancy would in fact be the same for each order of approximation. That is to say, the number of words to be discriminated would be the same in each set, and the total number of possible words would be the same. The only difference would be in the form of the redundancy, not in its amount. Under these conditions, where familiarity is equalized, it might not be surprising to find the lower orders of approximation as easy, if not easier, to discriminate as the higher orders of approximation, because these words can differ in more ways.

What is clear from these experiments is that people have learned the particular signification rules of real English, and that the more familiar patterns are easier to recognize under conditions of stimulus impoverishment. That what we are dealing with here is familiarity of particular patterns, not amount of redundancy, can readily be appreciated if we transposed the various letters in English for high orders of approximation (if we exchange all "e's" and "x's," for example). Such transposition of letters would not affect the amount of constraint or redundancy, but would affect the particular signification rules used. Most obviously, also, it would affect recognition thresholds.

Replacement of deleted letters

An even more direct attack on the problem of knowledge and use of the particular redundancy rules is to determine the extent to which material can be deleted without serious consequences in terms of full recognition or comprehension of the material. In a redundant language more letters are used than are minimally necessary to convey a given amount of information. This statement does not mean that we can simply get rid of some of the letters as actually used, since there will always be some uncertainty for any letter unless the total constraint for the particular letter is 100 percent.

In Chapter Seven, we noted that constraint for single letters in the middle of very long sequences is 100 percent, or very nearly so. Since we can find rare cases where even such middle letters cannot be reinserted with perfect accuracy, it is clear that no amount of deletion of letters can lead to perfectly accurate reproduction. If we cannot reinsert single isolated deletions with perfect accuracy, then certainly we cannot expect perfect accuracy if, say, 10 or 20 percent of letters are deleted.

A measure of amount of redundancy in printed English does not, therefore, directly tell us how many letters can be deleted from the language and still allow perfect reproduction, nor does it tell us what level of accuracy should be expected. It is experimental question, and one to which Chapanis (1954) first provided an empirical answer. He used many different prose passages, and deleted $\frac{1}{10}$, $\frac{1}{5}$, $\frac{1}{4}$, $\frac{1}{3}$, $\frac{1}{2}$, and $\frac{2}{3}$ of the letters, either on a regular deletion basis or on a random deletion basis. After the deletions, the material was collapsed, so that no direct indication of the loci of the deletions was given to the subjects. His data, from ninety-one subjects, are given in Fig. 8.4.

With regular deletion, approximately 90 percent of the missing letters were correctly restored with as much as 20 percent deletion, but accuracy fell off rapidly after that. With random deletions, accuracy was somewhat poorer for low amounts of deletion, but somewhat better for the higher amounts of deletion. This better accuracy for the higher amounts of deletion is undoubtedly due to the fact that with random deletion occasional longer sequences of letters occur, providing cues for the actual message, while these longer sequences can never occur with regular deletion. For example, if two letters out of three are deleted on a regular basis, each letter is actually given with no adjacent letters; but if the letters are deleted on a random basis, two or three letters will occasionally be given in a row.

Chapanis also found that there were important differences in subjects in their ability to carry out this task. He used a few code experts, for example, and found that they were substantially better than the average subject, although subjects who had as good a verbal

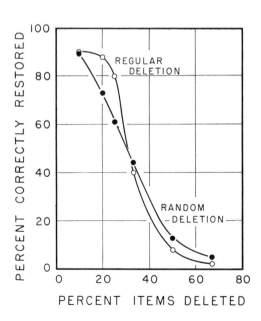

FIG. 8.4. Accuracy of reconstruction of printed English when various percent letters are deleted. After deletion, the material was collapsed. Deletions were spaced either regularly or randomly. (After Chapanis, 1954.)

ability as the code experts did just as well on this task. Thus the extent to which redundancy is used by human subjects does depend on their level of skill in using the language.

In a similar experiment, Miller and Friedman (1957) confirmed Chapanis' results, and also showed that the accuracy with which such mutilations can be handled depends on the actual form of the mutilation. Chapanis had used a collapsed set of letters, which Miller and Friedman refer to as abbreviation. In addition, Miller and Friedman used substitution, where an incorrect letter was substituted for the correct one; indicated substitution, where the location of the incorrect letter was indicated; deletion, where the letter was taken out and the space left blank; and insertion, where incorrect letters were simply inserted between the correct letters. Subjects were most accurate with insertion, where all of the correct letters actually occurred plus some incorrect ones. In fact, with this mutilation method, their subjects were able to reconstruct essentially perfectly (that is, median values were 100 percent) with 30 percent insertions.

These two experiments confirm, while providing actual empirical functions, general expectations about ability to reproduce material which has been deleted. As we noted above, it should be impossible to obtain 100 percent accuracy even with low rates of mutilation (except perhaps where all correct information is actually given, as with the insertion procedure), because letters deleted on any general statistical basis will leave some residual uncertainty. On the other hand, if the deletions or mutilations are made on a basis which deliberately takes out those letters which in fact convey the least information, it should be possible to have considerably more mutilation without serious loss of comprehension. For example, Carson's study (1961) showed that beginning letters carry much more information than middle letters, and probably end letters also carry more information. Therefore, there will be much less loss of information if middle letters are deleted than if end letters are.

Miller and Friedman actually tried a variety of planned mutilations (they use the term coherent abbreviation). They found that the most successful method was to delete (and then abbreviate) all of the vowels and spaces. With such a procedure, there was an average abbreviation of 48 percent, and their subjects were able to reproduce 93 percent of the omitted letters. Since total redundancy is on the order of 60 percent, it is clear that this method comes reasonably close to providing an efficient method of recoding English without destroying its basic comprehensibility for the intelligent reader. Very possibly even better abbreviation could be accomplished with some combination of vowel deletions and deletions of consonants from the middle of words, particularly the longer words. However, any reduction in length due only to deletions within words cannot be fully efficient, since there is some constraint across words as well as within words.

Positional effects

As we noted in Chapter Seven, redundancy is defined, for practical purposes, as the constraint on single letters after very long sequences of letters. However, constraints can and do operate backward as well as forward, and on the middle or any other part of a finite sequence of letters. The amount of constraint existing for any letter position depends both on the number of letters available for prediction and also on the positions of these letters relative to the one being predicted. As was suggested in Chapter Seven, prediction will always be better for any number of predictors when the letter being predicted is in the middle of the total sequence, rather than at the end. Actually, there is a systematic relation between amount of constraint and the letter position for randomly selected sequences.

Figure 8.5 shows this relation for nine-letter sequences, when the amount of constraint is computed solely from the contingent uncertainties from Newman and Gerstman (1952). The reason for this curved relation is simply that the closer two letters are to each other,

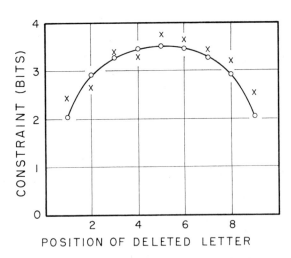

Fig. 8.5. Constraint as a function of position of letters in nine-letter sequences. The open circles are computed from Newman and Gerstman (1952) contingent uncertainties. The x's are data from Garner and Carson (1960).

the greater is the contingent uncertainty between them, and as the deleted letter (the one to be predicted) moves toward the center of the sequence, the number of large contingencies increases while the number of smaller ones decreases. That is to say, the total number of contingencies remains the same, since the number of letters from which the prediction is done remains the same, but their magnitudes increase. The data obtained by Garner and Carson (1960) for nine-letter sequences are plotted on the same graph for comparison purposes, and it is clear that the extent to which humans use redundancy is related to the amount of it available. Similar functions were obtained for other lengths of sequence, and, as was shown in Fig. 7.4, the overall relation between the predictions and the obtained constraints is good.

Miller and Friedman (1957) obtained similar curves for accuracy of letter guessing with five-, seven-, and eleven-letter sequences. Their data also show, somewhat more clearly than do the Garner and Carson data, a tendency for greater accuracy at the ends of sequences than at the beginnings. Any mathematical analysis will show a completely symmetrical function, so that this tendency must indicate a difference in the extent to which humans can make use of the redundancy. It seems likely that the effect is due to the normal pattern of reading from left to right.

These relations and experiments have dealt with randomly selected sequences of letters, in which sequences may begin with spaces, with first letters of words, or with any other letter within a word. The bow-shaped relation is a general statistical relation. We would naturally expect that similar relations would exist within sequences which are actual word units, and indeed Carson (1961) has shown that such a relation does exist. However, the relation is much sharper when word units are used. Carson's data show that the second and third letters of words have almost fifty percent constraint, when they are known to be the second or third letters of words, which is much greater constraint than exists for such lengths of letter sequences chosen at random.

The beginnings and ends of words carry the greatest information, and the middle letters of words are the most redundant. Does this fact have any effect on how words are perceived? Data from an experiment by Haslerud and Clark (1957) show that it does. They required subjects to read nine-letter words which were presented tachistoscopically for 40 msecs at a rather low level of illumination. The accuracy with which various letters were reported is shown in Fig. 8.6.

These data show that the first and last letters of the word are per-ceived much more accurately under these conditions. Since the subjects were trying to read the entire word, their best strategy would be to attempt to perceive accurately the most informative parts of the word, which are the beginning and the end. Thus it would appear that humans have learned to read in such a way as to make maximum use of the information in words.

In a related experiment, Bruner and O'Dowd (1958) reversed pairs of letters at the beginning, in the middle, or at the end of six- and

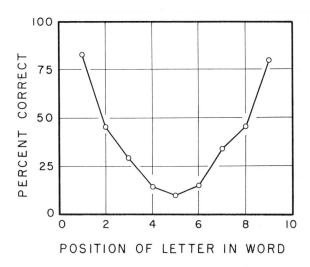

POSITION OF LETTER IN WORD

FIG. 8.6. Perception of letters as a function of position of letters in nine-letter words. Words were exposed tachistoscopically for 40 msec. (After Haslerud and Clark, 1957.)

eight-letter words. These words were presented tachistoscopically, and subjects were required to report the entire word. Reversals of letters in the middle of words were much less disruptive than reversals at the ends, a result which again corresponds with the fact that the middle letters carry much less information. These authors also found that beginning reversals were more disruptive than end reversals. This result may be due to reading habits, but it is also possible that the completely symmetrical relation for constraint and letter posi-tion does not hold for letters within words. End letters may be more redundant than beginning letters, and we have no clear-cut data on this point.

Interword constraints

Words are considerably less predictable than are letters, and even single words deleted in the middle of very long passages cannot be replaced without considerable error. Morrison and Black (1957) have studied the effect of different numbers of word deletions in sentences of eleven, twelve, or thirteen words. They deleted one to six of the words and required subjects to attempt to replace the missing words. Their data are given in Fig. 8.7. In this figure, one curve was obtained when the positions of the deletions were indicated and the other when the positions were not indicated. While accuracy is slightly

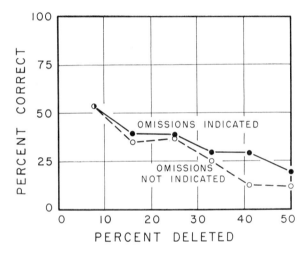

Fig. 8.7. Percent of deleted words in sentences correctly replaced. Sentences were eleven, twelve, or thirteen words long, and positions of deleted words were indicated for the upper curve only. (Data from Morrison and Black, 1957.)

greater when the positions of the deletions are indicated, the difference between the two conditions is not very great. What is of most interest is that when even a single word is deleted from a sentence, it can be replaced with an accuracy no greater than 50 percent.

A comparable amount of deletion of single letters leads to a much greater accuracy. For example, in the data of Miller and Friedman (1957), over 90 per cent of middle letters of eleven-letter sequences were correctly replaced. Actually, as we shall see later, it is remarkable that an accuracy as high as 50 percent can be obtained, because the uncertainty of single words, even in the middle of long sequences, is quite high.

Similar results, however, have been obtained by Aborn, Rubenstein, and Sterling (1959), who deleted single words at four different positions in sentences either six, eleven, or twenty-five words long. Their overall accuracy of replacement was slightly more than 40 percent, and while eleven-word sentences provided greater accuracy than six-word sentences, increasing length to twenty-five words produced no improvement in accuracy. These authors' results also showed that accuracy was slightly greater for words deleted from the middle of sentences than for words deleted at the ends, although initial words were correctly replaced far better than final words.

Thus, when complete sentences are used as the language sample, final words are not predicted as easily as initial words. This result is at some variance with results obtained with letter distributions. However, we must remember that the same result might be obtained with letters if single deletions were made from whole words rather than from random samples of letters. Just as the word is a psychologically meaningful unit, and letter structure within words is not the same as letter structure for random samples of letters, so also word structure within sentences is undoubtedly not the same as word structure for randomly selected sequences of words. Unfortunately, we do not have in this area many directly comparable experiments, which, if they existed, would allow us a better picture of the role of sentence structure in the use of redundancy by humans.

In this type of experiment, subjects are usually simply required to replace missing words and are scored on accuracy. Aborn and Rubenstein (1958) have shown that subjects not only can replace missing words with moderate accuracy, but can also estimate the probability of a given word's being correct rather well. These authors required their subjects to write down eight different words which could be used to replace a single deleted word in a sentence, and also to rank the words in order of decreasing likelihood of occurrence. Using the total number of responses as a measure of actual probability of occurrence, they found quite good agreement between the estimates of probability and actual use of the various words.

An interesting aspect of this experiment is the fact that the subjects apparently had little difficulty in finding eight different words to use for each deletion, words which could actually make the completed sentence meaningful. It is clear that there is considerable uncertainty for words even with a reasonably large amount of context given.

In a similar type of experimental task, Shepard (1962) required his subjects to produce as many words as they could in a 5-minute period. He used random selections of material, with number of context words (words actually presented) ranging from none through forty. In every case the omitted word which the subjects were to fill in was in the middle of the total sequence, so that the context should have been maximally restrictive. His results for this experiment are shown in Fig. 8.8. Clearly the number of words produced decreases as the context becomes more restrictive, and with forty words of context (twenty words on each side) slightly fewer than ten words were produced by the average subject. When no context was presented, the task was essentially simply free association, and an average of nearly a hundred words was produced in the 5-minute period.

Shepard was interested in comparing the rate of word production to the actual uncertainty of the words in the various contexts, so he obtained an independent estimate of the uncertainty of the words. His procedure was to have the subjects guess at the first letter of the missing word until they had it correct, then to guess at the second letter, then the third letter, etc. From the distributions of guesses, estimates of the uncertainty per letter positions were obtained, following the Shannon procedure. Then the uncertainties of these several letter positions were summed to give an uncertainty for the word itself. This procedure is equivalent to obtaining a total uncertainty by summing a series of uncertainty terms as was indicated in Eq. 5.7.

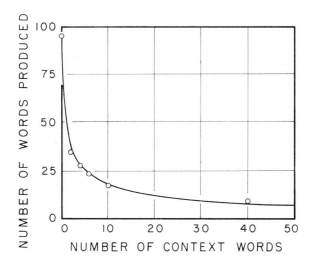

Fig. 8.8. Rate of word production as a function of the constraint imposed by context words. The ordinate shows total words produced per subject in a 5-minute period. The abscissa is the number of context words within which the produced words had to fit. (Data from Shepard, 1962.)

His data obtained from this procedure are shown as the open circles of Fig. 8.9, and the parallel between this function and that of Fig. 8.8 is obvious. Thus the rate of producing words (or total number which a subject can produce) is directly related to the uncertainty of words. A lot of words can be produced where the uncertainty is high, and only a few where it is low.

The association of rate of word production with uncertainty has also been shown by Goldman-Eisler (1958a,b), but in a somewhat different manner. She had subjects utter spontaneous speech, and then measured the pauses between words. She also had subjects guess successive words in these sentences to determine points of high and low uncertainty in the sentences used. She found that pauses in spontaneous speech were associated with points of high uncertainty. In another experiment, she had subjects read these sentences and replace words which had been omitted. The delay in replacement of the words was again greater with the more uncertain words. Thus she has established that pauses in speech are preludes to points of high uncertainty, a fact which is quite congruent with the relation between reaction time and stimulus or response uncertainty. The more alternatives a speaker has at a given point in his speech, the greater will be the time required to produce one of these alternatives.

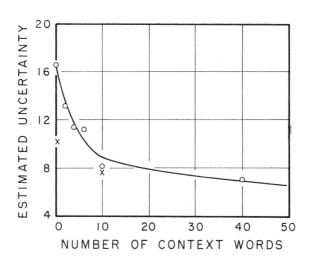

Fig. 8.9. Estimates of uncertainty of words. The open circles are data from Shepard (1962), and are obtained from a guessing procedure with context symmetrical on both sides of the word to be guessed. The x's are estimates from Carson (1961) for zero context and 31-letter unidirectional context.

There is an apparent contradiction in these results of Goldman-Eisler and those of Shepard. Notice that Shepard's subjects produced words faster (that is, they produced more words in a given period of time) with high uncertainty, while Goldman-Eisler's subjects took longer to produce a single word. The difference probably lies in the procedure. When subjects are instructed to produce as many words as they can, then the more possibilities there are the faster they can go. However, when they are instructed to produce (and thus select) just one of these words, then the reaction time is greater.

Estimates of word uncertainty

A word might be said about these estimates of word uncertainty themselves. It is difficult to obtain meaningful measures of amount of redundancy for words, partly because of the large vocabulary, and partly because of the difficulty of determining the distributional uncertainty of the words actually used. Furthermore, this uncertainty will vary considerably depending on the author whose material is being used—far more than the distributional uncertainty of letters will vary. Nevertheless, these estimates of uncertainty can be very meaningful. It is only the conversion into redundancy which is ambiguous.

We might compare these estimates of Shepard with estimates obtained in a similar fashion from the Carson (1961) data. If we take Carson's data for no prior context (Fig. 7.5.), and add the successive letter uncertainties up to five letters (for a rough average length of word), then we have another estimate of the uncertainty of single words. This value for the Carson data (plotted as an x in Fig. 8.9) is a little over 10 bits, compared to the value given by Shepard of 16.3 bits. The discrepancy is large, and it is likely that the true value lies in between. Shepard's value corresponds to a vocabulary for single words of over eighty thousand (with the unlikely assumption of equal probabilities). Since newspaper material was used in his experiments, such a figure is considerably too high. On the other hand, the value obtained from Carson's data suggest a vocabulary of not much over one thousand words (although it would have been larger if we had estimated for longer words). The true value surely lies somewhere between these two.

We can also compute an estimate of uncertainty of words from Carson's maximum context condition, and this value, plotted as an x in Fig. 8.9 also, is just under 8 bits, compared to Shepard's value for ten context words of just over 8 bits. In other words, these values agree very closely. It is interesting to note, however, the differences in experimental conditions under which they were obtained. For Carson's data, subjects had approximately five words of prior context only, while for the condition plotted as comparable, Shepard's subjects had five words of prior context plus five words of subsequent context. The fact that these two experimental conditions give estimates of word uncertainty so nearly the same suggests that with words the bilateral context is not particularly advantageous compared to unilateral context. As we saw earlier, with letters the same total amount of context is much more valuable when distributed evenly on the two sides of the letter to be predicted than when it is entirely on one side. The Shepard data, as compared to the Carson data, suggest that this effect is not as evident with words as it is with letters. It seems very likely that a function relating position of word deletion to constraint would be much flatter than it is for letters.

We have, of course, some evidence that verifies this assumption. The experiment by Aborn, Rubenstein, and Sterling (1959), with deletions of words in sentences, shows some advantage to words deleted near the middle, but relatively little. For example, with six-word sentences, initial words were correctly replaced 38 percent of the time, final words 26 percent of the time, and medial words 42 percent of the time. This function becomes flatter with longer sentences, except that the final word is still the most difficult to replace.

Associative effects

In any real language the probability that a given word will be used by a subject is determined not just by the general topic of the material but also, and most heavily, by the sentence structure itself. If, for example, a sentence is given with the only verb deleted, acceptable replacements come only from the class of verbs. Such structural constraints are determined entirely by the words within the sentence itself, because grammatical structuring extends beyond sentences to only a very slight extent. Thus any constraint produced on a given word position by language units larger than sentences must almost certainly be due to general topical associations, rather than to grammatical structure. For example, suppose we are given the sentence, "The prediction of the _____ behavior of a population is formulated in statistical terms." It is clear that we need an adjective (or an adjectival noun), but there are many adjectives which could make that sentence meaningful. If, however, the preceding material has been discussing use of words, phrases, etc., then the probable words will be narrowed down considerably to words within the general context of language, speech, etc.

Even though constraints operating over word sequences longer than sentences appear not to be very great, they do operate to some extent. E. Miller (1956), for example, showed that tachistoscopic recognition thresholds for sentences were improved if the various sentences were given in a meaningful rather than a random order. Bruce (1958) showed that intelligibility of sentences heard in noise is a function of the extent to which a prefacing word is topically appropriate to the sentence. In other words, if a prefacing word gives a correct "set," then intelligibility is better.

In a similar type of experiment, Cofer and Shepp (1957) measured recognition times for words as a function of the nature of a preceding standard word. When the preceding word was a synonym of the test word, recognition times were faster, and the closer the degree of synonymy, the faster the recognition time.

In an experiment reported by Howes and Osgood (1954), subjects were required to write down a word association to a series of four stimulus words. The word produced was affected primarily by the last word given, but it was still affected to some extent by at least one preceding word. The stimulus words selected were themselves not normally associated, so that it was possible to demonstrate an independent effect of words preceding the last stimulus word.

These experiments, which we need not treat with any further detail here, show that perception and use of words is affected by factors other than constraints within words or sentences. While these effects are not large, they cannot be entirely ignored. Furthermore, the data of Howes and Osgood suggest that even these effects do not operate over large spans of words. Whatever associations there are, they are produced over relatively short spans of words. While we cannot extrapolate directly from simple word associations to content associations extending over sentences, it does seem likely that very long-term constraints in language are not of great importance. This assumption, of course, agrees well with the generally found lack of long term effects. In particular, the very small decreased constraint found by Shepard (1962) when he increased the context from ten to forty words indicates that such long-range constraints are of little importance.

REDUNDANCY AND VERBAL LEARNING

Thus far we have discussed the ways in which redundancy in language is used by humans, either in affecting accuracy of perception or in affecting the ability to reproduce a message unit when part of the total message has been deleted. However, language is something which is learned, and the extent to which redundancy affects learning of a language is of considerable psychological interest.

Learning and order of approximation to English

A first attempt at using information concepts in the study of learning was made by Miller and Selfridge (1950). These authors constructed lists of words with various orders of approximation to English, and the lists were generated by the Shannon procedure described above. If fourth-order approximations were desired, for example, a subject would be given three successive words and be asked to add a fourth word that could actually occur in the sequence. Then another subject would be given the last three words, and would add a fourth again, and so on. The order of approximation is determined by number of words which a subject is given before he adds the next word. For zero-order approximations, words are chosen from a dictionary listing of words, all words with equal probabilities.

Lists of ten, twenty, thirty, and fifty words were constructed for each of several orders of approximation, and these lists were read to the subjects one at a time. After a subject had heard each list, he wrote down all of the words he could remember. The results of this free-recall method for two different lengths of list are given in Fig. 8.10. It is clear that the order of approximation to English does

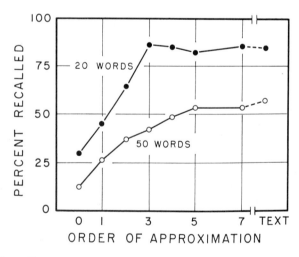

FIG. 8.10. Immediate recall of words as a function of the degree of approximation of the words to actual English. Lists of two different lengths were used as indicated. (After Miller and Selfridge, 1950.)

affect ability to learn the list. In constructing the first order lists, incidentally, these authors actually used the same words that were generated by subjects for the higher order approximations, but in a scrambled order. Thus any differences in learning for first or higher orders of approximation are clearly due to the sequences of the words, and not to the words themselves.

One point of considerable interest shown by the curves in Fig. 8.10 is that the curves flatten out at such relatively low orders of approximation. In other words, complete English text is not necessary to obtain good learning, but only a form of English in which near-word associations are familiar to the subject. For example, the actual list used by Miller and Selfridge for third-order approximation, twenty words, is "family was large dark animal came roaring down the middle of my friends love books passionately every kiss is fine." Such lists of words still constitute nonsense in the strictest sense, just as the words used by Miller, Bruner, and Postman (1954) are nonsense words. Because of these results, Miller and Selfridge argue that it is the short-range, familiar relationships between words, rather than meaning per se, which facilitates learning.

These results, which have been confirmed by van de Geer (1957) and by Sharp (1958), show that immediate recall for lists of fixed length is strongly affected by the similarity of the lists to actual English. A logical extension of this finding is that the immediate memory span for such lists of words would be greater, the more nearly the material resembles real English. Marks and Jack (1952) obtained immediate memory spans for several orders of approximation, with the results shown in Fig. 8.11. Here, as we would expect, the span increases with increased order of approximation, but unlike the previous results, the span for continuous text is considerably longer than for fifth order of approximation.

Thus, to some extent, at least, the effect of order of approximation depends on the method of learning and of scoring. For memory span, the words must be recalled perfectly and in the correct order. Part of the difference in these results may have been the requirement of correct order, but it seems likely that scoring for perfect reproduction may be of considerable importance also. In one part of Sharp's experiment, the number of perfect scores was recorded, and with this scoring method there was considerable improvement in recall from fifth to ninth orders of approximation. Thus the Miller and Selfridge results, with their suggestion of little improvement beyond about the fourth order of approximation, are probably due to the scoring method, and it is quite likely that complete meaning of the type obtained with

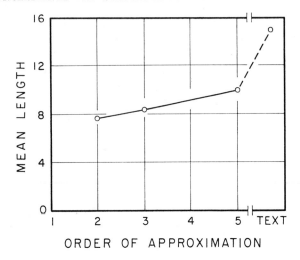

Fig. 8.11. Immediate memory span for words as a function of order of approximation to English. (Data from Marks and Jack, 1952.)

continuous text is important for total recall. Perhaps, then, meaning per se, not just short-range associations, does facilitate learning and recall.

Rubenstein and Aborn (1958) have extended the relationship between language uncertainty and learning ease by computing for several different passages a word prediction score, and showing that this prediction score is positively correlated with learning ease. They had subjects attempt to guess in sequence all the words of a given passage, and determined, for the entire passage, the mean number of correct guesses per word. Passages with low numbers of correct guesses were then assumed to have higher uncertainty per word than passages with high numbers of correct guesses. The correlation between learning and prediction was found to be .73. Thus ease of learning can be experimentally manipulated by varying the predictability of the sequences of words, or it can be found to vary with real English passages which differ in amount of predictability. In either case, the experiments are showing the same thing, namely, that learning, at least as measured by free recall, is closely related to the sequential predictability of the words in the passage learned.

Another experiment which shows that differences in order of approximation beyond about the fourth or fifth order are important is one by Moray and Taylor (1958). This experiment was not concerned with learning, but rather with distraction. Subjects were given simultaneously two sets of verbal material, one set presented separately to each ear. To one ear went continuous English prose. To the other ear went material with different orders of approximation to English. The subjects were required to read along (out loud) with the non-continuous material, and errors of omission and commission were recorded. With this technique, errors continued to decrease beyond the seventh order of approximation at least. Thus it is very clear that changes in order of approximation in English can be meaningful to quite high levels, and even though the uncertainty decreases more slowly with the higher orders of approximation, performance measures (including learning, with the appropriate technique) do show an effect of the decreased uncertainty.

Learning of artificial constraint

So far in this section we have discussed the effect of language redundancy on learning under conditions in which the redundancy of the actual language is used, and the experimental variable is simply the amount of this redundancy used. Experiments can be done, however, with quite artificial languages. Pollack (1953b), for example, has carried out a systematic investigation of the effects of number of alternatives per message element and number of elements, using sequences of consonants and numerals. He showed that the optimal length of message was relatively independent of the number of alternatives per element, and that total information transmission with such a method is maximum with the largest number of alternatives.

While Pollack used no sequential constraints in the sequences he generated, Miller (1958) did use such constraints with sequences of letters. He used four consonants ("g," "n," "s," and "x"), and generated essentially a series of nonsense words of length 4 to 7. Subjects were required to learn with a free-recall procedure lists of nine of these nonsense words. One of these lists had words (strings of letters) which were generated by random selection of the four consonants. The other list had words which were generated by sequentially constrained rules. These rules, for example, allowed the words to start only with "s" or "n," and always required that they finish with "g." Furthermore, a "g" could never occur except at the end of a word. Intermediate letters were constrained in slightly more complicated ways, but no letter could be followed by more than two other possibilities, and sometimes could be followed by only one. For example, a beginning "n" could be followed only by another "n," and only "s" or "x" could precede the final "g." Such an "x" in turn could be preceded only by an "s," although the "s" before the "g" could be preceded by "x"

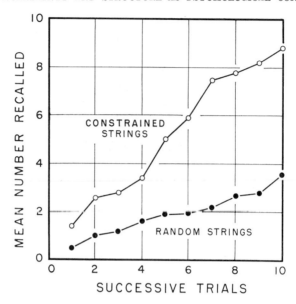

Fɪɢ. 8.12. Free recall of strings of letters when the strings have been generated randomly or by rules which produce sequential constraints. (After Miller, 1958.)

or "n." These rules were highly restrictive, and led to an uncertainty of slightly more than half a bit per letter on the average.

The learning results from these two kinds of lists are given in Fig. 8.12, which show that the constrained strings of letters were learned much more easily than were the random strings. However, if the rate of acquiring information is measured by taking into account the difference in uncertainty between the two lists, then the constrained strings are much less efficient ways of acquiring information.

Even earlier, Aborn and Rubenstein (1952) had carried out a similar experiment with sequences of nonsense words. Their subjects were required to learn messages about thirty-two words long, and these messages were composed of sequences of sixteen possible nonsense monosyllables. Different messages were generated by restricting the sequences of words that could occur. With a random sequence, the uncertainty per word was 4 bits. However, with one type of restriction, for example, two groups of words were used, and these groups alternated. Pairs of words always were chosen so that the first word came from one group of eight words, thus having an uncertainty of 3 bits. The next word of the pair was then chosen from a subgroup of four, depending on the particular first word of the pair. Thus the second

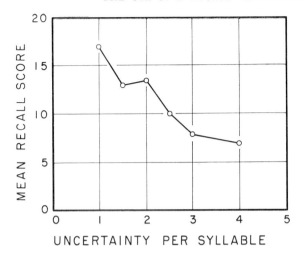

Fɪɢ. 8.13. Immediate recall for strings of nonsense syllables as a function of the uncertainty per syllable. Uncertainty was varied by constraining the order in which syllables could occur, as in a grammar. (Data from Aborn and Rubenstein, 1952.)

word of the pair had an uncertainty of 2 bits, giving an average uncertainty of 2.5 bits per word. Similar kinds of restrictive rules were used to give average uncertainties per word ranging from 1 to 4 bits.

In the Aborn and Rubenstein experiment, the learning results for immediate recall are given in Fig. 8.13, where once again it is clear that learning is made easier when constrained sequences of words are used. In a further related experiment, these same authors (Rubenstein and Aborn, 1954) confirmed this result, but found in addition that increased study time before recall increased the differences due to constraint of the word sequences. Again, the result shown is the one common to most experiments of this type: If the learning scores are corrected for information per word, then the more constrained series are less efficient. In other words, while it takes longer to learn random sequences, the amount of information gained per unit time is greater than for constrained sequences.

Some methodological problems

As has been necessary so often before, some serious consideration must be given to methodological problems of the use of redundancy in verbal learning. I have been using the more general term *constraint* in these sections to avoid, temporarily, the question of what constitutes redundancy in these verbal learning experiments. However, to understand the role of redundancy in verbal learning properly, we must consider the nature of the constraints used or generated in relation to the actual experimental task.

First, let us consider those experimental tasks in which a single passage must be learned by the subject, even though the single passage is itself rather long. In a really strict sense, we cannot talk about the redundancy of such a single passage, because there is no specified parent population of passages from which this one passage is drawn. When, however, the passage is generated by introducing sequential restrictions between the words which can be generated, we can consider such a passage to be redundant by exactly the same reasoning that we use to estimate the redundancy of a real language, namely by estimating the average uncertainty of the elements (letters or words) in the single passage. In such a case, the actual measurement of the amount of redundancy is a measurement of the redundancy of an assumed subset of passages which could have been generated, and from which this particular passage was drawn.

Clearly, in such single passage learning the redundant passages should be easier to learn, because each successive word is less uncertain and there is, in fact, less to learn. The clearest case of this type of learning task occurs in the Aborn and Rubenstein experiments involving sequences of nonsense syllables constrained sequentially by various rules. Here the subject is required to learn and reproduce a single passage, and his ability to learn it is going to be affected by his ability to learn and use the sequential rules by which the passage was generated. For example, if a simple alternation of two groups of words is used, as soon as the subject learns the nature of the alternation (in the actual experiments he was told exactly what the rules were) his recall accuracy must improve, if for no other reason than that his chance level of performance has improved.

Next, let us consider those experiments in which a set of words is used, with no constraining rules operating between the words within the set, but with constraining rules operating on the generation of the words themselves. The Miller experiment on constrained sequences of letters is such an experiment. In this type of experiment, the subject must learn, as part of a single set, several different sequences of letters, and the problem of total number of words to be learned becomes part and parcel of the definition of redundancy. Thus redundancy cannot be defined solely in terms of the letter constraints operating within the words, but must be defined in terms of the number of words in the set compared to the number which could have been generated.

In a strict sense, Miller's experiment is an experiment on the form of redundancy, not on the amount of it. He used constrained or random lists of words each containing the same number and lengths of words; with four alternative letters the total number of words in the parent population of words is the same. Therefore the redundancy is the same. The difference between the two lists of words lies not in how much selection (redundancy) was used, but rather in which *particular* words were selected.

To illustrate this point more completely, the actual letter strings used by Miller as one of his lists of *random* strings are: "gnsx," "nsgxn," "xgssn," "sxnngn," "xgsxxs," "gsxxgns," "nsxxgsg," "sgxggnn," and "xxgnsgg." In this list, all four letters actually occur in the initial position, but for any given initial letter only two letters can follow it, and in the case of an initial "n," only "s" follows it. Thus in this list as actually seen by the subject, there is considerable constraint operating within the list, or between the letters within the word. In fact, as we saw in Chapter Five, the total amount of constraint in the constrained and random lists is identical. Only the form of constraint is different.

The importance of either the amount or the form of redundancy depends to a considerable extent on the nature of the task. Miller used, as his primary task, free recall learning, and we have already noted that such learning is primarily related to the amount of internal constraint, and that the optimum form of such redundancy is that with high contingencies between letters. Miller's constrained lists provide exactly these needed high contingencies. If the task were one requiring discrimination, however, then this same form of redundancy would provide poorer performance. Miller notes that when subjects were required to search for a particular item from among lists of random or constrained strings of letters, the search time was considerably greater for his constrained strings, because (as he notes) they are more similar to each other. In other words, discriminability of the constrained lists was poorer than discriminability of the random lists, just as we saw when visual patterns were constructed with similar restrictive rules.

I mentioned in Chapter Five the work of Horowitz (1961). Here, the nature of the particular learning task is shown to be related to the effectiveness of redundancy. Horowitz used high- and low-similarity lists of nonsense words, and found that high similarity was best for free recall (thus confirming Miller's note on his constrained strings), but that low similarity was best for serial learning. Horowitz generated his low-similarity lists by increasing the number of different letters which were used for the high-similarity lists, thereby increasing the number of words which could have been generated. In other words, he increased total constraint, or the size of the parent population of words. By this process, he also increased redundancy. Thus, his low-similarity lists were more redundant than his high-similarity lists, and he obtained exactly the result we would expect: that free recall was better with low redundancy (high intralist similarity). And the opposite result was obtained with the serial learning method, a method which requires discrimination between words, although this result may be related to the form of redundancy as well as to its amount.

OPTIMUM FORM OF REDUNDANCY

As I have just been saying, the usefulness of redundancy to human subjects is not just a question of its amount, but also its form. It is in fact difficult, at times, not to feel that the form of the redundancy is a more critical factor than its amount. This question has been of concern to communication engineers, who have done considerable work in determining optimum methods of coding for communication in noise. It seems likely that the problem is even more important to psychologists.

The data of Miller on redundant strings of letters suggest, insofar as his experiment is one on form of redundancy rather than amount, that in language high correlation between pairs of letters is more useful than the more complicated forms of constraint involving higher-order interactions. As we noted, his two types of list really differ only in form of redundancy, and the major difference is the complexity of the constraining rules for his "random" lists. For tasks other than free-recall learning, however, the optimum form of redundancy may be different.

For auditory communication in noise Pollack (1958) has provided some evidence that mere repetition of a word is not an efficient form of redundancy. He compared two message procedures, one of which he calls repetition, and the other network selection. Repetition was exactly what the word suggests. If the word to be heard in noise was "firefly," the speaker simply repeated the same word three times in succession. For the network selection procedure, the process was somewhat more complicated. Three words were spoken in succession, the final word being the one to be recorded by the listener. The first word could be one of two: "cargo" or "oxcart," for example. Each of these words could itself be followed by two others, and each of the second words could then be followed by two others. Thus each word spoken narrowed the final possibilities down by one half, and the three words in succession carried three bits of information. A typical sequence here might be "cargo duckpond firefly," in which the last word was the one to be recorded. In essence, the function of the earlier words was simply to decrease the set of possible words which could come later, and had much the same effect as a restriction of vocabulary size has in improving accuracy.

Pollack's results showed unambiguously that the network selection procedure was considerably superior to simple repetition. The reason is perhaps obvious, namely that correlation of errors is minimized with the successive selection procedure. For whatever reasons a word is not heard correctly the first time, those same reasons will continue to exist to some extent on successive repetitions, and the best way to avoid error repetition is to use an entirely different word. In a list of eight possible words, for example, the subject may not be sure whether the correct word is "firefly" or "vampire," but if he knows that "vampire" may be preceded by "oxcart" and "starlight," and that "firefly" may be preceded by "cargo" and "duckpond," then he can determine which of the final words is the correct one if he has heard either of the preceding words correctly. If "firefly" is simply repeated, the confusion between "firefly" and "vampire" may also be repeated.

In an extension of the principle of independent successive words, Pollack (1959b) has also shown that even when repetition is used, accuracy of perception of words in noise is better if the successive repetitions are as independent as possible. He found that if the word is repeated by the speaker's actually repeating the word in a continuous noise, perception was better than when the first spoken word and the noise were recorded, and the recording was then simply played back to obtain the repetition. When the recording is used, of course, whatever accidental factors in the speech and the noise occurred once to hinder perception will occur again in exactly the same fashion. When independent speech is used, with independent noise, then accidental factors can still occur to hinder perception, but they will not be the same factors as occurred on the first presentation. Thus redundancy should be provided in such a way as to minimize correlation of error.

The optimum form of language redundancy depends on the particular task required of the human in his use of the language. Where the critical aspect of a task is discrimination between words, or between letters, then each element should convey as much information as possible independently of all of the other elements. If two elements become completely correlated, then to perceive these two elements is no better than to perceive one, and this form of redundancy is inefficient. Thus if we were to generate a series of words with a given amount of redundancy, and wanted optimum form of redundancy, we would minimize correlations between pairs of letter elements; that is, we would try to keep the contingencies as low as possible. The redundancy would be put in the form of interactions.

If, on the other hand, our intent is to generate a series of words which can be most easily memorized, or whose spellings can most easily be learned, we would probably want to use high correlations between pairs of letters. The difference we are discussing is, of course, the difference between internal and external constraint. In any language system, both must be learned. However, the ideal form of redundancy for each is not the best for the other since for external constraint we want high discriminability (calling for low contingent uncertainties between pairs of letters), but for internal constraint we want ease of learning the structure, and here the more easily perceived and learned simple contingencies are most useful.

Miller's constrained strings of letters are easier to learn to spell or to free recall, while his random strings are easier to discriminate. His constrained strings have high contingencies between letters, while his random strings have lower contingencies. This difference, and its relation to type of learning or discrimination task is quite general, as we can see by referring back to our discussion of form of redundancy in Chapter Five. Suppose we generate strings of letters from the A and from the C sets of patterns from Table 5.2. We might have,

A: AAAA, ABBA, BABB, BBAB

and

C: AAAA, ABBB, BAAA, BBBB.

These two lists of strings of letters have exactly the same amount of redundancy, since each set of four is selected from sixteen possible strings, but the C list has higher pair contingencies than does the A list. I showed in Chapter Five that the C list is poorer for discrimination purposes, but it seems fairly obvious that it is easier to learn, if by "learn" we mean remember the actual sequences of letters—learning the internal constraint. (A rather casual free-recall experiment, with my wife as the subject, showed one-trial learning for the C list, and three-trial learning for the A list.)

COMMENTARY

The material discussed in this chapter is really concerned with two basically different problems, problems which correspond to the distinction I made in Chapter Five between signification and structure. To refresh ourselves, signification refers to the actual relational rules which exist for symbols, and signification can exist for either internal or external structures. Thus *dog* in one language system can signify *chien* in another language system; but *dog* can also signify all the words which commonly occur in association with it in English itself. Thus meaning, in the signification sense, is all of the words which are related to a given word. Structure, on the other hand, refers to the total amount of relatedness existing in an entire closed system of symbols.

Most of the experiments reported in this chapter have been concerned with the extent to which the actual relational rules of printed English are understood by the average person, and thus affect his performance. The extent to which these relational rules can affect performance is naturally a function of the amount of structure which exists in the stimulus material, since an amount of structure is prerequisite to the existence of particular relational rules. Thus the amount of structure or redundancy in English can affect performance in many different ways, but its effect, as usually measured, depends on prior learning and familiarity with the particular relational or signification rules of the language.

In its simplest form, we have seen that subjects can directly replace missing elements in language, either letters or words. Their ability to do so obviously depends on two factors: First, there must exist in the stimulus material an amount of structure or redundancy; and second, the subject must know the particular signification rules which are operative with the given amount of structure. Thus that printed English is redundant is in itself no guarantee that a subject can replace the missing letter in "sav_d." He must know the particular signification rule for this set of letters, and must make use of his knowledge to insert the missing "e."

The more the stimulus material allows the subject to make use of his familiarity with the signification rules of English, the more accurate will his performance be. In similar fashion, the ability of a subject to recognize a word correctly will depend on the extent to which the presented word or sequence of letters resembles actual English, so that once again he can make use of his prior familiarity with the language.

The chief value of these experiments is in demonstrating that humans do understand the nature of their own language, and that their understanding affects performance involving verbal stimuli and even responses. However, these experiments fail, in large part, to attack the more fundamental problem, which is to determine the value and role of redundancy (as an amount and as a form) in perception and learning. To illustrate this failure, let us suppose that we do an experiment in which we construct two sets of words and require free-recall learning of these two sets. One set consists of actual English words; the other set consists of words formed at random by taking all of the letters from the first set of words, placing them in a hat, and drawing them out at random. We, of course, make sure to match the two lists for total number of words and for lengths of words.

Now it is obvious that English speaking subjects will learn, by free recall, the set of actual English words much faster than the set of nonsense words. We might even be tempted to say that we have demonstrated that redundant words are learned more easily than non-redundant words, but this seductive conclusion is quite wrong. In actuality, these two sets of words have exactly the same amount of redundancy. We have only demonstrated that familiar words are easier to learn than unfamiliar ones, and have demonstrated absolutely nothing about the role of redundancy in free-recall learning.

To talk about the effect of amount of redundancy, or amount of structure, we must do something quite different from what is required to demonstrate that subjects are familiar with the internal significations of the language. In Chapter Five I stated that redundancy should make free-recall learning more difficult, but this result is not intuitively expected until we are very clear what increasing the amount of redundancy does to a list of words to be learned by free recall. Perhaps the best way of looking at this problem is to examine again some methods of creating redundancy.

Suppose that we generate eight different "words" by using three-letter words with two possible letters in each position. Our complete set of eight words is: AAA, AAB, ABA, ABB, BAA, BAB, BBA, and BBB. This list of words is completely nonredundant, since the list includes all the words that could be generated. Now if we decide to make these words redundant, we do so simply by increasing the number of letters per word. We might use the words: AAAAA, AABAB, ABABB, ABBBA, BAAAA, BABAB, BBABA, and BBBBB. This list of words has 2 bits of redundancy in it, which we have achieved by increasing the maximum possible uncertainty of the words to 5 bits, not by decreasing the actual word uncertainty. Now if we compare the rate of learning of these two lists of words, with free recall, it seems fairly obvious that the second list will be more difficult to learn than the first. It will be more difficult because there is, in fact, more to be learned. Discrimination learning will not be particularly aided with the redundant words because the total external constraint has not been changed. In fact, evidence presented earlier suggests that the redundancy will aid discrimination only when there is some need for it.

This example is a clear-cut case of the effect of amount of redundancy on verbal learning, and it should make free recall more difficult. In this example the stimulus uncertainty of the two lists has been kept constant, so that there is no ambiguity about the fact that the second list is more redundant than the first.

It is possible to maintain the same stimulus uncertainty while increasing redundancy in still another way, and that is by increasing the number of alternatives for each letter position. Thus we can have lists with the same number of words, and with the same number of letters per word, but with different numbers of possible letters per letter position. For example, we can form eight words from three letters: ABC, ABA, ACB, BAC, BCA, BAB, CCA, and CBC. This list of words has the same stimulus uncertainty (external constraint) as the first list, but, again, there is greater redundancy, because the number of possible words is twenty-seven, rather than just eight. And again it seems certain that this redundant list will be more difficult to learn by free recall.

Form of redundancy is still another matter. When experimental word lists have the same number of words, the same number of letters per word, and the same number of alternative letters per position, then any differences between these word lists are entirely differences in the form, not the amount, of redundancy. In this regard, the distinctions made in Chapter Five are almost certainly valid here. When learning of the internal structure is required, then the optimum form of redundancy will be that which maximizes the contingent uncertainties between the pairs of letters. Thus, in free-recall learning, we want the constraints to consist of high probabilities of particular pair combinations, whereas, for discrimination purposes, the pair contingencies should be minimized.

There are, to my knowledge, no experiments which have deliberately kept stimulus uncertainty constant while changing systematically the amount of redundancy, except for the Horowitz experiment on intralist similarity. Thus we have no direct evidence concerning the effect of amount of redundancy on learning, and cannot be positive that my expectations concerning its effect are valid. There are some experiments, particularly the Miller experiment, however, which have shown that my expectations with respect to the effect of form of redundancy are valid.

The expectation that free-recall learning should be more difficult with redundant stimulus words seems at first glance to be at variance with the results of experiments on learning of single passages, where sequential constraints definitely make the material easier to learn. Here, however, we have a very tricky problem that is much like the problem of defining the redundancy of a unique pattern, discussed in Chapter Six. When a single passage is to be learned, then the sequential constraints rather literally reduce successive word uncertainty, so that clearly there is less to be learned. The effect of such constraints is the same as if in free-recall learning of a set of words we reduce the uncertainty per word. Such a reduction, with the length of the list held constant, is equivalent to a decrease of redundancy, since we decrease the total number of words from which the list was drawn, thus decreasing total constraint and redundancy. For the single passage problem, when sequential constraints are introduced, we do much the same thing, since we reduce the total number of passages which can be formed, and thus reduce redundancy. So perhaps the two problems are not so different after all.

SUMMARY

Human subjects are aware of the particular nature of the redundancy in their language, and this awareness can be demonstrated in a number of ways. Subjects are able, for example, to produce distributions of letters and use words in proportion to their actual occurrence in English. In addition, recognition accuracy of words is affected by the probability of occurrence of the words in English, even though there is some indication that the effect is due primarily to the frequency with which subjects use words rather than to a direct perceptual effect.

Knowledge of sequential constraints can also be demonstrated by direct performance of subjects. They can replace missing letters or words in sequences of letters or words with considerable accuracy, and their accuracy in such a task corresponds well with the amount of predictability or constraint available in the presented stimulus materials. Thus replacement of deleted letters in the middle of random sequences is better than replacement at the ends of such sequences.

Similarly, recognition accuracy for letters in words depends on the position of the letters in words. The high-information end letters are recognized more quickly, but reversal of such letters affects recognition accuracy more than does reversal of the low-information middle letters.

Several experiments on learning have shown that learning is better whes the patterns of letters or words correspond to those in actual English. Furthermore, the introduction of artificial sequential constraints improves the learning of single passages.

There is little research directly relevant to the question of effect of amount of redundancy on the learning of lists of words, although there are experiments relevant to the question of the form of redundancy. We have, however, every reason to expect that redundancy should make free-recall learning more difficult, and one experiment indirectly confirms this expectation. Form of redundancy may be as important a factor in free-recall learning as amount, and here the available results confirm our expectations that high contingencies between letter pairs should aid free-recall learning.

It is not entirely clear whether discrimination-learning tasks, such as serial learning, are aided by increased redundancy, but there is some suggestion that such learning is improved.

CHAPTER NINE

Other Sequential Behavior

OUR DISCUSSION IN CHAPTER EIGHT makes clear that humans do learn and use sequential characteristics of the language. Language is certainly one of the most important behavior media, and one which involves fairly complicated sequential constraints which must be understood if the language is used either as a stimulus or as a response. However, there are many other forms of behavior which involve sequences of stimuli and/or responses as well. In fact it is tempting to say that there is no aspect of human behavior which does not involve sequential characteristics. Actually, of course, there are many behavioral situations in which the sequential nature of the behavior is of minor importance and thus can safely be ignored. Nevertheless, I feel that investigation of temporal or sequential aspects of behavior has not received the attention it deserves.

Our experimental literature is rather limited in discussions of sequential aspects of behavior. There are essentially just two areas of research which have been explicitly concerned with sequential problems, and these are the problem areas we will discuss. The first of these has to do with the learning of sequential characteristics of stimulus series; and the second has to do with those studies of perceptual-motor skills which have emphasized continuous movement, or tracking behavior.

LEARNING OF SEQUENTIAL DEPENDENCIES

There are many experiments dealing with the ability of humans to respond to a series of events which occur on a probability basis only.

284

For example, a subject may be asked to guess the outcome of the next stimulus occurrence by stating which of two alternative stimuli he thinks will occur. In order to guess better than chance, the subject must first learn something about the probabilities of the alternative outcomes or stimuli. In most such experiments, the only concern has been with the subject's ability to learn (and reproduce with his responses) the average probability with which the various outcomes occur. Some few experiments, however, have been concerned with the sequential dependencies of the response series, or have deliberately introduced sequential dependencies into the stimulus series itself.

One of the first experiments of this sort was done by Hake and Hyman (1953). In their experiment, subjects were required to guess which of two stimuli would occur. The experimental variables included not only the average probability of occurrence of each stimulus but also conditional probabilities, so that the probability of occurrence of a given stimulus depended on which stimulus had last occurred. Data for two of their experimental conditions are given in Fig. 9.1. For each of these conditions the overall probability of an H (one of their two stimulus symbols) was .50, and on the average the subjects gave H responses just about half the time, as expected. But for the top curve in this figure, the conditional probability of an H following an H was .75, while the same conditional probability for the lower curve

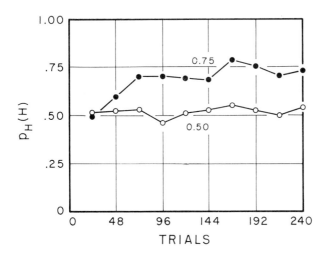

Fig. 9.1. Sequentially dependent response probabilities as a function of learning trials for two different stimulus sequential probabilities, as indicated in the graph. (After Hake and Hyman, 1953.)

was .50. The conditional probabilities plotted are those of the subjects' responses, and it is quite evident that not only are the first order probabilities matched, but also the conditional probabilities.

These results, which have since been confirmed in more detail by Anderson (1960), show that subjects can learn at least these simple sequential dependencies in a fairly short time. Both the results plotted in Fig. 9.1 and Anderson's results show that the conditional probabilities are matched quite accurately after about fifty trials. With language, of course, there is usually considerable overlearning by the time a psychologist gets the adult human into his experiment, but in these probability experiments no particular prior experience with stimuli of this sort is likely. Thus we can assume that the learning actually takes place within the period of the experiment.

Hake and Hyman have argued that there is some question as to whether the subjects actually learn the statistical properties of the sequence. They feel that the subject primarily responds in terms of his successes in guessing over very short runs, and that the overall result that the subjects' conditional probabilities match those of the stimulus series is a somewhat incidental effect due to changed probabilities of being correct for certain short run patterns of guesses. Whether or not subjects actually do learn the overall statistical structure is not a question we can answer now, but we do know that learning (at least of a sort) occurs when what must be learned are sequential dependencies. Furthermore, such learning can occur when the probabilities are made dependent on the response, rather than having an independent set of stimulus probabilities. Shelly (1958), for example, has shown that in a four-choice learning problem, subjects can learn alternation patterns when they are reinforced for not repeating a response.

These experiments have dealt primarily with rather simple conditional probabilities, in which the probability of a given stimulus is dependent only on the preceding stimulus. Data from Bennett, Fitts, and Noble (1954) suggest that dependencies operating over more than pairs of stimuli are much more difficult for subjects to learn. In this experiment, subjects were required to predict events when five alternative stimuli were used. In one experiment, the stimulus series was generated so that only ten of the possible twenty-five sequential pairs of stimuli occurred, and with these stimulus series subjects were able to produce much better than chance performance. But in another experiment, where the occurrence of a given stimulus depended on two preceding stimuli, little or no learning occurred.

Thus there is some meager evidence that learning of statistical characteristics of sequential events is not very good when the response must depend on more than just one preceding stimulus. This point is of some importance to us, in helping to understand why verbal learning (free recall, in which the words on a list must be learned) seems to be best when the internal constraint is composed primarily of simple contingent uncertainties. Learning of first-order conditional probabilities involves only the learning of contingent uncertainties, while learning dependencies extending over longer lengths may involve both contingencies and interaction terms, or could even involve just interaction terms. We do not know what uncertainty terms were involved in the Bennett, Fitts, and Noble experiment, but it would be interesting to determine whether such learning depends on the exact nature or form of the sequential constraints.

When we consider the rather complex nature of the sequential dependencies involved in normal language, it is more than a little surprising that subjects seem to be able to learn only such short sequence lengths. That such poor learning is not restricted to situations in which only probabilities can be learned is shown by Galanter and Smith (1958), who required subjects to learn repeated sequences (sequences which repeated themselves exactly after a fixed number of trials), so that the series was completely predictable. In their data, for example, a five-unit sequence of 01001 required a mean of 125 trials, or 25 complete cycles of the pattern, before it was learned. While median scores were somewhat lower, this still seems like very slow learning. Even so, such perfectly predictable sequences are learned much more rapidly than statistically predictable sequences, since Bruner, Wallach, and Galanter (1959) showed that when occasional errors were introduced into the fixed sequences, learning was much slower. Such occasional errors, of course, essentially change the sequence from one which is completely repetitive to one which simply has probabilistic sequential dependencies.

There are at least two possible reasons for this apparent difficulty of subjects to learn reasonably complicated and long sequences of stimuli—a difficulty which seems at variance with the obvious fact that humans do learn such statistical sequences in the language they use. One of these reasons has to do with the way experiments are ordinarily run compared to the way in which we actually learn the language. Usually the subject in the experiment is required to start guessing the next stimulus in the sequence at the beginning of the experiment. The consequence of this is that he is trying to perceive both the statistical structure of the stimulus sequence and the outcome of his own guesses. Thus there is a statistical structure to his sequence of successes and failures as well as a structure to the stimulus series itself. In real life we do not learn the language by immediately trying to guess letter or word sequences; rather, we listen, or look, at the language as it exists. Such passive observing may be a far more effective way of learning internal structure of sequences than active interference in the sequence.

This possibility is suggested by the results of another aspect of the Bruner, Wallach, and Galanter experiment. They required some of their subjects simply to observe the first three stimuli in the sequence, and not to begin responding (guessing) until the fourth stimulus was due. Since these authors were using a three-unit cycle, their subjects saw one complete stimulus cycle before responding, and they learned the sequential pattern somewhat faster than did the subjects who began responding immediately. Thus even this small amount of passive observing aided learning of the structure of the sequence.

The other possible reason for this apparent difficulty of sequence learning has to do with whether in real life we ever really learn time patterns. When we read a printed page we do not carefully expose one letter, or even one word or phrase, at a time—and most certainly we do not immediately try to predict the next letter or word. Rather, we see an entire sequence of letters and words—as a space pattern, not as a time pattern. There is little, if any, need for our learning the statistical structure of the printed language as a time pattern, if indeed it is easier to learn it as a space pattern. It is true that the spoken language occurs as a time pattern, but with only a reasonable memory we can effectively convert it into a space pattern. In fact, this may be the real advantage of passive observing of a time sequence, compared to active participation in the sequence—that it is easier to use memory to perceive the time pattern as a static space pattern.

There is little need to discuss this problem further, because we have so very little data to go on. There is little question that we have a lot more to learn about this problem than we already know.

PERCEPTUAL-MOTOR SKILLS

There are many forms of behavior in which the sequential aspects of either the stimuli or the responses are important, and particularly where the stimulus sequence involves some degree and form of redundancy. In some cases, the redundancy in the stimulus series need not be learned per se, but it can still affect perceptual performance of a related nature. For example, Senders and Cohen (1955) have shown that the accuracy of dial reading increases with repeated presentations of the same dial position (that is, when the dial positions are completely redundant). These authors used as many as ten consecutive identical dial positions, and accuracy of reading continued to improve over most of the trials.

In a later experiment, Cohen and Senders (1958) showed that dial reading was more accurate when the dial positions changed in a regular ascending or descending order rather than in a random order. At first glance this result may appear to have been obvious, since with repeated exposures of the same stimulus positions subjects can easily perceive the identity of position. It must be remembered, however, that the dial readings improved when scored against true position. If subjects simply perceived that the positions were identical, they might well just repeat the response previously made. Subjects, however, change their response in the direction of the true position.

Maximum information rates

Tasks in which sequential aspects of the stimulus and response are most important, however, are those tasks which require a continued motor response to a continued series of stimuli. These tasks usually go under the name of psycho-motor skills, or perceptual-motor skills. Various attempts have been made to determine the upper information rate at which humans can carry out continuous tasks of this sort. Quastler and Wulff (1955), for example, have determined information transmission rates of 22 to 24 bits per second for such tasks as piano playing and typewriting. Quastler (1955) cites studies which suggest that this maximum rate may be as high as 30 bits per second for other tasks.

If there were a single figure which was relatively independent of experimental conditions, then such a figure would be quite valuable in establishing a limiting condition for human performance, and we could use this value as a standard against which to compare performance in other experimental situations. The information rates which have been obtained experimentally, however, show considerable variation, and as I have pointed out before it does not seem too profitable to be concerned with establishing limiting values. Klemmer and Muller (1953), for example, obtained maximum rates of just slightly greater than 10 bits per second with a task in which keys were pressed in response to varying light patterns, and this value was the maximum they obtained under a variety of experimental procedures.

It does not seem too profitable, therefore, to look for single figures, or constants of performance. Rather, it would seem somewhat more profitable to look for patterns of performance as a function of experimental variables, particularly variables of an informational nature. Our main concern here will be to look at sequential aspects of the task.

Motor discrimination

In most human experiments, particularly those in which there are discrimination limits, we usually think of the perceptual side of the problem as providing the limiting factor, and normally arrange our experiment so that motor discrimination is very good, at least as compared to the perceptual discrimination. Information concepts, however, are as applicable to the problems of motor discrimination as they are to perceptual discrimination, and may in any task provide the limiting factor.

Fitts (1954) has most clearly shown the relevance of information concepts to the study of motor skills. He carried out a series of experiments in which the precision of the required manual movement and placement was the critical experimental variable. In one task, subjects were required to tap two plates back and forth, and the width of the two plates was varied from one condition to another. In another task, subjects were required to transfer discs from one pin to another, and the experimental variable was the size of the hole in the disc. In a third task, subjects were required to transfer pins from one set of holes to another, and the size of the holes with respect to the size of the pins was the experimental variable. In all of these experiments, the total amount of movement was also systematically varied.

Fitts used the logarithm of the ratio of the tolerance for the final placement to the total amplitude of movement as an index of amount of information required per response, and used the average time per response in combination with the uncertainty per response to determine information transmitted per second. As a first approximation, Fitts showed that information transmission is approximately constant for these various experimental conditions. Thus information output is a more meaningful measure than average accuracy or time alone.

Even here, however, the meaningfulness of reducing a total motor task to single information concepts is of only first-order value. Annett, Golby, and Kay (1958) carried out a more detailed analysis of the peg-transferring task, and came to the conclusion that only the final positioning movements showed any variation due to the relative difficulty of the task, and that the gross positioning movements are relatively unaffected by the precision required for the final movement. They found that information transmission rates were relatively constant when based on the individual movement elements, but were not so when based on total movement times. Thus while information concepts may be valuable in the study of motor skills, it seems unlikely that any single measure of performance in informational terms can be very successful.

Perceptual anticipation, or advance information

The brief discussions of maximum information rates and motor discrimination have been given somewhat for purposes of completeness, but more importantly as contrasting background for the main theme of this chapter. Information concepts can be used to determine maximum rates of performance, or speed of response can itself be used as a dependent variable. However, the essence of a perceptual-motor task lies in the required coordination of two series—a stimulus series and the corresponding response series. It is not enough to know that a response can be carried out at a particular rate; rather, we are primarily interested in the extent to which a human can accurately follow a predetermined series of stimuli, stimuli whose time and amplitude characteristics are both important.

There is, of course, a large literature on factors affecting accuracy of "tracking" behavior, which is what we are now talking about. We shall not attempt any major discussion of most of this work, because much of it is quite outside the realm of information concepts. We do, however, want to discuss enough work to establish the relevance of some information concepts to these problems.

Of considerable importance is the role of anticipation or prediction of the stimulus series in carrying out a well-coordinated response to the series. Leonard (1954) has shown that even with random sequences of stimuli, performance can be improved if the subject is given advance information concerning the next stimulus. In his experiment, the stimulus was one of five lights, and the subject had to touch a corresponding disc with a stylus. After the correct disc had been touched for each stimulus, the subject then had to touch a center disc, followed by the next discriminative response, and so on. Thus there was always a neutral response before each discriminative response. In one condition, the next light came on only after the center disc was touched, while in a second condition, the next light came on as soon as the correct disc had been touched and before the center disc was touched. Thus in this latter condition, the subject knew what his next discriminative response was to be before touching the center disc; he had advance information. Under this condition, the subjects were able to respond substantially faster. Thus the total sequence of actions was carried out faster when the subject was responding behind the stimulus, or alternatively, when he was able to anticipate his response, by knowing in advance of the required response what the designated stimulus was.

Poulton (1957b,c) has emphasized the importance of perceptual anticipation and prediction in skilled movements, and has himself carried out several experiments relevant to this problem. He has shown (Poulton, 1952a), for example, that pursuit tracking is more accurate than compensatory tracking (with simple harmonic courses, and handwheel tracking), and he argues that the primary difference lies in the degree to which the target course can be predicted. In pursuit tracking, two pointers are seen—one representing the stimulus course and the other representing the response course. Thus with such a display the subject has a clear picture of the stimulus course alone, and can easily anticipate its future position. With the compensatory display, on the other hand, the indicator simply shows the discrepancy between stimulus position and response position, and does not show in an uncomplicated manner the stimulus course alone. Poulton also showed that the value of anticipation was greater with a simple harmonic course—that is, a highly redundant course.[1]

Related to this finding is another experiment (Poulton, 1957a) in which either the input or the output display was blanked out for short periods of time. Thus the information the subject received about the stimulus or about the response was less than maximum. The results of this experiment showed that loss of stimulus information was more deleterious than loss of response information, thus confirming the importance of perceptual anticipation. In still another experiment, Poulton (1957b) showed that the more predictable a course is, the more accurately it can be responded to when the target course is partly obscured visually.

In another experiment, carried out at about the same time, Conklin (1957) delayed the display of response information in both pursuit and compensatory displays, with both random and predictable target courses. His main findings completely support the importance of anticipation in perceptual-motor skills, in that he found delay much

---

[1] It is interesting that perception of the stimulus sequence alone appears to be necessary for effective tracking as well as for simple learning of stimulus sequences, as we saw above. Compensatory tracking produces a perceived sequence in which the stimulus series is contaminated by the response, just as required responding in the guessing experiments produces a contamination of the stimulus sequence as perceived by the subject. Passive observing of a stimulus sequence may well be of real value to the subject.

more deleterious with compensatory tracking, which allows little perceptual anticipation; in addition, delay was completely destructive of accuracy with random target courses, which allow essentially no anticipation.

Thus, we can assert with little hesitation that tracking performance will be better under experimental conditions which permit or provide advance information or perceptual anticipation. Such conditions may involve the type of display itself, since if a stimulus or target course is literally shown in advance of the required response, advance information is given. However, more important for our consideration is the fact that stimulus redundancy itself makes perceptual anticipation possible. With completely random sequences, the subject who is tracking can have no advance information, and the only way he can know what his response is to be before actually making it is to respond after the stimulus has occurred. With redundant stimuli, however, he can project the target course into the future on the basis of the past history of the course, and thus have advance information about the next target position.

REDUNDANCY AND RESPONSE LAG

The human performing a tracking task needs to know what any particular response is going to be in advance of actually making that response, for optimum performance. As we have seen, there are basically two different ways in which a person can obtain such advance information.

The first of these is the obvious one. The subject in an experiment is directly given information about the next stimulus before the time which is specified for him to make a response. Such advance information can be provided in a variety of ways. A target course may, for example, be exposed in advance of the time at which response is required by presenting to the subject something like a 1- or 2-second portion of the stimulus course, with instructions to respond to the middle of the exposed course. On the other hand, if only the instantaneous—or discrete—stimulus is presented, this stimulus may be known well in advance if the target course is a highly predictable course. Thus redundancy is one means by which advance information may be obtained also.

The second way in which a person can obtain information in advance of his response is to provide it himself by delaying his response until sometime after the particular stimulus to which he is responding has occurred. Thus at any given instant the subject in a tracking experiment may be responding to an item or particular stimulus which occurred one, two, or more time units before. The net effect of such a response lag, or delay, is that the subject is responding at all times to a stimulus which occurred some time ago, while he is looking at the stimulus which defines a response which he will make at some time in the future. By delaying his response, then, the subject obtains what is for him advance information. Insofar as he is able to respond more accurately by delaying his response, we would expect a subject in an experiment to delay his response.

It would seem from this discussion that there should be little reason for a subject to delay his response, or produce a response lag, if he has a redundant stimulus series, since if the series is sufficiently redundant he has advance information from the series itself, and does not need to delay his response in order to obtain it. On closer examination of the problem, however, we shall see that with some redundant series there is still a good reason for the subject to delay his response, because the same factors which make it possible for him to have advance information from the redundancy make it possible for him to have even more information if he delays his response.

Sequential reproduction or time matching

Before discussing this problem further, we might do well to consider the nature of the task which the usual subject has in tracking a stimulus sequence. Ordinarily there are two requirements which the subject must satisfy, and to a certain extent these two requirements are in contradiction to each other.

The first of these requirements is that the subject reproduce the actual sequence of stimuli as accurately as possible, maintaining the same time relations within the sequence as originally existed. A telegrapher taking code, for example, is expected to reproduce the original message, and while time relations between successive letters are not required, it is required that the actual sequence of original letters be preserved in the telegrapher's reproduction. In such a task, there is no penalty normally attached to the telegrapher who lags behind the transmitted message by several letters, or even as much as half a minute. If the telegrapher can produce copy more accurately by lagging half a minute than by trying to keep up with each letter, then he is permitted to lag. He certainly should be encouraged to lag if his accuracy can be improved by doing so.

The other requirement is that the subject reproduce or match a stimulus accurately in time. In compensatory tracking, for instance, the display which the subject sees is the instantaneous discrepancy between the stimulus value and the response value. Similarly, when we drive an automobile down a winding road, we must match the car's course to the actual road with precise time relations. It is not satisfactory to reproduce, with the car's course, the exact course of the road, unless the two courses coincide in time.

Obviously if a person is required to carry out a tracking task in which both a time matching and a reproduction criterion exist, he will be in some conflict, since if he lags to allow greater reproductive accuracy he will decrease the accuracy of his time matching. On the other hand, if he attempts to maintain accurate time matching, then his reproductive accuracy must suffer. Very few tracking tasks emphasize just one of these criteria to the complete exclusion of the other, but many tracking tasks clearly make one aspect of the problem more important than the other. The telegrapher, for example, wants to produce his copy as quickly as possible after the actual transmission, if for no other reason than that he might forget it if he doesn't. However, there is no great urgency in a time sense, and he certainly will lag whenever it will aid his reproduction accuracy to do so. The man driving down a very winding road, however, must match his course to the road in a time sense, even if he loses some reproduction accuracy in the process. Thus it is permissible to smooth out the course by occasionally crossing the middle line, as long as his course coincides in time with the road's course. Unlike the telegraph operator, however, the driver of a car may not lag in his response, even for half a second, in order to increase his reproduction accuracy, because the consequences of the lag are far greater than the consequences of a slight decrease in reproduction accuracy.

Thus most tracking tasks, whether real life or laboratory, involve both a time requirement and an accuracy of reproduction requirement, and the human tracker will ordinarily make some compromise between these two requirements, the degree of compromise being determined by the relative importance of the two requirements. If the time-matching requirement is paramount, then no compromise will be made. On the other hand, if the time requirement is not an absolute requirement, then we can expect the operator to introduce some lag into his response. He will not, however, introduce such a lag unless he expects to gain in accuracy of reproduction.

Our problem for the moment is to determine the circumstances which should make it advantageous for a human tracker to lag in his response. We have already seen that some lag is necessary to allow perceptual anticipation, so that the tracker knows what his response is going to be in advance of his actually making the response. There is an additional consideration, however, and that has to do with the accuracy of the anticipation. If a response lag can provide the tracker with more accurate information about the stimulus course or sequence, then the tracker will produce a response lag. And it is in this connection that redundancy plays a role.

Effect of time lag on constraint

We noted above that redundancy of a stimulus sequence is one means by which a tracker can obtain advance information about the stimulus course, so that the tracker can anticipate his response. It might seem, therefore, that with redundant stimulus sequences there should be little reason for the tracker to delay his response, since if the redundancy itself gives him advance information, he does not need to produce a response delay in order to obtain the equivalent of perceptual anticipation. The redundancy which can give the tracker advance information, however, can give him even more accurate information if he delays his response. Thus the same factor which seems to make a response lag unnecessary in fact makes it profitable for the tracker to delay his response, since by delaying it he can maximize his obtained information.

The advantage of a delayed response is due to the fact that the middle of a long sequence of stimulus values is, with a redundant sequence, more predictable than is the end of a sequence of the same length. This factor has already been mentioned in connection with the redundancy of printed English, and is responsible for the bow-shaped curves shown in Figs. 8.5 and 8.6, in which it is shown that missing middle letters are more easily reinserted than are end letters. In a similar fashion, if a tracker responding to a redundant stimulus sequence delays his response, he will at any instant be responding to a stimulus which is in the middle of a sequence of stimuli, while if he responds to the last stimulus presented he will be responding to the end of a stimulus sequence. If he has any need for improving his accuracy of perception, he will tend to delay his response in order to obtain the better predictability, or constraint, which the entire sequence has on the middle stimulus.

The exact amount of advantage which can be gained from such a delay, as well as the amount of delay which will give the maximum advantage, depend on the particular nature of the redundancy. We can, nevertheless, see some general relations between delay and redundancy which must exist by considering certain limiting conditions. Figure 9.2 illustrates, in a most general way, the relative advantage of prediction of middle stimuli compared to prediction of end stimuli

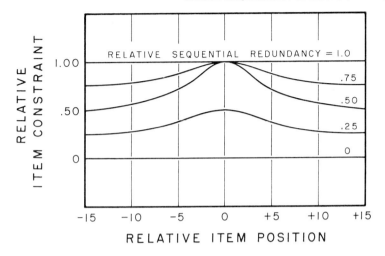

FIG. 9.2. Relative constraint per item as a function of the item position in a sequence, for different relative amounts of sequential redundancy. Sequential redundancy is the constraint on the last letter of a long sequence. An item at the 0 position is in the middle of a long sequence, and other item positions are before or after this middle position. The exact shapes of such curves would depend on the particular uncertainty terms involved in the sequential constraint.

for different relative amounts of redundancy. The two limiting amounts of redundancy give a very simple picture. If there is no redundancy in the stimulus sequence, then end stimuli cannot be predicted with greater than chance accuracy, and the middle letters cannot be predicted any better. Thus, with no redundancy, prediction is no better in the middle than at the ends.

The other limiting condition is if the stimulus sequence is perfectly predictable (has a relative redundancy of 1.00). In this case a stimulus at the end of a given sequence is completely predictable, and so also is a stimulus in the middle of such a sequence. Thus all stimuli are again equally constrained by the other stimuli, and there is no advantage to prediction of middle stimuli compared to prediction of end stimuli.

It is only with intermediate amounts of redundancy that there can be any advantage to middle prediction compared to end prediction; and thus only in these cases can a response lag provide more accurate stimulus information. In Fig. 9.2 there are three general curves for intermediate amounts of redundancy, and the relative advantage of middle prediction over end prediction can be seen to be a function of the amount of redundancy.

If relative redundancy is .75, then end stimuli are constrained by that amount (this is the definition of sequential redundancy, from Chapter Seven). Relative middle prediction in this case could be as great as 1.00 (the maximum), so that a delayed response could lead to an improvement of .25 in relative predictability or constraint. If relative redundancy is .25, then middle prediction might be as great as twice this amount, or .50, and once again middle could be better than end prediction by as much as .25 relative constraint. On the other hand, if relative redundancy is .50, then constraint of middle stimuli could again be as great as the maximum of 1.00, which is .50 better than the equivalent constraint for end stimuli.[2]

Thus we can see that with redundant sequences of stimuli, there can be a gain in accuracy with a response lag, because both forward and backward constraints can operate, while with no response lag only forward constraints can operate. Furthermore, the relative gain in constraint due to a response lag will be maximum with a relative redundancy of .50. In consequence, if there is an advantage to the tracker in delaying his response, this advantage should be at a maximum with a relative redundancy of .50, and we would therefore expect a maximum lag with such redundancies.

Figure 9.3 illustrates schematically the kind of response lag we would expect as a function of relative redundancy. As we have noted, with relative redundancies of 0 or 1.00, there can be no informational advantage in lagging, and we would thus expect none—for that purpose. However, with no redundancy, the tracker would ordinarily lag in order to obtain perceptual anticipation, thus the curve shows a lag greater than zero. With full redundancy, however, the stimulus sequence is completely predictable, thus always known in advance. Thus no lag for purposes of obtaining simple advance information is necessary, since the tracker already has it.

With intermediate amounts of redundancy, however, we would ex-

---

[2] These relations between redundancy, or constraint on end stimuli, and the maximum possible constraint on middle stimuli must be considered as approximations only. In the first place, the exact relation between end constraint and middle constraint depends on the precise set of uncertainty terms involved, as illustrated in Tables 7.1, 7.2, and 7.3. Secondly, I have been unable to prove what the maximum possible middle constraint is for any given amount of end constraint. The relations shown in the tables in Chapter Seven make it clear that maximum middle constraint can be close to twice the end constraint, but it seems unlikely to me that it can be exactly that much. In other words, it seems unlikely that middle constraint can be simply the sum of the two unilateral constraints. What is clear, however, is that maximum middle constraint cannot exceed twice the end constraint, or twice the redundancy.

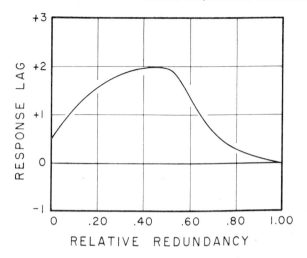

Fig. 9.3. A schematic function showing the effect of relative redundancy on response lag in a serial task. The exact shape of such a function, including its maximum lag, would depend on the particular pattern of sequential redundancy.

pect greater response delays—delays which increase the accuracy of the stimulus information. Since the maximum gain is for a relative redundancy of .50, we would also expect that trackers will delay maximally under that condition. We cannot know the exact shape of the function shown in Fig. 9.3, and to a very large extent it would depend on the exact nature of the redundancy. To illustrate, in a Markov series there would be little value in delaying the response more than one stimulus, since no additional information can be obtained beyond the one step over which the Markov process operates. However, the general characteristics of such a function must certainly be those shown in Fig. 9.3.

Are there any data to support the notion that response lag should be a function of amount of redundancy? There are no direct tests of this concept, but we do have suggestive data. Noble, Fitts, and Warren (1955), for example, note that in a tracking task with moderately slow sinusoidal target courses, subjects keep tending to get out of phase with the stimulus and then suddenly to go back in phase. In other words, the subjects have a tendency to lag in their response, but since this tendency is contrary to the instruction to stay "on course," they oscillate between getting out of phase and getting back in phase. A more pertinent experimental finding has been reported by Garvey and Mitnick (1957), who required tracking of continuous rate or continuous acceleration courses. They found consistently greater lags with the acceleration courses, which are less predictable for the average subject than are the rate courses. In other words, less lag was found with the more completely predictable target course.

Effect of memory

The amount of lag which we would normally expect is not simply a function of the redundancy in the stimulus series itself. Clearly if the subject lags in his response, he may suffer some memory loss concerning the most accurate single predictor of where his response should be, which is the stimulus to which he is presumably responding. In other words, to delay to get more information is fine as long as you don't forget more than the additional information you get, and some sort of memory factor must put limits on the delay, regardless of the nature of the redundancy.

It seems unlikely, however, that memory is a serious limiting factor in most realistic situations, since short-term memory seems to be more than adequate for the usual tracking problem. Pollack, Johnson, and Knaff (1959), for example, determined the running digit span for auditorally presented numbers. Their subjects were read a series of digits, and at a warning signal were required to reproduce as many of the digits as they could, counting backwards from the stop. Sometimes the subjects knew in advance how long the total sequence was going to be, and sometimes they did not. These running digit spans as a function of rate of presentation are given in Fig. 9.4. While it is clear that the digit span is larger for the slower rates, and for known total lengths of digits, it is also clear that a digit span of about six is obtainable even under poorer conditions. Such a span should be more than adequate for most situations.

In a similar type of experiment, Poulton (1958) had subjects copy in block letters simple prose material, and, with fast rates of presentation, found that subjects could copy as much as forty letters behind. In another experiment, Mackworth (1959) forced subjects to respond behind a random series of stimuli, and found no serious consequences of this forced lag up to two stimuli behind the one being responded to. Thus clearly we could expect subjects to perform quite adequately with a self-produced lag in order to take advantage of the redundancy, with no serious loss in performance due to the lag if the lag does not exceed two information units beyond the stimulus to which the response is being made. In other words, if subjects are attempting to use a total predictive sequence as long as five units, they can easily be expected to remember this long a sequence in a "running" fashion, and

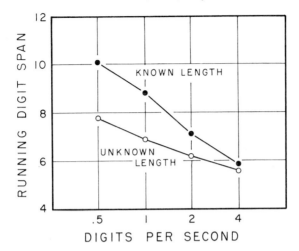

FIG. 9.4. Running digit span for auditory presentation as a function of rate of presentation for known and unknown message lengths. Subjects were required to reproduce digits at the end of a longer sequence of either known or unknown length. (After Pollack, Johnson, and Knaff, 1959.)

also to respond to the middle item of the sequence with no loss in accuracy due to the delay itself.

The need for redundancy

I have presented here an argument that optimum use of redundancy in a series of stimuli would require that subjects lag a moderate amount in their responses with intermediate amounts of redundancy. Clearly, whether such a lag will actually occur in an experiment will depend on considerations other than the nature of the redundancy itself.

Certainly one of the most important factors to the subject in determining whether he will lag in his response is the experimenter's instructions to the subject, and the subject's interpretation of the instructions. Normally a subject is given instructions which emphasize a time criterion of accuracy, rather than a course criterion of accuracy. In other words, the subject will be scored in terms of his matching of the stimulus course at the time the stimulus course actually occurs. For scoring purposes, the stimulus course and the response track are aligned in time, and then the scoring is in terms of deviation of the two courses. With such an instruction, there is a penalty (insofar as subject error leads to penalty) to the subject in delaying his response, since the delay can only lead to greater error. Suppose, however, that the subject is given instructions that he is to recreate, as accurately as possible, the actual stimulus course, preserving all of the time relations within the course itself. These instructions should lead to lag, since the subject can maintain response coordination more accurately if he delays his response to obtain maximum information.

There is another critical factor which will determine whether a subject will delay his response with a redundant stimulus series, and that factor is the accuracy with which the stimulus series can be perceived without redundancy. Suppose that the subject is given a task of tracking with a stylus directly on a moving target, and that the target moves (changes position) just once a second. If the target is clearly visible, then we would expect only enough delay to allow a coordinated response, since there will be little ambiguity to the subject about his response. In such a tracking task, it should make very little difference whether there is any redundancy in the stimulus sequence or not, since he can easily track with close to perfect accuracy any target course presented.

Suppose, however, that the target begins to change position more rapidly, and that a certain amount of random error is introduced into the target course. Now there will exist some ambiguity about the correct target position at any instant in time, and if the course is partially redundant there will be some advantage in delaying the response in order to obtain more accurate information about the true target position. Noise does not have to be introduced in a direct fashion for there to be some advantage in the redundancy, with the consequent response lag to maximize the value of the redundancy. Any ambiguity or increased task difficulty may make the redundancy valuable to the subject. For example, the visual conditions may be poor so that clear discrimination is impossible, or the rate of the stimulus presentation may be too great for individual reaction to each successive stimulus.

Still another factor which may make the redundancy valuable to the subject is the total task requirement. Bahrick and Shelly (1958) have clearly shown the value of redundancy when the task requirement is increased. They used a task in which key-pressing responses to four possible lights were required, with stimuli presented once every 0.58 sec. Four different degrees of redundancy were used: a random series, with no redundancy; another series in which four pairs of successive stimuli occurred twice as often as the other twelve pairs, with a redundancy of 2 percent; a third series in which just four of the pairs of successive stimuli occurred nearly all the time, with a redundancy of 13 percent; and a series which repeated itself every fourth stimulus, with a consequent redundancy of 100 percent. When these four different series were used alone, there was no real difference in performance as a function of the redundancy—in fact, performance in terms of correct hits was nearly perfect regardless of the amount of redundancy.

In another condition, however, the subjects were required to carry out the same task with one hand while they simultaneously carried out a similar task of key pressing to a set of randomly presented auditory stimuli. Naturally the addition of the second task produced a deterioration in performance, but the amount of the deterioration was directly related to the amount of redundancy, as shown in Fig. 9.5. The greatest decrement in performance occurred with the random series, and the least decrement occurred with the completely redundant series of stimuli. Thus the redundancy had no apparent effect on performance as long as the task was easy enough, but once the task was made more difficult the value of the redundancy became immediately apparent.

The need for redundancy as the critical factor in determining whether redundancy affects human performance has appeared several

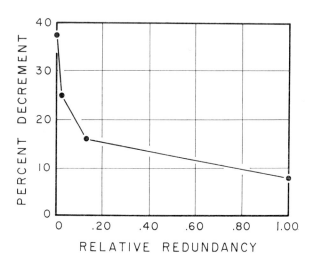

FIG. 9.5. Relative performance on a serial key-pressing task as a function of sequential redundancy. The stimuli were presented visually, but another task was carried out simultaneously in which key-pressing to auditory stimuli was required. Decrement is relative to performance on the same task without the additional auditory task. (After Bahrick and Shelly, 1958.)

times in this book. Many different experiments, on form perception and on verbal learning, for example, have shown no apparent value to redundancy (even for discrimination tasks), and sometimes have shown redundancy to be detrimental to performance. A common finding also is that redundant stimuli may provide more accurate response or faster learning but at a cost in information transmission.

It should be clear that redundancy per se is not necessarily a valuable characteristic of stimuli used in human experiments. In fact, it can be detrimental, depending on the form in which it comes. When redundancy occurs in the form of sequential constraint, there is little reason to expect any detrimental effects of the redundancy as long as performance is measured in terms of direct accuracy, not in terms of information transmission. The reason is that sequential constraints in no way add to the complexity of the stimuli, thus should not make the task more difficult. There are other situations, however, in which the addition of redundancy, as I have pointed out in regard to perceptual discrimination problems, is an addition of stimulus complexity. If the stimuli are easily discriminable without redundancy, then we might well expect an increase in errors as the stimuli are made more complex. Similarly, if eight nonsense words are to be learned with free recall, increasing redundancy by increasing length of the words will most likely make the task more difficult, because the addition of the redundancy is in fact an addition of something to be learned.

The purpose of redundancy is to offset the effects of other negative performance factors, whether these factors be errors in stimuli, poor discrimination, too great a task load, or too great a rate of presentation. We have every reason to expect, under such circumstances, that redundancy will aid performance as long as the redundancy is appropriate to the nature of the task. Thus we would not expect the kinds of response lags we have been discussing to occur in any human task where there is sequential redundancy, but only in those tasks where the human operator has some real need for the redundancy.

COMMENTARY

In Chapter Eight, we discussed the use of language statistics by humans, and many studies have clearly demonstrated that adult humans are rather thoroughly aware of the complex sequential dependencies existing in a real language, and that they can use these statistical characteristics to predict or replace missing elements. Furthermore, the sequential constraints of language are truly statistical in nature, in that a particular letter or word is predictable only in a probabilistic sense. Rarely is a letter or word the only one which can occur in a given context. Rather, there will be several possible letters or words with unequal probabilities, and humans seem to have done a rather good job, by the time they are grown up, in learning these statistical distributions.

This being the case, the most surprising aspect of laboratory experiments on the learning of statistical dependencies is that what can be learned is so very limited. The available evidence suggests that simple contingencies of adjacent symbols can be learned fairly easily, but that longer sequences, even when invariable in nature, are learned only with difficulty. What is the difficulty? Perhaps it is that the laboratory experiments provide too artificial a task for the subject. Or perhaps it is that complex and probabilistic sequences can be learned, but only with considerable training. Adults have had, after all, a rather long time in which to learn the statistical nature of their language. Perhaps it is, as I have suggested, that learning of sequential characteristics is much easier when subjects can see relatively long sequences as a space pattern rather than as a time pattern.

Whatever the difficulty, it is evident that experimentally we have just barely scratched the surface with this type of problem. We do not know what kinds of sequences are learned most easily, whether simple contingencies are easier to learn than interaction terms, what influence the amount of constraint has on the rate of learning, or whether rate of learning depends only on the amount of constraint and not on the residual uncertainty.

Our knowledge of informational factors in perceptual-motor skills is not much better off, again particularly in regard to factors that should be operative with sequentially presented stimuli. Most of our discussion in this area has been discussion of what should happen with regard to sequential constraint variables, and it is rare that we can say that such and such does happen.

Of particular interest, I feel, are the timing relations involved in continuous perceptual-motor activity as these relations should be affected by the amount and nature of sequential redundancy. That under certain circumstances a human operator should lag in his response is a fact which we can establish only with anecdotal evidence, and not with direct and controlled laboratory experimentation.

The anecdotal evidence that the kinds of relations we have discussed do affect human performance is abundant. Watch a stenographer taking dictation, and you will see that she lags behind the spoken material. Or watch her type material from a dictated record, where she can control the rate of the material. She does not stop the record when she is up with the material, but she allows the recorded material to get ahead of her. In other words, she deliberately uses a response lag.

Leonard Carmichael has pointed out to me that a characteristic of fast readers is that they read "ahead of themselves." In reading out loud, for example, the reader is looking at material ahead of what he is actually reading, thus lagging in his response. Even when reading to himself, the fast reader is in the same sense looking ahead of the material which is being absorbed at any given instant. Good reading should require exactly such behavior, for in looking ahead the reader is making maximum use of redundancy, and the uncertainty of the material he is reading at any instant is held to a minimum.

Another illustration of the effects of the redundancy on the amount of lag is provided by telegraphers. When a telegrapher receives normal code, he lags behind the auditory material in copying, but he does not lag in this fashion when he is copying special code material. Special code material is, for the telegrapher, non-redundant material, since he does not know the statistical structure of the coded material. And I have pointed out that the only advantage of a response lag in copying such material is the small lag which allows perceptual anticipation. Lag for purposes of gaining more accurate information is of no value, since information cannot be gained unless there is redundancy.

The effects of noise on the lag can easily be seen by observing people using a telephone. When the telephone line is providing very clear communication, and the listener does not hear a particular word, or wants confirmation on a particular word or phrase, he will interrupt and ask for confirmation rather quickly. On the other hand, a person listening on a noisy line waits longer before asking for confirmation. In our terms, the listener with a clear line may be reasonably sure that the talker in fact made a mistake and he responds rather quickly when he wants confirmation, while the listener with a noisy line is less sure that a mistake has been made and waits for additional context, hoping thereby correctly to understand the ambiguously heard word or phrase.

This last illustration is somewhat similar to a monitoring task. When a human is used to monitor another human or a machine which is putting out a sequence of letters as in ordinary English, his job is to make no response unless something is wrong. Then he should make some sort of corrective response. Here again, if real language is being used, the human can rarely be sure that a mistake has been made if he attempts to make his decision at the instant each word is printed out, because all of the prior context is normally insufficient to reduce his uncertainty reasonably close to zero. If he waits, in order to obtain both antecedent and subsequent context, he will be able to correct mistakes as long as the mistake rate is not extremely high. The important point here is simply that, in such a task, response lag is absolutely necessary for the best performance of the monitoring job.

It is interesting that sequential redundancy in a stimulus series can both prevent and produce a time lag in the response. When the stimulus material is completely unambiguous, so that even with a non-redundant series there is no uncertainty about the stimulus, then time delay will be introduced only for purposes of providing simple perceptual anticipation, and a long time delay would be of no value. Under such perceptual conditions, the introduction of redundancy may, by providing advance information, eliminate the necessity of the response lag, which after all has the same purpose. And it might not be necessary that the redundancy be complete. Quite possibly a relative redundancy of .75 would provide sufficiently accurate advance information to eliminate response lag.

If stimulus material is ambiguous in any fashion, however, the redundancy must be used to obtain information about the stimulus material itself. In this case the redundancy, rather than eliminating the response lag which occurs to provide advance information, will introduce a further response lag, now in order to provide more information. This fact means that the amount of lag should be a systematic function of the amount of noise, or stimulus ambiguity, although the amount of lag will interact with the amount of redundancy. Certainly for intermediate amounts of redundancy, the lag should increase monotonically with the amount of noise.

The special value of a relative redundancy of .50 is certainly intriguing. In Chapter Seven, when discussing the redundancy of printed English, I suggested that probably the critical factor which determines the redundancy of English is the effect of redundancy on prediction in the middle of long sequences, and that redundancy is probably added to the language until essentially perfect prediction, or error correction, can occur for isolated letters in the middle of sequences. A value not much above .50 is what is required just to produce perfect prediction in the middle of sequences. Here again, we have seen that a relative redundancy of .50 should produce the maximum response lag for purposes of maximizing information obtained about the stimulus sequence.

Redundancy comes at a cost—more stimuli must be used to transmit the same information. This cost must always be a deterrent in any real information system. In a sense, you get the most gain for the least relative cost for redundancies on the order of 50 percent, because lesser amounts of redundancy will give little extra prediction in the middle compared to the ends; and greater amounts of redundancy will not improve prediction in the middle at all. Thus there is some reason to feel that printed English has evolved very closely to an optimum condition.

SUMMARY

Humans can learn not only distributional probabilities of a stimulus series; they can also learn sequential probabilities if these exist. The experimental evidence available suggests that learning of sequential constraints which exist over more than a very small number of steps is very difficult, although constraints operating only between adjacent pairs of stimuli are learned easily. This relative difficulty of learning longer constraints seems oddly at variance with our known ability to use such constraints in our language. This difficulty of learning may be due to the interference of the response sequence with perception of the stimulus sequence. It may also be due to an inherent difficulty in learning time sequences—a difficulty which may not exist for the learning of space sequences such as we ordinarily see with printed languages.

There are many perceptual-motor tasks in which a continuous, or continuing, response is required to a stimulus series which may be redundant, or sequentially constrained. There is considerable evidence that response to any sequence is more accurate if the subject has advance information about the stimuli so that he can anticipate his response. If such advance information is not provided by the nature of the task, then subjects ordinarily will provide it themselves by delaying their response with respect to the stimulus series. Such a delay allows the subject to be responding to one stimulus while he is seeing the stimulus which determines his next response. Thus in effect the delay provides advance information.

Redundancy in a stimulus series can also provide such advance information, because the redundancy makes the stimulus series predictable, so that the subject can project the stimulus series into the future. With sufficient redundancy in a series, then, the response lag normally produced should be eliminated. On the other hand, if there is any ambiguity about the stimulus series, the redundancy will help to reduce the subject's uncertainty about the stimulus, and thus about his response. In order to make maximum use of the redundancy, however, the subject must delay his response so that he obtains both forward and backward prediction rather than just forward prediction. The maximum information gain from a delayed response should occur with relative redundancies of about .50. Thus, the amount of delay will depend on the amount of redundancy. It will also depend on the need for the redundancy, as determined by the instructions, the task difficulty, and the amount of noise in the stimulus series.

CHAPTER TEN

Concept Formation

THERE EXISTS WITHIN PSYCHOLOGY a class of experimental problems usually called concept formation problems. The term *concept* is not the best-defined term in psychology, but certainly the experimenters on concept formation are using the term in the sense of a general idea which can be applied to a number of specific instances. While we use the term concept in ordinary conversation with connotations quite different from those involved in discrimination, absolute judgment, learning, etc., the experimental paradigm within which concept formation problems are usually carried out is in reality quite similar to the experimental paradigms used for these other classes of problems. It might be profitable, therefore, to examine the concept formation problem by analogy and contrast with these other problems— problems which we have already discussed to some extent.

THE NATURE OF A CONCEPT PROBLEM

In an experiment on concept formation, a subject is presented with a set of stimuli, either successively or simultaneously, and is required to respond differentially to the various stimuli to demonstrate that he can either learn or use some rule which determines which responses go with which stimuli. Such an experimental procedure, where a series of stimuli is presented and the subject responds to each, is fundamentally not different from the procedures used in discrimination, absolute judgment, or learning experiments. There are, however, two basic characteristics of such experiments which are necessary for them

310

to be concept formation experiments, rather than one of the other types.

The first of these required characteristics is that the same response must be used for more than one stimulus. If each stimulus has a distinctive response, then no requirement that a general idea be applied to specific instances is involved. The subject must be able to demonstrate that he can correctly apply the same rule in responding to at least two different stimuli before he can be considered to be using a concept.

In Chapter Five, we discussed at considerable length the amount and form of constraint produced when stimuli are *selected* from a larger group of stimuli, and also briefly noted that no redundancy is produced when stimuli are pooled to require a common response. An experiment in which one response is required for several different stimuli has a superficial resemblance to the experiment in which a subgroup of stimuli is selected from a larger set, but this resemblance is somewhat deceptive. The distinction operationally, however, between experiments on judgment or learning and experiments on concept formation can be very slight.

The use of one response for more than one stimulus in an experimental set of stimuli is not unique to problems on concept formation. Bricker (1955a), for example, used eight different stimuli in an identification and reaction time experiment, but some of his experimental conditions involved using fewer responses than stimuli so that he could determine the effect of response uncertainty independently of stimulus uncertainty. The same procedure has been used in other reaction time experiments, but these have not usually been considered as experiments on concept formation.

Eriksen and Hake (1955a), in their experiment on absolute judgments of visual size, used fewer response categories than stimulus categories. In a strict sense such an experiment can be considered as a problem in concept formation, because the subject is required to use a common response for a group of stimuli defined by a size rule. Thus the general idea of a size range is applied to specific instances, and our requirement for a concept is satisfied. Again, however, such experiments are not normally considered relevant to concept formation, and the reason relates to the second requirement for concept formation problems.

This second required characteristic is that the stimuli must be multivariate in nature. Thus the Eriksen and Hake experiment is not accepted as a concept formation problem because the stimuli varied on only a single dimension. This multivariate requirement makes it possible for the experimenter to determine a priori which variables are relevant to changes in the response, and which variables are irrelevant to these changes. Then the subject is given the task of determining which variables are relevant, and once he has learned this fact he can respond correctly to a large group of stimuli with a single response by ignoring stimulus differences which exist only with respect to the irrelevant stimulus variables. For example, if the stimulus can be one of the four possible combinations of large and small, white and black, cats, then he can learn to say "yes" to the two large cats, ignoring whether they are black or white, and he has learned the concept of "largeness" which he can use in the two specific instances of large black cat and large white cat.

Kinds of response system

The actual kinds of responses used in concept formation problems may vary considerably, and these variations occasionally are confusing in relating one experiment to another. Table 10.1 illustrates sche-

Table 10.1

Different response systems which can be used with eight stimuli formed from three dichotomous variables. The last three systems can be used in concept formation problems.

Stimulus Variable			Response System			
v	w	x	1	2	3	4
1	1	1	A	A	A	A
1	1	0	B	A	A	A
1	0	1	C	A	B	$\bar{A}$
1	0	0	D	A	B	$\bar{A}$
0	1	1	E	B	C	$\bar{A}$
0	1	0	F	B	C	$\bar{A}$
0	0	1	G	B	D	$\bar{A}$
0	0	0	H	B	D	$\bar{A}$

matically four different kinds of response system which can be applied to eight different stimuli which are generated from three dichotomous variables. One of these response systems does not provide a concept problem, but the other three do, in various ways.

The first response system, which is included only for comparison purposes, is the type that would be used with eight different stimuli if we were studying reaction time, discrimination, absolute judgment, or even learning. Each stimulus is assigned a completely distinctive, a unique, response. For example, stimulus 111 is assigned response A, stimulus 110 is assigned response B, etc. If the response is very appropriate to the stimulus, so that no learning is required, then we might be interested in speed of reaction, or accuracy of discrimination. If, however, the responses initially have no obvious relevance to the differences in the stimuli, then we would be studying paired-associates learning, and our interest would be in how rapidly the subject can learn which response goes with which stimulus. For such an experiment we would require or assume that the stimuli are all quite discriminable and that the only real problem is the learning of the association.

In the second response system, the stimuli are grouped so that one response, A, is appropriate to four of them and another response, B, is appropriate to the other four. In the particular method of assignment used, the response is completely correlated with stimulus variable v, and is completely uncorrelated with the other two stimulus variables. Thus in the process of learning, the subject must (presumably) learn that variable v is the appropriate one, and that the other variables should be ignored. Actually, of course, the correct response can be learned to each of the eight stimuli without the conscious identification of the correlation between response and variable v, since it can be learned as a rote association. If learning has occurred by such a process, then we have concept formation only in a most artifactual sense. Normally, subjects are required to verbalize the rule by which they respond in order to preclude such a possibility.

The third response method is an extension of the second, in that stimuli are grouped according to a rule, except that now we use four groups of two stimuli each rather than two groups of four stimuli. Logically, of course, the procedure has not changed the nature of the problem at all. With this response system the response is correlated with combinations of stimulus variables v and w, and is completely uncorrelated with variable x. Since there are four combinations of two dichotomous variables, then four distinctive responses are used, rather than the two required with the second response system. With the second response system, one stimulus variable was relevant to the response, and two were irrelevant, but with this third response system, two variables are relevant and one is irrelevant. Once again, of course, such a response system could be learned by rote and could be essentially the same as any other paired-associates learning problem.

The fourth response system is essentially a variation on the third system, since the concept is again defined in terms of two variables, so that two variables are relevant and one is irrelevant. In this system, the subject is required to make a positive response when the concept conditions have been satisfied, and to make a negative response when the conditions have not been satisfied. ($\bar{A}$ simply means not A.) In this commonly used response system, the correct concept is that v and w each equals 1, and whenever these values occur, the subject says something like "correct," "yes," or "that's right." When the concept does not occur, he may make a verbal response which is negative, or he may make no response at all. Occasionally, he simply fails to select such stimuli, thus indicating a negative reaction.

A comparison of these last two response systems is of some interest because in both cases the concept is defined in terms of two variables and there is one irrelevant variable, but a greater degree of discrimination is required in the third system than in the fourth. In information terms, with the third system 2 bits of discrimination are required, while in the fourth system only 0.81 bit is required. This difference is one which has not been used experimentally. The fourth response system also adds another problem which we shall discuss later, and that is whether the nature of the response is an important variable. In the fourth system not only are the two responses used with different frequencies, but one of them is positive while the other is negative. It is quite possible, of course, to assign a positive response, B, to the last six stimuli in the fourth system, rather than the negation of A, and such a difference would have no effect whatsoever on the informational analysis. This difference may be of considerable relevance psychologically, however.

Thus a concept formation experiment needs to have a multivariate set of stimuli plus some grouping of the stimuli. If each stimulus has a unique response, then no concept formation is involved. Neither, on the other hand, would we consider the problem to be one of concept formation if all stimuli have the same response, since we would be unable to demonstrate discrimination in the use of the concept. A concept formation problem cannot, then, be too dissimilar from a paired-associates learning problem or a discrimination problem, because discrimination is necessary in order to demonstrate that a concept is in use.

Of some interest also is the role of the irrelevant variables. With response systems 2 and 3, the role of the irrelevant variables is to make possible having more than one stimulus per response. With the third system, for example, if stimulus variable x were eliminated we would have just four different stimuli and four responses, so the problem would again be a paired-associates problem. However, the addition of the third stimulus variable as an irrelevant variable makes possible two stimuli per response. In the process, the third stimulus variable adds confusion to the task given the subject. With the fourth response system, the use of irrelevant stimulus variables is less necessary. Suppose in this case that the third variable were eliminated. Now we would have two responses, one of which has a unique stimulus but the other of which is used for three different stimuli. Would not such a problem still be one of concept formation? Probably so, in which case the role of the irrelevant stimulus variable must be entirely to increase the difficulty of learning.

The nature of the stimuli used in concept formation experiments usually makes these experiments quite unlike discrimination or absolute judgment experiments, since the stimuli used are ordinarily quite discriminable. The difference between a concept problem and a paired-associates learning problem, however, is much less obvious, and the only essential difference is that in the concept problem there is greater stimulus uncertainty than response uncertainty due to the addition of irrelevant variables.

UNCERTAINTY AND CONCEPT FORMATION

In a paired-associates learning problem, one response is assigned to each stimulus. Thus the response uncertainty is made equal to the stimulus uncertainty, which itself is determined by the number of different stimuli. In a concept problem, stimulus uncertainty is made greater than response uncertainty, since a larger number of different stimuli is used than there are different responses. Thus the problem as defined by the experimenter is one in which the external constraint (or information transmission) is equal to the response uncertainty. In other words, once the problem is learned, the stimulus-response matrix is one in which each stimulus defines a unique response, but each response does not define a unique stimulus. The contingent uncertainty between stimuli and responses will thus be limited by the response uncertainty, and if there is no response equivocation (the condition after complete learning), then the contingent uncertainty will be the same as the response uncertainty. Thus the addition of irrelevant stimulus variables in a concept problem has the effect of increasing stimulus uncertainty. However, since the information transmission is limited by the response uncertainty, this increased stimulus uncertainty is in the form of stimulus equivocation.

Irrelevant information

Recently a series of experiments has been carried out to determine the relation between stimulus uncertainty and rate of concept learning. In these experiments, stimulus uncertainty was increased by the addition of irrelevant variables to the stimuli, while response uncertainty was held constant. Thus the additional stimulus uncertainty is additional stimulus equivocation, and is not accompanied by increased response uncertainty.

Archer, Bourne, and Brown (1955) used a basic procedure involving the third response system of Table 10.1, in which 2 dichotomous relevant variables were always used, with four discriminative responses. Thus response uncertainty was always 2 bits. Stimulus uncertainty, however, was varied by the addition of irrelevant dichotomous variables, so that each additional variable provided 1 bit of extra stimulus uncertainty. Since they used a minimum of one irrelevant variable, their minimum stimulus uncertainty was 3 bits (2 bits of relevant and 1 bit of irrelevant information).

These authors used four buttons to be pushed as the responses, and visually presented stimuli which could vary in form, size, brightness, stability of contour, speed of movement, horizontal direction of movement, and vertical direction of movement. Various pairs of these variables were used as relevant, and one or more of the others were used as irrelevant variables. Their subjects continued learning until a criterion of thirty-two consecutive correct identifications had been achieved. The results of this experiment, with errors before reaching criterion as the dependent measure, are shown in Fig. 10.1. (A parallel function is obtained if time to solution is used rather than errors to solution.) These results clearly show that an increase in stimulus uncertainty leads to an increase in the difficulty of the problem. While these authors did not use the limiting case of no irrelevant stimulus variable, I have extrapolated their function to an assumed value of ten errors, which seems like a reasonable number of errors for learning a four-item paired-associates problem (it certainly should be no greater). Insofar as this value is correct, it would seem that even the addition of a single irrelevant variable adds considerably to the difficulty of the task.

Similar results concerning stimulus uncertainty have been obtained by Bourne (1957) and by Bourne and Pendleton (1958), who also showed that the rate of learning is decreased when only partial information as to correctness of response is made available. Gelfand (1958) obtained a similar function for stimulus uncertainty and

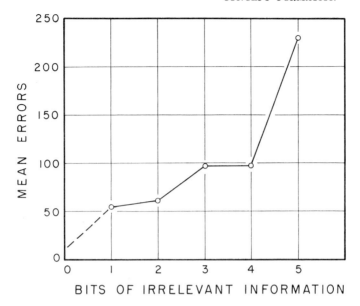

FIG. 10.1. The effect of amount of irrelevant information on solution of a concept problem. Each bit of irrelevant information represents one additional variable. (After Archer, Bourne, and Brown, 1955.)

showed, in addition, that some of the deleterious effects of a large amount of irrelevant information can be offset with favorable sets induced by prior training.

Positive and negative instances

As indicated previously, a special problem arises when the fourth response system is used, a system in which the psychological nature of the less frequently used positive response may be quite different from that of the negative response. While previous research had indicated some difficulty in concept learning when the stimuli presented were primarily negative instances (instances of what the correct concept was not), Hovland (1952) pointed out that the difference might well be due to the differential amounts of information provided in the two cases.

It should be clear that it is possible to "solve" a concept formation problem with fewer stimuli presented than the total number possible, if the stimuli presented are selected properly so as to show the correlation of the response with the relevant variable. For example, from Table 10.1, if the subject knows there are only two possible responses with response system 2 (and knows that they will occur equally often), then if stimuli 111 and 011 are presented, he has already established that the response is correlated with variable v and not with the others. Similarly, with response system 3, four stimuli will correctly define the response system. For example, stimuli 111, 110, 100, and 010 will define the four correct responses. The first two show that the stimulus variable x is irrelevant, and that A is appropriate for patterns beginning 11. The next two establish which stimulus pattern goes with B and with C, and D is determined by elimination.

With this type of analysis I am assuming rather simple types of concepts in which the response system is directly correlated with one, two, or more stimulus variables, and not with unique combinations of them. In terms of uncertainty analysis, I am assuming no interactions—an assumption which is not actually necessary, as we shall see later.

Hovland carried out a detailed informational analysis of the amount of information provided by positive and negative instances, for concept problems in which there are only two possible responses, as in our fourth response system. In such a system, the less frequently occurring response is usually designated as the positive concept, although again such a procedure is not logically necessary. Hovland's analysis was primarily concerned with the minimum number of positive and negative instances required to define the concept correctly, and with the amount of information (in terms of reduction of possible hypotheses) which each successive stimulus presentation gave. He argued that it was not possible to compare the effectiveness of positive and negative instances in concept formation unless the same amount of information was made available with the two types of stimuli. The number of positive or negative stimuli required for complete specification of a concept can be drastically different, and the amount of difference depends on the particular nature of the problem.

In our example of Table 10.1, for instance, two positive instances are necessary to specify the concept, while five negative instances are necessary. On the other hand, with sixteen stimuli defined by four dichotomous variables, three of them relevant, then just two positive stimuli are required, but ten negative stimuli, to completely define the concept. A much more extreme example occurs when we have five stimulus variables with five levels of each, making a total number of possible stimuli of 3125. If the concept is defined in terms of one specific level of each of four of these variables, then there are five positive stimuli, only two of which are required to specify the concept, but 628 of the 3120 negative stimuli are required to specify the concept completely.

Hovland and Weiss (1953) carried out a series of experiments on this problem. Their basic procedure was to present a series of positive instances or a series of negative instances, but in either case the total number of stimuli presented was exactly the minimum number necessary to specify the concept. Under these circumstances the number of subjects solving the problem was considerably greater when positive instances were used than when negative instances were used. On the possibility that the total number of items with which the subject must deal was the critical factor, they also carried out some comparisons in which the number of positive instances required was approximately the same as the number of negative instances required.

Under these conditions the experimentally obtained difference between the two procedures was reduced, although there still was a substantial advantage to the positive instances. Thus apparently, even when information factors are thoroughly controlled and equated, there is an advantage to the presentation of the positive instances— an advantage which must be due entirely to psychological factors involving how the subject conceives and structures his problem. It would be of some interest here to use two responses which are completely neutral, such as A and B, rather than A and not A.

While we can compute the minimum number of positive or negative instances (or mixture of positive and negative) required to specify a concept completely, there is no reason to suppose that the exact order in which these stimuli are presented is not of considerable importance. Hovland and Weiss actually made some comparisons of presentations of mixed positive and negative instances, and found that the order was not of great importance.

More recently, however, Detambel and Stolurow (1956) have shown the sequence of stimulus presentations to be important. Their stimuli were formed from three trichotomous variables, giving a total of twenty-seven stimuli. Only one variable was relevant, and three different responses were to be learned to correlate with the three levels on that one variable. They used two different sequences of the twenty-seven stimuli for training purposes, and then a fixed sequence for the test, with the dependent variable being the number of subjects who were entirely correct on the test sequence. The two different training sequences were identical in terms of the sequence of correct responses, but differed in the degree to which the irrelevant stimulus variables were correlated with the relevant stimulus variable from trial to trial.

The highly correlated series was called a high-synchrony series, and the other a low-synchrony series.

To illustrate, with high synchrony, two successive stimuli might be HHH followed by MLL, so that when the first (relevant) variable changed the other two variables also changed. With low synchrony, we might have HHH followed by MHH, so that when the relevant variable changed the other two variables did not change. Obviously there are limited degrees of freedom in arranging such sequences with a fixed set of stimuli, but considerable variation in the pair correlation can be achieved.

The results of this experiment are given in Fig. 10.2, where number of solvers is plotted for the two different training series. The overall difference due to synchrony was sizable, but the most interesting aspect of this experiment was that the extent to which synchrony in the stimulus series affected problem solution depended on the intelligence (scholastic ability as measured by ACE scores) of the subjects. For high-intelligence subjects there was no difference, but the low-synchrony series made it possible for the low-intelligence groups to solve the problem as successfully as the high-intelligence subjects solved either series. In other words, low synchrony makes the problem easier to solve, but if the subject is bright enough, he can solve it anyway.

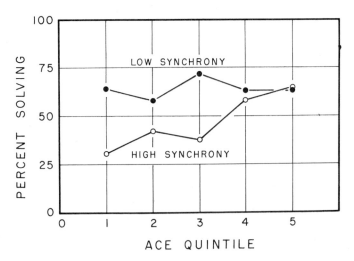

Fig. 10.2. Effect of scholastic aptitude (ACE score) and synchrony of the stimulus series on concept solutions. (After Detambel and Stolurow, 1956.)

STIMULUS REDUNDANCY

By far the most common procedure in experiments on concept formation is to use all the possible stimuli which can be generated with the given number of relevant and irrelevant variables. If, for example, we have two trichotomous irrelevant variables and one trichotomous relevant variable, as in the Detambel and Stolurow experiment, then all of the twenty-seven stimuli which can be generated from these three variables are actually used. And if we have three dichotomous relevant variables plus two dichotomous irrelevant variables, then all of the thirty-two possible stimuli are used.

There is, however, no fundamental reason why all of the possible stimuli should be used. We can satisfy the conditions for a concept formation experiment when less than all of the possible stimuli are used, since the requirements simply are that each response be assigned to more than one stimulus and that the stimuli be multivariate. In a sense, the experiment of Hovland and Weiss on the minimum number of positive or negative instances necessary to specify a concept is a step in the direction of using redundant stimuli, since fewer than the total possible number of stimuli are actually presented to the subject. This procedure was not, however, deliberately aimed at investigating the role of redundancy per se.

Forms of redundancy or internal constraint

We have discussed at some length the fact that selection of fewer stimuli than can be generated with a given number of variables produces a redundant set of stimuli. The number selected compared to the number which could have been selected determines the amount of stimulus redundancy; and which particular stimuli are selected determines the form of the internal constraint.

In Chapter Five, when we were first discussing this problem, we noted that the form of internal constraint also uniquely determines the form of the external constraint, since the terms involved in one are directly derivable from those involved in the other. This exact relationship between the form of internal and external constraint, however, depends on a condition which we were assuming at that time but are not assuming now—that each stimulus is assigned a unique response. The nature of a concept problem is that several different stimuli are all assigned the same response. This method of assignment of responses to stimuli leads to considerably greater freedom in the relations which can exist between the forms of internal and external constraint.

This fact, which we shall discuss more fully later, affects the form of the external constraint, but it has no relevance whatsoever to the form of the internal constraint. Thus in a set of stimuli used for a concept problem, the number of stimuli selected (relative to the number which could have been selected) still determines the amount of internal constraint in the stimuli; and the particular selection of stimuli uniquely determines the form of the internal constraint. Nevertheless, the assignment of the response system determines the relation between the internal constraint and the concept problem which the subject must solve.

One more comment needs to be made before discussing some particular ways in which internal constraint can be used in a concept problem, and that is the relation between redundancy and total constraint. In Chapter Five, I showed that total constraint equals external constraint plus internal constraint. This relation is still essentially true for the concept problem, but there is an added consideration which must be taken into account. Previously we were discussing the case where each stimulus is assigned a unique response; that is, there was no stimulus equivocation or response equivocation. In such a case, the total constraint is limited by the maximum stimulus uncertainty which the given number of variables can produce. Thus if there is a fixed number of stimulus variables, then any increase in internal constraint must be accompanied by a decrease in external constraint. In a sense, then, the internal constraint comes out of, or from, the external constraint.

In a concept problem, however, we have (by definition) more stimuli than responses, so that there is stimulus equivocation. Since there is some stimulus equivocation, the total constraint in a concept problem is less than the maximum possible constraint, or maximum possible stimulus uncertainty. Therefore, it is possible to hold the number of responses (external constraint) constant, and to increase internal constraint by selection of stimuli, thereby increasing the total constraint, *with the same number of stimulus variables*. This cannot be accomplished if there is a unique response for each stimulus. In the concept problem, the additional constraint, both internal and total, literally comes from the stimulus equivocation, since the stimulus equivocation is decreased by exactly the same amount that the internal constraint is increased.

A simple numerical illustration may help clarify this relation. Suppose we have five dichotomous variables and generate all the thirty-two possible stimuli. We use four different responses and assign them to the four combinations of two relevant variables, with a resultant 2 bits of external constraint. This assignment means that eight different stimuli are all called the same response, so that there is 3 bits of stimulus equivocation. Now we select just eight of these stimuli for actual use, maintaining the same 2 bits of external constraint. Now, however, just two stimuli are called the same response, so that there is just 1 bit of stimulus equivocation. And the selection of eight out of thirty-two stimuli has produced 2 bits of internal constraint, the 2 bits which was formerly stimulus equivocation. In more general form,

$$U_y(x_1, x_2, \ldots x_n) + U(y{:}x_1{:}x_2{:}\ldots x_n)$$
$$= U(y{:}x_1, x_2, \ldots x_n) + U(x_1{:}x_2{:}\ldots x_n) + U_y(x_1, x_2, \ldots x_n). \quad (10.1)$$

In this equation, which is analogous to Eq. 5.15, y is the response variable, and $x_1, x_2, \ldots x_n$ are the various stimulus variables. In other form these terms are

$$SE + TC = EC + IC + SE,$$

where SE is stimulus equivocation, TC is total constraint, EC is external constraint, and IC is internal constraint. In our former equation, stimulus equivocation was zero, and thus was not considered. In this form, however, we can see that exchanges can go on between stimulus equivocation and either internal or external constraint; but since stimulus equivocation occurs on both sides of the equation, any exchange involving it on one side must be accompanied by equivalent exchanges on the other side. So if internal constraint is increased by a decrease in stimulus equivocation, so also must total constraint be increased.

Let us return to the role of redundancy in concept problems. Table 10.2 shows schematically a set of redundant stimuli which could be used in a concept problem. These stimuli are formed from four dichotomous variables, so that the maximum stimulus uncertainty is 4 bits. Only eight of the sixteen possible stimuli are actually used, however, so this set of stimuli has 1 bit of internal constraint. In this particular illustration, all of this internal constraint consists of the contingent uncertainty between variables u and v, which are perfectly correlated.

Now the use and meaning of this redundancy depends both on the number of different responses assigned and on the particular assignment. There are two major forms of simple redundancy which can be used in concept problems, and several more complicated forms, depending on the particular assignment of responses to stimuli.

Table 10.2

Redundant stimuli which can be used with different
response systems in concept formation problems.

Stimulus Variable				Response System			
u	v	w	x	1	2	3	4
1	1	1	1	A	A	A	A
1	1	1	0	A	B	B	A
1	1	0	1	A	B	C	B
1	1	0	0	A	A	D	B
0	0	1	1	B	A	A	C
0	0	1	0	B	B	B	C
0	0	0	1	B	B	C	D
0	0	0	0	B	A	D	D

First is *relevant stimulus redundancy*. In this form, the redundancy occurs entirely with respect to those stimulus variables which are made to be relevant to the concept. In the first response system of Table 10.2, the response is completely correlated with variables u and v, which are themselves completely correlated. Thus with this response system, two variables are relevant, and are redundant with respect to each other. On the other hand, variables w and x are irrelevant and are uncorrelated with each other as well as with the two relevant variables and the response variable.

The second major form of redundancy is *irrelevant stimulus redundancy*, in which the relevant dimension or dimensions are uncorrelated, but the irrelevant dimensions are correlated. Response system 3 is an example of this form of redundancy. In this system, four different responses are used, and are assigned to the four different combinations of w and x. Thus the multiple contingent uncertainty between (w, x) and the response is 2 bits. Now u and v are irrelevant variables, since neither is correlated with the response or either of the relevant variables, but they are correlated with each other, so that all of the redundancy is due to the correlation between the irrelevant variables.

There are many other forms of redundancy which can be used, and two others are illustrated in Table 10.2. In the second response system, for example, just two different responses are again used, but the response variable is uncorrelated with any single stimulus variable, and is also uncorrelated with all pairs of variables except the (w, x) variable, with which the contingent uncertainty is 1 bit. Since, however, the two simple contingent uncertainties involved in this multiple contingency are zero, it follows that the total predictable uncertainty is in the interaction term involving (w, x) and the response. This particular illustration is one which would not ordinarily be used in concept formation problems, because normally the concept is directly identified with simple contingent uncertainties. There is no reason why it need be, however.

The fourth response system also is used only to illustrate a more complex but possible system of redundancy. In this case, again with four responses, the responses are assigned so as to correlate perfectly with the four possible combinations of the v and w variables. Thus the multiple contingent uncertainty between these two variables and the response is 2 bits. However, variable u is perfectly correlated with variable v, so that the multiple contingent uncertainty between the response and stimulus variables u and w is also 2 bits. The responses are completely uncorrelated with variable x, and this variable is completely uncorrelated with the other three stimulus variables as well. Therefore, variable x is clearly an irrelevant variable. All three of the other variables are relevant, however, but two of them are redundant with respect to each other.

Some experimental data

Some experiments on concept formation with redundant stimuli have been reported by Bourne and Haygood (1959), with the simple forms of redundancy. Their basic procedure involved either two or four different responses to stimuli generated by several dichotomous variables. They used variables such that either the relevant variables were completely redundant or the irrelevant variables were completely redundant, but none of the more complex forms of response system. With reference to Table 10.2, they used response systems equivalent either to the first or to the third system described, although they used a larger number of redundant variables on occasion than I have illustrated.

In one experiment, Bourne and Haygood always used two responses, but added relevant variables to increase the redundancy. In other words, they simply added variables which were completely correlated with the one relevant variable used as a minimum. They also used one, or three, or five irrelevant variables, and these variables were always uncorrelated with each other as well as being uncorrelated with the relevant variables. Their results are shown in Fig. 10.3, where mean errors are plotted as a function of the number of redundant relevant variables. It is clear that an increase in number of redundant

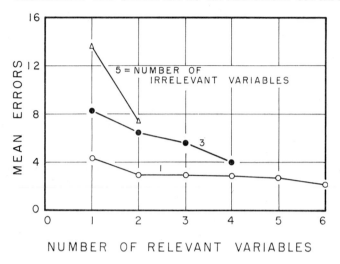

NUMBER OF RELEVANT VARIABLES

FIG. 10.3. The effect of number of relevant variables on solution of concept problem. Relevant variables were completely redundant. Each curve is for a different number of irrelevant variables as indicated, and these variables were independent. (After Bourne and Haygood, 1959.)

relevant variables improves performance, but that this improvement is itself related to the number of irrelevant variables. In particular, as the number of irrelevant variables (and therefore stimulus uncertainty) increases, the greater the gain due to addition of redundancy in the relevant variables. In fact, there is the suggestion that concept learning would be about as good with five irrelevant variables as with one, if the number of redundant relevant variables was five or six. These cases were not used in the actual experiment due to the difficulty of obtaining a large enough total number of variables.

In another experiment, Bourne and Haygood increased the number of irrelevant variables, but in a redundant manner. In this case an increase in number of redundant variables leads to poorer concept learning, as shown in Fig. 10.4, and this result holds with either one or two independent relevant variables. This result is particularly interesting, since an increase in number of redundant irrelevant variables in no way increases the stimulus equivocation, but is actually concomitant with an increase in redundancy. Thus we have a situation here in which an increase in redundancy leads to poorer performance. A comparison of Fig. 10.4 with Fig. 10.3 shows, however, that an increase in redundancy due to a reduction of actual stimulus uncertainty does give better performance, when the response uncertainty is held constant. For example, with one relevant variable and five non-redundant irrelevant variables, the mean errors to criterion was over thirteen, while with the same number of variables but with all five irrelevant variables made redundant, the mean errors to criterion was approximately seven.

In both of these cases the maximum possible stimulus uncertainty is 6 bits, but in the latter case only 2 bits was used, with 4 bits being redundant. This decrease in actual stimulus uncertainty (or increase in redundancy), therefore, leads to improved performance. While detailed comparisons of these two sets of data are not possible due to the fact that they were obtained in two separate experiments, it seems reasonable to conclude that the deleterious effects of number of irrelevant variables comes about both as a result of the number of stimuli which are possible and as a result of the number which are actually used. An increase in the number possible with no increase in the number used leads to some deterioration, but even greater deterioration results when the stimuli are both possible and used.

While we have discussed these and other concept formation experiments primarily within the framework of various information concept, it is clear from these results that there exists no simple relation between any one or two information concepts and the rate

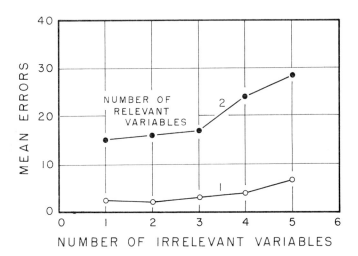

Fig. 10.4. The effect of number of irrelevant variables on solution of concept problem. In this case all irrelevant variables are redundant, but the two relevant variables are independent. (After Bourne and Haygood, 1959.)

at which the concepts are learned. As we have noted, no single measure of amount of redundancy, percent redundancy, or stimulus uncertainty uniquely determines rate of learning. And it is even more unlikely that these relations would be simple if variations in the nature or pattern of the external structure were introduced. The chief value of the use of information concepts, it seems to me, is in providing an analytic framework within which to carry out such experiments. It is likely that any final explanatory system will be more in the nature of present learning theories, and Bourne and Restle (1959) have shown that a learning-theory type of explanation fits the results of these experiments quite well. This is not the proper place, however, to go into the details of this type of explanatory theory.

FORM OF EXTERNAL CONSTRAINT WITH NON-REDUNDANT STIMULI

When each stimulus is assigned a unique response, as we were assuming in Chapter Five, there exists no problem concerning the form of external constraint unless redundant stimuli are used. In other words, if each stimulus has its own response, and all possible stimuli are used, then the form of the external constraint is invariant and consists solely of simple contingent uncertainties between the stimulus variables and the response variable. Only when there is some selec-

Table 10.3

Symbolic representation of eight different stimuli formed from three dichotomous variables, and four response systems for which the eight stimuli are arranged into two groups of four each. These are the stimuli and response systems used by Shepard, Hovland, and Jenkins (1961).

Stimulus Variable			Response System			
v	w	x	I	II	IV	VI
1	1	1	A	A	A	B
1	1	0	A	A	A	A
1	0	1	A	B	B	A
1	0	0	A	B	A	B
0	1	1	B	B	B	A
0	1	0	B	B	A	B
0	0	1	B	A	B	B
0	0	0	B	A	B	A

Table 10.4

An uncertainty analysis for the four systems of response to the
eight stimuli divided into two groups of four each given
in Table 10.3. (y is the response variable.)

Uncertainty Term	Response Systems			
	I	II	IV	VI
$y\!:\!v$	1.00	0	0.19	0
$y\!:\!w$	0	0	0.19	0
$y\!:\!x$	0	0	0.19	0
$\overline{yvw}$	0	1.00	0.12	0
$\overline{yvx}$	0	0	0.12	0
$\overline{ywx}$	0	0	0.12	0
$\overline{yvwx}$	0	0	0.07	1.00
Σ	1.00	1.00	1.00	1.00

tion of stimuli does the question of the form of the external constraint arise.

When, however, more than one stimulus is assigned the same response, with the resultant stimulus equivocation, there arises the
problem of the particular method of assigning responses to the stimuli.
Thus also there arises the question of what form of external constraint
exists. We have just been discussing the form of external constraint
with redundant stimuli, but the problem can exist as well with non-
redundant stimuli.

Shepard, Hovland, and Jenkins (1961) report a series of experiments
in which they used six different methods of assigning dichotomous
responses to eight stimuli formed from three dichotomous variables.
There are, incidentally, only six fundamentally different ways of
making these assignments, since various changes in the meanings of
the variables will lead to the same pattern of uncertainties. Four of
these types of response classification are shown in Table 10.3. We are
using only four of them because the other two provide patterns of
uncertainties much like those provided by system IV. The actual
uncertainty components for each of these systems are shown in Table
10.4, where the basic nature of the differences between these response
systems can be seen.

System I, for example, has the response variable perfectly correlated
with stimulus variable v, and since all stimulus variables are uncorrelated (due to the fact that all possible combinations exist), the
response variable is uncorrelated with any other stimulus variable

or combination of variables. In many ways this is the simplest possible type of classification, and corresponds most closely to what we normally mean by a concept problem. With this system, variable v is relevant, and the other three variables are completely irrelevant. The subject learning to use this system has a relatively easy task.

System II is slightly more complicated in that the response is uncorrelated with any single stimulus variable, but is perfectly correlated with combinations of variables v and w. The rule is, similar to an illustration used previously, simply that whenever these two variables have the same value, the correct response is A; and when they have different values, the correct response is B. The application of this rule, of course, can be more difficult than it seems from this statement of it, because in practice the two stimulus variables, while each dichotomous, do not necessarily have the same value. Since the response variable is uncorrelated with either variable v or w, but has a multiple contingency of 1 bit with the combination of these two variables, then the entire contingency is contained in an interaction term, as indicated in Table 10.4. As a concept problem, this response system requires that the subject be aware of two stimulus variables which are relevant, and learn to ignore the third.

Response system IV is still further complicated, and in terms of the uncertainty analysis is the most complicated of all. Each response, for this system, occurs three times out of four with one of the two values of each variable. For example, when v has a value of 1, then A occurs three times and B once. Similarly for the other two stimulus variables. This fact means that there is a correlation between each stimulus variable and the response, but not a complete one; and the actual contingent uncertainty is 0.19 bit. In addition, each pair of values provides 0.50 bit of contingent uncertainty, since some combination values completely specify the response while other combinations leave complete response uncertainty. For example, when v and w each has a value of 1, the response is always A, but when v has a value of 1 and w has a value of 0, then half the time the response is A and the other half of the time it is B.

This response system means that each of the three-variable interactions has a value of 0.12 bit. In addition, there is a small four-variable interaction. This pattern of uncertainties means that no pair of stimulus variables can completely specify the correct response, and that none of the three variables can be ignored by the subject as being irrelevant to the concept. The verbalization of the concept in this case is much more complicated: When both v and w have values of 1, the response is A, and when they have values of 0, the response is B.

When v and w have different values, ignore variable w and look at pairs of v and x; if these two have values of 1, then the response is B, and if they have values of 0, the response is A.[1]

The last response system, VI, is one in which the response is completely uncorrelated with any single stimulus variable, and is also completely uncorrelated with any pair of these variables. Thus no simple contingency or multiple contingency from two predictors is greater than zero. However, the total multiple contingent uncertainty still has a value of 1 bit, all of which is in the four-variable interaction term.

The pattern of uncertainties for this response system certainly looks less complicated than the pattern for system IV. Yet psychologically there is quite a difference between them. For system IV, all variables must be noted to obtain a complete specification of the response, but noting any two variables still provides considerable decrease in uncertainty. In system VI, however, no information can be obtained from any pair of variables. Thus in order to obtain any reduction in uncertainty at all, the values of all three variables must be noted.

In a sense, we can say that all variables are completely relevant with this system, but that all variables are only partially relevant with system IV. The concept in this last case, while complicated, can still be stated verbally: If v and w have the same value, then respond B if x is 1, and A if x is 0. If v and w have different values, then respond A if x is 1 and B if x is 0. And once again, the application of this rule in practice may be much more difficult when the different stimulus variables do not have the same values.

In one experiment, Shepard, Hovland, and Jenkins used pairs of pictures as their stimulus variables. One pair was nut or bolt; another pair was candle or lightbulb; and the third pair was violin or horn. One value from each pair was presented simultaneously, and subjects were required to learn the correct response for each triple picture. Some of their data for mean errors during learning are shown in Fig. 10.5, a set of results which leaves little ambiguity that learning of concepts is more difficult when the pattern of uncertainties includes higher order contingencies and interactions. The results show a direct

---

[1] It should be clear that these verbalizations are in symbolic form only, and that the application of the verbalization in actual practice is much more complicated. While we are using 0 and 1 to symbolize the two values of each variable, in an actual experiment each variable would have two values but they might be entirely different things. For example, we might use large and small, black and white, squares and triangles. If actual values of 0 and 1 are used, then the verbalization might be even simpler than I have stated. In this case, for example, an odd number of zeros calls for A, and an even number of zeros calls for B.

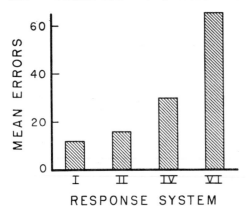

Fig. 10.5. Mean number of errors made in concept formation as a function of the type of response system. See Table 10.3 for type of response system. (Data from Shepard, Hovland, and Jenkins, 1961.)

relation between difficulty of learning and the number of variables which must be noted before the concept can be specified.

In another experiment, these same authors used three geometric figures as variables, each of which could be large or small. They required their subjects to state the rule for the concept, and then used the percent of subjects getting the correct concept and the time required to arrive at the concept as dependent measures. These results, with different stimuli and different methods lead to exactly the same conclusion as above, in that more time was required and less accuracy was obtained, the more variables the subject had to use for his concept.

These results in no way contradict one's intuitive feelings about which of the various response systems should lead to most rapid performance. The more complicated the rule for the concept, the more we should expect the concept to be difficult to learn. In information terms, we see that simple contingencies (between single stimulus variables and the response variable) are the most easily learned, a result which has appeared in other connections; and that interaction uncertainties are the most difficult to learn. Perhaps this result is not so surprising when we realize how difficult it is at times to visualize a set of data in which there is an interaction.

COMMENTARY

The literature on concept formation does not lend itself easily to understanding or interpretation in terms of the ideas discussed in this book. The reason is that primary emphasis has been placed on the ability of the subject to abstract the one or more relevant dimensions of the stimulus, so that the major concern has been on the nature of the relevant variables of the stimulus, and little attention has been paid to the nature of the irrelevant variables. In fact, very often the exact nature of the irrelevant variables as seen by the subject cannot clearly be specified. Yet it is self evident that the process of selecting relevant variables is simultaneously the process of rejecting irrelevant variables.

If there is any one thing which seems of paramount importance to me, it is that we, as experimenters, must be able to specify exactly the nature of the stimuli used in an experiment, the nature of the responses, and the required relations (significations) between them. If we use a non-redundant set of stimuli in a concept experiment, the problem of specifying the nature of the stimuli is quite simple, since all possible combinations of the variables are seen by the subject. If the stimuli are redundant, however, the problem is much more complex, and the nature of the problem as seen by the subject may change considerably from one set of redundant stimuli to another depending on the exact form of the redundancy.

In most concept experiments, only the relevant variables are controlled in any systematic fashion; moreover, quite often the number of variables occurring in the stimuli is far greater than required for the number of stimuli actually presented. In other words, the stimuli are in fact redundant, but no account is taken of the amount or the form of this redundancy. And yet it seems to me that the exact amount (and form) of the redundancy is probably one of the most important factors determining the rate of concept learning.

Bourne and Haygood (1959) have shown, as we have noted, that an increase of stimulus redundancy with the addition of correlated relevant variables improves concept learning, but that an increase of stimulus redundancy with the addition of correlated irrelevant variables hinders concept learning. In these experiments, actual stimulus uncertainty was held constant (that is, the number of stimuli used was the same), so that the addition of the redundancy in no way affected the total number of different stimuli seen by the subject. The redundancy only affected the nature of the stimuli, and the two different kinds of redundancy differed only in respect to which stimuli from the total set of possible stimuli were actually seen by the subject. Thus a simple change in the form of the redundancy either improved or impaired concept learning.

Relatively simple forms of redundancy were used in these experiments: The additional variables were perfectly correlated with either the relevant or the irrelevant stimuli. However, other forms of redundancy can be used as well, and it is quite possible that different effects might be obtained with these other forms.

To use a simple example, suppose that we have three dichotomous variables, and from the eight possible stimuli we select four to use, giving us 1 bit of stimulus redundancy or structure. We might use the following symbolic stimuli: 000, 011, 100, and 111, and if we define the first variable as relevant for a dichotomous response, then the second two variables are irrelevant and perfectly correlated. This set of stimuli corresponds to one of the sets used by Bourne and Haygood, with one relevant and two irrelevant redundant variables.

Again, we might choose another set of stimuli from the eight possible: 000, 011, 101, and 110. We can again define the first variable as relevant, and the other two are once again irrelevant since neither of them is correlated with the relevant variable. There is a great difference, however, between this set of stimuli and the one given just above; the difference is that in this second set of stimuli the two irrelevant variables are uncorrelated with each other as well as being uncorrelated with the relevant variable. In both cases we have one relevant and two irrelevant variables, and in both cases the amount of stimulus redundancy is 1 bit. The only difference is in the form of stimulus redundancy.

Should this difference in the form of redundancy make a difference in concept learning? I think that it might, and that the reason has to do with the subject's perception of the structure of the set of stimuli. Let us once again suppose, as we have before, that the kind of structure most easily perceived by a subject is that involving simple contingencies between stimulus variables. If this supposition is true, then a subject will be able to perceive internal structure (structure within the set of stimuli itself) fairly easily in the first set of stimuli, since two of the stimulus variables are perfectly correlated. However, his task is defined in terms of external structure, since he must learn to make a discriminating response to the stimuli. In other words, he is required to respond differentially to the stimuli. The subject, however, enters into an experiment with a set to determine the structure in the total situation, and the nature of the redundancy is such that structure is easily perceived in the stimuli themselves. Unfortunately, the only structure which exists within the stimuli is that within the subset of irrelevant variables—the very stimulus variables which he must learn to ignore. His external structure relates to the relevant variable, to be sure, but the subject must first learn to ignore the internal structure of the irrelevant variables.

With the second set of stimuli, there is no easily perceived internal structure in the set of stimuli. There is still 1 bit of redundancy, but this 1 bit is in the form of the interaction involving all three stimulus variables, and is much less easily perceived by the subject. Thus the only structure the subject can easily find is the external structure— the relation between the response and the relevant variable. It seems more than possible that the subject will learn the concept faster with this second set of redundant stimuli than with the first set, because in the second set there is no interference from an easily perceived structure which is irrelevant to his task.

Because of the small number of variables in our illustration, there might not be an appreciable experimental effect of this difference. Still, the same principle can be applied to much more complicated sets of stimuli, even though there are limits operating on the number of simple contingencies which can exist with dichotomous variables, as we discussed them in Chapter Five.

It is obvious here that I am making an assumption, namely, that in any experimental (or other) situation the subject is searching for structure. Normally, we define the concept task in terms of the required external structure, and we decide when the subject has performed adequately in terms of his demonstrated correct use of the defined external structure. The point I want to stress is simply this: The subject searches for structure, but the internal structure of the set of stimuli may be as important to him as the external structure to the experimenter. Thus the ease or difficulty of a concept problem almost certainly cannot be solely a function of the amount of external structure, or the amount of stimulus equivocation. It must also be a function of both the amount and form of internal structure. Or perhaps we can state the problem more simply by stating that concept learning must also be a function of the internal structure of the stimuli as perceived by the subject.

The suggestion that the perceived internal structure should be within the subset of variables which are defined as relevant is contained in the experimental results of Bourne and Haygood, since the same amount of redundancy produces better performance if the structure as perceived by the subject is within the subset of relevant stimuli than if it is in the subset of irrelevant stimuli. I am simply extending this point to suggest that redundancy which leads to little perceived structure (redundancy primarily involving interactions) may have little deleterious effect even if it does involve the irrelevant stimuli, and might even have an advantageous effect. Certainly there should be an advantageous effect if there is perceived structure within the relevant variables, and no perceived structure within the irrelevant variables.

Suppose, for example, the following three sets of redundant stimuli:

A	B	C
000	0000	0000
001	0011	0011
110	1100	1101
111	1111	1110

If in each set we define the first two variables as relevant, then in each set of stimuli we have two redundant relevant variables. In set A, there is 1 bit of redundancy, and all of it is in the contingency between the two relevant variables. This redundancy should aid concept learning when compared to learning with all eight possible stimuli, one of which is relevant. In set B we have added 1 bit more of redundancy, and have put it in the contingency between what are now the two irrelevant variables. Thus the total of 2 bits of redundancy is contained in easily perceived contingent uncertainties, and the subject can perceive both the relevant and the irrelevant variables as structured. We know that the addition of this correlated irrelevant variable will make concept learning more difficult.

The critical set of stimuli is set C, where we have again added 1 bit of redundancy compared to set A, but its form is such that there is no easily perceived structure within the two irrelevant variables, since they are uncorrelated. In other words, the additional redundancy is contained in interactions. It is quite possible that the addition of this irrelevant redundancy may aid concept learning compared to set A, since there is now provided a clear differentiation between the relevant and the irrelevant variables. The subject will quickly perceive the internal structure in the relevant variables, but the irrelevant variables will be perceived as unrelated to each other and also to the two structured variables. Thus the subject's perception of the internal structure is consonant with his task of relating these stimuli to an external variable.

To summarize, if the subject's perceived structure in the stimuli is not related to the external variable, he will have interference in his task. If his perceived structure is related to the external variable, he will have facilitation. Possibly, if the relevant variables are perceived as structured, and the irrelevant variables as unstructured, he will have facilitation because he will more quickly differentiate between the relevant and the irrelevant variables.

SUMMARY

The basic experimental paradigm for what is called a concept problem is quite similar to the paradigm for a paired-associates learning task or an absolute judgment problem, in that a series of stimuli is presented and the subject must learn to use different responses for different stimuli. There are two essential characteristics of the task, however, which make it different from these other tasks and thus define it as a concept problem. First, the subject must use the same response for more than one stimulus. In uncertainty terms, this requirement means that there is stimulus equivocation. Second, the stimuli must be multivariate in nature, so that one or more of the variables can be defined as relevant to the response differentiation required, and the others as irrelevant. The number of irrelevant variables, of course, determines the amount of stimulus equivocation.

If the entire set of stimuli which can be formed from a given number of variables is used in an experiment, then we have a non-redundant set of stimuli. In this case, with a fixed number of relevant variables, the addition of irrelevant variables increases stimulus uncertainty and stimulus equivocation. The effect of such an increase is clearly to increase the difficulty of concept learning.

When fewer stimuli are used than can be formed with a fixed number of variables, then we have a redundant set of stimuli, and the form and amount of redundancy become important variables. If redundancy is added to a fixed number of stimuli by adding variables which are correlated with the redundant variable, then the redundancy aids concept learning. If, however, variables are added which are correlated with the irrelevant variable, then the redundancy hinders concept learning.

This result makes it clear that the form of the external constraint or structure is an important variable in concept learning with redundant stimuli. When there exists stimulus equivocation, as is necessarily true in a concept problem, then the form of the external constraint can be varied, even with no stimulus redundancy, by the method of assigning responses to stimuli. Experimentally it has been shown that methods of assignment which make the minimum number of variables relevant are the most efficient for concept learning.

It is suggested that the form of the external structure within a set of redundant stimuli may be an even more important variable than shown so far, since all forms of structure are not equally perceivable by subjects. Probably an ideal form of structure is that which is perceived within the set of relevant variables, and structure within irrelevant variables is probably best if it is in the form of the less easily perceived interactions.

CHAPTER ELEVEN

Final Commentary

IN CHAPTER ONE, I expressed some attitudes toward the material to be presented in this book. In particular, I disclaimed any intent to present a theory of information, at least to present a general theory or a theory of information in the communication sense. Perhaps the reasons for my disclaimer are now a little more apparent. It is true that the mathematical base for the material presented in this book comes from modern information theory, but its value to me is less in providing a measure of information than in providing a very general mathematics for purposes of multivariate analysis. It is the generality of the uncertainty measure which has been so useful.

Insofar as this book is theoretical, it is more concerned with a theory of structure than with a theory of information. While my initial development treated psychological material more or less as problems of information transmission, the concepts of structure introduced in Chapter Five form the essence of the book. In fact, I would have preferred to start the book at that point, since the earlier material is easily subsumed under the topic of external constraint, and can be treated in a more general fashion by considering the role of external constraint in relation to the parallel role of internal constraint.

Even if we consider that I have presented a theory of structure, it certainly is not a complete theory. Rather, it is an attempt to use these concepts of structure to provide a logical analysis of several classes of psychological problem. Also, there are many kinds and aspects of psychological problem which are concerned with things other than the structure of variables. Especially the problems of signification, both internal and external, form a large class of psychological problem over

338

and above that of general structure. I feel that structure, in the sense of my use of the term, is in many ways a more fundamental problem, if for no other reason than that an amount of structure is prerequisite to the existence of significations.

I have tried to develop some of the more general ideas by dealing with specific problem areas. It becomes obvious that I am making some basic assumptions which underlie my treatment of the material, and at times I have specifically stated some of these assumptions. Nevertheless, it might be well, by way of a final commentary, to state some of the more important of these assumptions in summary form.

1. *Uncertainty is prerequisite to structure.* This statement is, of course, not really an assumption, but a fact. When stated in mathematical terms, it is an obvious fact, since it is only saying that without variability there can be no correlation, and what we are talking about as structure is a form of non-metric correlation.

The reason for making a special point of this relation is simply that it has so frequently been misunderstood when we apply the concept of structure. It sounds reasonable to say that structure is the lack of uncertainty, but the statement is wrong. Structure is *related* uncertainty, not the lack of it, and to have structure is to have uncertainty. Furthermore, to increase structure is also to increase uncertainty, and it is this aspect of the problem which is conceptually so important.

To add redundancy is to add uncertainty, or variability, not to reduce it. The addition of uncertainty does not per se, however, produce redundancy, since the uncertainty must be added in a meaningful way. But the addition of uncertainty is still prerequisite to the addition of redundancy. Thus redundancy, as one form of structure, is related directly to the amount of uncertainty, not inversely.

It is for these reasons that I have used a notation in which every term is symbolized as an uncertainty—to emphasize the fact that uncertainty and structure, or uncertainty and information, are the same commodity. Transmitted information is simply structured uncertainty, and total constraint is just a measure of how much of the total uncertainty exists in a structured, or constrained, form.

Structure is still the important kind of uncertainty, and unstructured uncertainty is equivocation, or noise, or error, whichever term you prefer. It is uncertainty which is unrelated to any other uncertainty.

2. *The search for structure is inherent in behavior.* This statement is an assumption, one which is implicit in many of the topical discussions in this book. People in any situation will search for meaningful relations between the variables existing in the situation, and if no

such relations exist or can be perceived, considerable discomfort occurs. The search for structure will occur with respect to either internal or external structure, but preferably for both. Thus we will try to perceive the relations which exist in the stimulus environment, but we will also try to relate our own behavior to the variations in the stimulus environment. In the first case we are attempting to perceive the internal structure which exists in the stimulus environment, and in the second case we are trying to provide external structure by relating our own behavior to the stimulus variations.

In addition to this general assumption, I suspect there is another aspect of the problem which was touched on briefly in Chapter Ten. This is the fact that we ordinarily expect external structure to occur primarily with respect to the structured part of the internal system of stimulus variables. In any given stimulus situation, there can exist subsystems of structure, and these subsystems may or may not be related to each other. In Chapter Ten, we discussed experiments in which the relevant variables were unstructured with respect to themselves, and the irrelevant variables were structured with respect to themselves, although by definition they were unrelated to the relevant variables and thus to the external response variable. We saw that the addition of such redundant irrelevant variables made concept attainment more difficult.

It seems to me that there is probably a general expectation that those variables in the environment which are related to each other should be those variables which are related to one's own behavior. In other words, when we try to perceive the structure in the environment, we are trying to determine which aspects of the environment have meaningful relations and which ones do not. Now if we see internal structure within one set of variables, we assume them to be the meaningful aspects of the environment; but if they are not related to our own behavior, we must break this assumption before we can relate our responses to the relevant variables.

To search for a concept is to search for external structure; but if internal structure exists, it will be sought out also. If these two structures are not both relevant to the task at hand, then ineffective performance will ensue.

In view of my first major point in this chapter, it should be pointed out that the search for structure is simultaneously the search for uncertainty, since structure cannot exist without uncertainty. True, structure does not necessarily exist because of uncertainty, but without the uncertainty there can be no structure. Stimulus deprivation experiments have highlighted the deleterious effects of a lack of stimulus uncertainty. Strictly speaking, these are not experiments on stimulus deprivation, since stimulation exists; rather, they are experiments on the lack of stimulus uncertainty or variability. I am not really sure that this difference is critical, however, since I feel that uncertainty and structure are so fundamental to behavior that stimulation without variability is effectively no stimulation at all. However, to say that the search for structure is also the search for uncertainty does not mean that any kind of uncertainty will satisfy the requirements. The search is for related uncertainty, for variability which can be meaningfully related to other variabilities.

This search for structure is so dominating a characteristic of behavior that it will be created if none exists; or if only a small amount exists it may be emphasized or elaborated. Any psychologist who has run psychophysical experiments where minimal or ambiguous stimulous differences exist is well aware of the dangers involved. Subjects will find any cue at all to which they can relate their responses, and if a small artifactual cue exists which is, strictly speaking, irrelevant to the defined task, the subject will nevertheless relate his responses to that artifactual cue. The entire literature on context effects in judgment shows the extent to which subjects maximize external structure by responding so as to maximize the possible correlation of their responses with the stimuli (that is, by maximizing the uncertainty of their responses, they are also maximizing the amount of uncertainty which can be externally structured by relation to stimulus differences). This pattern of responding occurs even though the instructions emphasize an absolute criterion (a criterion which presumes an exact and invariant signification).

To summarize my assumptions so far, statements 1 and 2, taken together, imply that behavior is primarily relational. The search for structure is simultaneously the search for uncertainty, and maximum uncertainty occurs where there are maximum differences in either the perceived world or in our responses.

3. *Structure can exist meaningfully only within specified systems.* When we are concerned about the experimenter's ability to specify the amount of uncertainty and the amount of structure, this statement is a fact and not an assumption. Nor will there be any serious disagreement with the statement. It becomes an assumption, however, when I extend it to say that for any individual it is also true. The subject who sees a single stimulus as structured does so only because he generates an implied set of stimuli against which the particular stimulus can be contrasted, or within which the particular stimulus can be subsumed. I have discussed this assumption in much more specific form

in Chapter Six, but I believe it to be a general characteristic, and not related to a particular problem of visual pattern perception.

In the discussion up to this point, I am agreeing to a considerable extent with classical Gestalt theory, although I have emphasized the problem of uncertainty in addition to that of structure. However, in the present matter I am disagreeing with classical Gestalt theory, and I feel that the major failing of such theory has been its assumption that it can deal adequately with the single stimulus pattern. Take the problem of figure reproduction, for example, where on reproduction after a time period we have such phenomena as leveling, closure, and sharpening. Only in rare cases can sensible prediction be made as to which phenomenon will occur with which figure. On the other hand, expectations about which phenomena will occur become much clearer when we experimentally specify a complete set of stimuli, rather than allowing the subject to generate his own set, but without our knowledge of what the set is.

Suppose we have a set of four figures: a circle, square, triangle, and trapezoid. Now suppose also that a small gap is put in each figure in approximately the same position on the bottom. We ask our subject to look at the figures, and a week later request him to reproduce them. Since the gap was a non-differentiating aspect of the four figures, it generates no uncertainty and thus is irrelevant to any system of relating these figures to some external criterion. Thus we would expect closure of the gap.

Suppose, however, that we give the subject four squares all of the same size, but put a gap on a different side of each figure. On later recall now the gap cannot close, because if it does the only differentiating cue is destroyed, and the subject has lost the only structure available. In this case, not only will we fail to get closure, but we very likely will get enhancement (sharpening) of the gap. In other words, sharpening will occur for those aspects of the figure which are differentiating, and closure, or perhaps leveling, will occur for those aspects which are non-differentiating.

We could carry this line of reasoning even further, by considering what might happen if we deliberately provide the external constraint. Suppose, for example, we use four different sizes of rectangle, and four different positions of a gap, to generate sixteen figures altogether. Now we require our subject to learn four different labels, correlated with the four sizes, but uncorrelated with the position of the gap, as in the typical concept problem. Later we again ask for reproduction of all sixteen figures. We might well expect closure of the gap but enhancement of the size differences. (Note well that I said enhancement of the size *differences,* not enlargement or contraction of a single size.)

4. *Structure as such is a property of systems.* Structure is an entire set of relations between variables, and its amount and form can be specified without statement of the particular significations which operate because of the structure. The structure can be perceived even without the ability to verbalize the significations. We can, for example, perceive the structure in music without being able to state the signification rules, and we can directly perceive that one musical system has more structure than another system.

It should be clear, however, that by structure I mean the totality of the relations between sets of variables, and do not mean the specific relations between the elements of a single pattern or mosaic. It is for this reason that I emphasize the need to specify entire sets of stimuli, rather than the unique stimulus, because the relations that I am talking about are relations between variables over the set of stimuli.

When I say that structure as such is a property of systems, I am implying that the structure as perceived is not a function of the particular elements of the individual combinations (or stimulus patterns). Thus a set of stimuli may have the elements transformed, but the structure can remain the same, just as in a factor analysis we can rotate the axes without changing the amount or the form of the structure. We are simply changing the ease of verbal description of the structure, perhaps, but are not changing the structure itself.

This point about structure per se being a critical variable in psychological work came out most importantly when we were discussing verbal learning. I pointed out then that experiments which simply vary the extent to which the material to be learned resembles English are not experiments on structure, or redundancy, but are simply experiments on the extent to which particular statistical significations are learned. However, the existence of structure itself can, and must, affect the rate of learning, and, insofar as it does, we must then consider structure as a meaningful variable in its own right—not simply the sum of the significations.

There is just one last comment I would like to make, and that concerns the extent to which some of the concepts and principles discussed in this book have a greater generality than I have tried to show. Some of the ideas expressed here can be used in a verbal, and thus less exact, form to describe other psychological problems. For example, we can think of all the behavior of a particular individual as a closed system of variables. The total variability, or uncertainty, of this behavior will then determine the maximum constraint which can exist for this system of variables and the totality of the external system of variables to which the person must relate. Now this total constraint can be divided into internal and external constraint, but the amount available for external relating is limited by the amount of internal constraint. Thus any given individual can be considered to face a decision concerning the extent to which he becomes structured internally (thus having his own integrated personality) and the extent to which he chooses to relate to the external world. The problem of balance between these two kinds of structure must be a real one.

In a similar vein, any group of persons can relate to itself or to individuals and groups outside itself. Once again, however, the total structure is limited by the uncertainty within the group, and the greater the amount of internal structuring, the less must be the external structuring.

I have not pursued topics which can be handled only at this verbal level, because I cannot specify exactly enough what the amounts and kinds of uncertainty and structure are. Rather, I have attempted to work at some realistic level of compromise—a compromise between exactness (with its frequent lack of generality) and maximum generality (with its concomitant lack of exactness). I hope that I have hit a fruitful degree of compromise.

Appendix

Values of $\log_2 n$ and $-p \log_2 p$. The entry is either n or p, depending on which column is read out.*

n or p	$\log_2 n$	$-p \log_2 p$	n o p	$\log_2 n$	$-p \log_2 p$
1	0.000	.0664	31	4.954	.5238
2	1.000	.1129	32	5.000	.5260
3	1.585	.1518	33	5.044	.5278
4	2.000	.1858	34	5.087	.5292
5	2.322	.2161	35	5.129	.5301
6	2.585	.2435	36	5.170	.5306
7	2.807	.2686	37	5.209	.5307
8	3.000	.2915	38	5.248	.5304
9	3.170	.3127	39	5.285	.5298
10	3.322	.3322	40	5.322	.5288
11	3.459	.3503	41	5.358	.5274
12	3.585	.3671	42	5.392	.5256
13	3.700	.3826	43	5.426	.5236
14	3.807	.3971	44	5.459	.5211
15	3.907	.4105	45	5.492	.5184
16	4.000	.4230	46	5.524	.5153
17	4.087	.4346	47	5.555	.5120
18	4.170	.4453	48	5.585	.5083
19	4.248	.4552	49	5.615	.5043
20	4.322	.4644	50	5.644	.5000
21	4.392	.4728	51	5.672	.4954
22	4.459	.4806	52	5.700	.4906
23	4.524	.4877	53	5.728	.4854
24	4.585	.4941	54	5.755	.4800
25	4.644	.5000	55	5.781	.4744
26	4.700	.5053	56	5.807	.4684
27	4.755	.5100	57	5.833	.4623
28	4.807	.5142	58	5.858	.4558
29	4.858	.5179	59	5.883	.4491
30	4.907	.5211	60	5.907	.4422

* These values were originally prepared at the Operational Applications Laboratory. Complete tables are available in Air Force Cambridge Research Center, Technical Report 54–50.

n or p	$\log_2 n$	$-p \log_2 p$	n or p	$\log_2 n$	$-p \log_2 p$
61	5.931	.4350	81	6.340	.2462
62	5.954	.4276	82	6.358	.2348
63	5.977	.4199	83	6.375	.2231
64	6.000	.4121	84	6.392	.2113
65	6.022	.4040	85	6.409	.1993
66	6.044	.3957	86	6.426	.1871
67	6.066	.3871	87	6.443	.1748
68	6.087	.3784	88	6.459	.1623
69	6.109	.3694	89	6.476	.1496
70	6.129	.3602	90	6.492	.1368
71	6.150	.3508	91	6.508	.1238
72	6.170	.3412	92	6.524	.1107
73	6.190	.3314	93	6.539	.0974
74	6.209	.3215	94	6.555	.0839
75	6.229	.3113	95	6.570	.0703
76	6.248	.3009	96	6.585	.0565
77	6.267	.2903	97	6.600	.0426
78	6.285	.2796	98	6.615	.0286
79	6.304	.2687	99	6.629	.0140
80	6.322	.2575	100	6.644	.0000

References

Aborn, M., and H. Rubenstein. Information theory and immediate recall. *J. exp. Psychol.*, 1952, **44**, 260–266.

Aborn, M., and H. Rubenstein. Perception of contextually dependent word-probabilities. *Amer. J. Psychol.*, 1958, **71**, 420–422.

Aborn, M., H. Rubenstein, and T. D. Sterling. Sources of contextual constraint upon words in sentences. *J. exp. Psychol.*, 1959, **57**, 171–180.

Adelson, M., F. A. Muckler, and A. C. Williams, Jr. Verbal learning and message variables related to amount of information. In H. Quastler (Ed.), *Information theory in psychology*. Glencoe, Ill.: Free Press, 1955.

Alluisi, E. A. Conditions affecting the amount of information in absolute judgments. *Psychol. Rev.*, 1957, **64**, 97–103.

Alluisi, E. A., and H. B. Martin. An information analysis of verbal and motor responses to symbolic and convential Arabic numerals. *J. appl. Psychol.*, 1958, **42**, 79–84.

Alluisi, E. A., and P. F. Muller, Jr. Verbal and motor responses to seven symbolic codes: A study in S-R compatibility. *J. exp. Psychol.*, 1958, **55**, 247–254.

Alluisi, E. A., P. F. Muller, Jr., and P. M. Fitts. An information analysis of verbal and motor responses in a forced-paced serial task. *J. exp. Psychol.*, 1957, **53**, 153–158.

Alluisi, E. A., and R. C. Sidorsky. The empirical validity of equal discriminability scaling. *J. exp. Psychol.*, 1958, **55**, 86–95.

Anderson, N. A. Effect of first-order conditional probability in a two-choice learning situation. *J. exp. Psychol.*, 1960, **59**, 73–93.

Anderson, N. S., and P. M. Fitts. Amount of information gained during brief exposures of numerals and colors. *J. exp. Psychol.*, 1958, **56**, 362–369.

Anderson, N. S., and J. A. Leonard. The recognition, naming, and reconstruction of visual figures as a function of contour redundancy. *J. exp. Psychol.*, 1958, **56**, 262–270.

Annett, J., C. W. Golby, and J. Kay. The measurement of elements in an assembly task—the information output of the human motor system. *Quart. J. exp. Psychol.*, 1958, **10**, 1–11.

Archer, E. J. Identification of visual patterns as a function of information load. *J. exp. Psychol.*, 1954, **48**, 313–317.

Archer, E. J., L. E. Bourne, Jr., and F. G. Brown. Concept identification as a function of irrelevant information and instructions. *J. exp. Psychol.*, 1955, **49**, 153–164.

Attneave, F. Psychological probability as a function of experienced frequency. *J. exp. Psychol.*, 1953, **46**, 81–86.

Attneave, F. Some informational aspects of visual perception. *Psychol. Rev.*, 1954, **61**, 183–193.

Attneave, F. Symmetry, information, and memory for patterns. *Amer. J. Psychol.*, 1955, **68**, 209–222.

Attneave, F. Physical determinants of the judged complexity of shapes. *J. exp. Psychol.*, 1957a, **53**, 221–227

Attneave, F. Transfer of experience with a class-schema to identification-learning of patterns and shapes. *J. exp. Psychol.*, 1957b, **54**, 81–88.

Attneave, F. *Applications of information theory to psychology.* New York: Holt, Rinehart, and Winston, 1959a.

Attneave, F. Stochastic composition processes. *J. Aesthet.*, 1959b, **17**, 503–510.

Attneave, F., and M. D. Arnoult. The quantitative study of shape and pattern perception. *Psychol. Bull.*, 1956, **53**, 452–471.

Augenstine, L., A. A. Blank, H. Quastler, and M. Wayner. *Flash recognition of familiar displays.* Control Systems Lab., University of Illinois. No. R-69, 1956.

Bahrick, H. P., and C. Shelly. Time sharing as an index of automatization. *J. exp. Psychol.*, 1958, **56**, 288–293.

Bar-Hillel, Y. An examination of information theory. *Phil. Sci.*, 1955, **22**, 86–105.

Battig, W. F. Some factors affecting performance on a word-formation problem. *J. exp. Psychol.*, 1957, **54**, 96–104.

Battig, W. F. Effects of previous experience and information on performance on a word-formation problem. *J. exp. Psychol.*, 1958, **56**, 282–287.

Beebe-Center, J. G., M. S. Rogers, and D. M. O'Connell. Transmission of information about sucrose and saline solutions through the sense of taste. *J. Psychol.*, 1955, **39**, 157–160.

Bendig, A. W. Twenty questions: An information analysis. *J. exp. Psychol.*, 1953, **46**, 345–348.

Bendig, A. W. Transmitted information and the length of rating scales. *J. exp. Psychol.*, 1954, **47**, 303–308.

Bendig, A. W., and J. B. Hughes, II. Effect of amount of verbal anchoring and number of rating-scale categories upon transmitted information. *J. exp. Psychol.*, 1953, **46**, 87–90.

Bennett, W. F., P. M. Fitts, and M. Noble. The learning of sequential dependencies. *J. exp. Psychol.*, 1954, **48**, 303–312.

Berlyne, D. E. Conflict and information-theory variables as determinants of human perceptual curiosity. *J. exp. Psychol.*, 1957a, **53**, 399–404.

Berlyne, D. E. Conflict and choice time. *Brit. J. Psychol.*, 1957b, **48**, 106–118.

Berlyne, D. E. Uncertainty and conflict: A point of contact between information-theory and behavior-theory concepts. *Psychol. Rev.*, 1957c, **64**, 329–339.

Berlyne, D. E. The influence of complexity and novelty in visual figures on orienting responses. *J. exp. Psychol.*, 1958a, **55**, 289–296.

Berlyne, D. E. Supplementary report: Complexity and orienting responses with longer exposures. *J. exp. Psychol.*, 1958b, **56**, 183.

Bevan, W. and W. F. Dukes. Preparatory set (expectancy)—an experimental reconsideration of its "central" locus. *Brit. J. Psychol.*, 1953, **44**, 52–56.

Binder, A. A statistical model for the process of visual recognition. *Psychol. Rev.*, 1955, **62**, 119–129.

Black, J. W. The information of sounds and phonetic digrams of one- and two-syllable words. *J. Speech Dis.*, 1954, **19**, 397–411.

Black, J. W. Predicting the content of short phrases. *Quart. J. Speech*, 1959, **45**, 299–303.

Bourne, L. E., Jr. Effects of delay of information feedback and task complexity on the identification of concepts. *J. exp. Psychol.*, 1957, **54**, 201–207.

Bourne, L. E., Jr. and R. C. Haygood. The role of stimulus redundancy in concept identification. *J. exp. Psychol.*, 1959, **58**, 232–238.

Bourne, L. E., Jr. and R. B. Pendleton. Concept identification as a function of completeness and probability of information feedback. *J. exp. Psychol.*, 1958, **56**, 413–420.

Bourne, L. E., Jr. and F. Restle. Mathematical theory of concept identification. *Psychol. Rev.*, 1959, **66**, 278–296.

Bricker, P. D. The identification of redundant stimulus patterns. *J. exp. Psychol.*, 1955a, **49**, 73–81.

Bricker, P. D. Information measurement and reaction time: A review. In H. Quastler (Ed.), *Information theory in psychology*. Glencoe, Ill.: Free Press, 1955b.

Broadbent, D. E. Information theory and older approaches in psychology. *Proc. 15th int. Congr. Psychol.*, Brussels, 1957, 111–115.

Broadbent, D. E. *Perception and communication*. New York: Pergamon, 1958.

Brogden, W. J., and R. E. Schmidt. Effect of number of choices per unit of a verbal maze on learning and serial position errors. *J. exp. Psychol.*, 1954a, **47**, 235–240.

Brogden, W. J., and R. E. Schmidt. Acquisition of a 24-unit verbal maze as a function of number of alternate choices per unit. *J. exp. Psychol.*, 1954b, **48**, 335–338.

Brown, J. Evidence for a selective process during perception of tachistoscopically presented stimuli. *J. exp. Psychol.*, 1960, **59**, 176–181.

Bruce, D. J. The effects of listeners' anticipations on the intelligibility of heard speech. Language and Speech, 1958, **1**, 79–97.

Bruner, J. S., J. J. Goodnow, and G. A. Austin. *A study of thinking*. New York: Wiley, 1956.

Bruner, J. S., G. A. Miller, and C. Zimmerman. Discriminative skill and discriminative matching in perceptual recognition. *J. exp. Psychol.*, 1955, **49**, 187–192.

Bruner, J. S., and D. O'Dowd. A note on the informativeness of parts of words. *Language and Speech*, 1958, **1**, 98–101.

Bruner, J. S., M. A. Wallach, and E. H. Galanter. The identification of recurrent regularity. *Amer. J. Psychol.*, 1959, **72**, 200–209.

Brush, F. R. Stimulus uncertainty, response uncertainty, and problem solving. *Canad. J. Psychol.*, 1956, **10**, 239–247.

Burton, N. G., and J. C. R. Licklider. Long-range constraints in the statistical structure of printed English. *Amer. J. Psychol.*, 1955, **68**, 650–653.

Cane, V. R., and V. Horn. The timing of responses to spatial perception questions. *Quart. J. exp. Psychol.*, 1951, 3, 133–145.

Carson, D. H. Letter constraints within words in printed English. *Kybernetik,* 1961, 1, 46–54.

Chapanis, A. The reconstruction of abbreviated printed messages. *J. exp. Psychol.,* 1954, 48, 496–510.

Chapanis, A. A rate of making complex decisions. *Amer. J. Psychol.,* 1957, 70, 650–652.

Chapanis, A., and R. M. Halsey. Absolute judgments of spectrum colors. *J. Psychol.,* 1956, 42, 99–103.

Cherry, E. C. The communication of information (an historical review). *Amer. Scientist,* 1952, 40, 640–663.

Cherry, (E.) C. *On human communication.* New York: Wiley, 1957a.

Cherry, E. C. On the validity of applying communication theory to experimental psychology. *Brit. J. Psychol.,* 1957b, 48, 176–188.

Cofer, C. N., and B. E. Shepp. Verbal context and perceptual recognition time. *Percept. Mot. Skills,* 1957, 7, 215–218.

Cohen, J., and A. J. Dinnerstein. Flash rate as a visual coding dimension for information. *USAF WADC Tech. Rep.,* 1958, No. 57–64.

Cohen, J., and V. L. Senders. The effects of absolute and conditional probability distributions on instrument reading: III. A comparison of a linear scale and two scales with expanded central portions. *USAF WADC Tech. Rep.,* 1958, No. 57–65.

Cohn, B. N. Projective methods and verbal learning. *J. abnorm. soc. Psychol.,* 1954, 49, 290–297.

Conklin, J. E. Effect of control lag on performance in a tracking task. *J. exp. Psychol.,* 1957, 53, 261–268.

Conover, D. W. The amount of information in the absolute judgment of Munsell hues. *USAF WADC Tech. Note,* 1959, No. 58-262.

Crossman, E. R. F. W. Entropy and choice time: The effect of frequency unbalance on choice-response. *Quart. J. exp. Psychol.,* 1953, 5, 41–51.

Crossman, E. R. F. W. The measurement of discriminability. *Quart. J. exp. Psychol.,* 1955, 7, 176–195.

Current trends in information theory. Pittsburgh: Univ. Pittsburgh Press, 1953.

Deese, J. Complexity of contour in the recognition of visual form. *USAF WADC Tech. Rep.,* 1956, No. 56-60.

Detambel, M. H., and L. M. Stolurow. Stimulus sequence and concept learning. *J. exp. Psychol.,* 1956, 51, 34–40.

Edwards, W. Reward probability, amount, and information as determiners of sequential two-alternative decisions. *J. exp. Psychol.,* 1956, 52, 177–188.

Edwards, W. Probability learning in 1000 trials. *J. exp. Psychol.,* 1961, 62, 385–394.

Engen, T., and C. Pfaffmann. Absolute judgments of odor intensity. *J. exp. Psychol.,* 1959, 58, 23–26.

Engen, T., and C. Pfaffmann. Absolute judgments of odor quality. *J. exp. Psychol.,* 1960, 59, 214–219.

Eriksen, C. W. Location of objects in a visual display as a function of the number of dimensions on which the objects differ. *J. exp. Psychol.,* 1952, **44,** 56–60.

Eriksen, C. W. Prediction from and interaction among multiple concurrent discriminative responses. *J. exp. Psychol.,* 1957, **53,** 353–359.

Eriksen, C. W., and H. W. Hake. Absolute judgments as a function of stimulus range and number of stimulus and response categories. *J. exp. Psychol.,* 1955a, **49,** 323–332.

Eriksen, C. W., and H. W. Hake. Multidimensional stimulus differences and accuracy of discrimination. *J. exp. Psychol.,* 1955b, **50,** 153–160.

Eriksen, C. W., and H. Wechsler. Some effects of experimentally induced anxiety upon discrimination behavior. *J. abnorm. soc. Psychol.,* 1955, **51,** 458–463.

Fano, R. M. The information theory point of view in speech communication. *J. acoust. Soc. Amer.,* 1950, **22,** 691–696.

Faverge, J. M. La théorie de l'information en psychologie expérimentale. *Année psychol.,* 1953, **53,** 463–476.

Faverge, J. M. Le modèle de la théorie de l'information en psychologie. *Proc. 15th int. Congr. Psychol., Brussels,* 1957, 116–122.

Fisher, R. A. On the mathematical foundations of theoretical statistics. *Phil. Trans. Roy. Soc. London, A,* 1922, **222,** 309–368.

Fisher, R. A. Probability, likelihood, and quantity of information in the logic of uncertain inference. *Proc. Royal. Soc. London, A,* 1934, **146,** 1–8.

Fitts, P. M. The information capacity of the human motor system in controlling the amplitude of movement. *J. exp. Psychol.,* 1954, **47,** 381–391.

Fitts, P. M., and R. L. Deininger. S-R compatibility: Correspondence among paired elements within stimulus and response codes. *J. exp. Psychol.,* 1954, **48,** 483–492.

Fitts, P. M., and J. A. Leonard. *Stimulus correlates of visual pattern recognition—a probability approach.* Columbus: Ohio State University, 1957.

Fitts, P. M., and C. M. Seeger. S-R compatibility: Spatial characteristics of stimulus and response codes. *J. exp. Psychol.,* 1953, **46,** 199–210.

Fitts, P. M., M. Weinstein, M. Rappaport, N. Anderson, and J. A. Leonard. Stimulus correlates of visual pattern recognition. *J. exp. Psychol.,* 1956, **51,** 1–11.

French, R. S. Identification of dot patterns from memory as a function of complexity. *J. exp. Psychol.,* 1954a, **47,** 22–26.

French, R. S. Pattern recognition in the presence of visual noise. *J. exp. Psychol.,* 1954b, **47,** 27–31.

Frick, F. C. The effect of anxiety—a problem in measurement. *J. comp. physiol. Psychol.,* 1953, **46,** 120–123.

Frick, F. C. Some perceptual problems from the point of view of information theory. *In Current Trends in Information Theory.* Pittsburgh: University of Pittsburgh Press, 1954.

Frick, F. C., and G. A. Miller. A statistical description of operant conditioning. *Amer. J. Psychol.,* 1951, **64,** 20–36.

Frick, F. C., and W. H. Sumby. Control tower language. *J. acoust. Soc. Amer.,* 1952, **24,** 595–596.

Fritz, E. L., and G. W. Grier, Jr. A study of information flow in air traffic control. In H. Quastler (Ed.), *Information theory in psychology.* Glencoe, Ill.: Free Press, 1955.

Gabor, D. Theory of communication. *J. I. E. E.*, 1946, **93**, 429–457.

Galanter, E. H., and W. A. S. Smith. Some experiments on a simple thought-problem. *Amer. J. Psychol.*, 1958, **71**, 359–366.

Garner, W. R. An equal discriminability scale for loudness judgments. *J. exp. Psychol.*, 1952, **43**, 232–238.

Garner, W. R. An informational analysis of absolute judgments of loudness. *J. exp. Psychol.*, 1953, **46**, 373–380.

Garner, W. R. Symmetric uncertainty analysis and redundancy of printed English. *Proc. 15th int. Congr. Psychol., Brussels*, 1957, 104–110.

Garner, W. R. Symmetric uncertainty analysis and its implications for psychology. *Psychol. Rev.*, 1958, **65**, 183–196.

Garner, W. R. Rating scales, discriminability, and information transmission. *Psychol. Rev.*, 1960, **67**, 343–352.

Garner, W. R., and D. H. Carson. A multivariate solution of the redundancy of printed English. *Psychol. Rep.*, 1960, **6**, 123–141.

Garner, W. R., and H. W. Hake. The amount of information in absolute judgments. *Psychol. Rev.*, 1951, **58**, 446–459.

Garner, W. R., and W. J. McGill. Relation between information and variance analyses. *Psychometrika*, 1956, **21**, 219–228.

Garvey, W. D. Operator performance as a function of the statistical encoding of stimuli. *J. exp. Psychol.*, 1957, **54**, 109–114.

Garvey, W. D., and L. L. Mitnick. An analysis of tracking behavior in terms of lead-lag errors. *J. exp. Psychol.*, 1957, **53**, 372–378.

Geer, J. P. van de. Psychologische toepassingen van de informatie-theorie. *Ned. Tijdschr. Psychol.*, 1957, **12**, 295–328, 333–357.

Gelfand, S. Effects of prior associations and task complexity upon the identification of concepts. *Psychol. Rep.*, 1958, **4**, 567–574.

Gershuni, G. V. O razlichenii zvukovym analizatorom cheloveka slozhnykh razdrazhenii s vozrastaiushchim kolichestvom informaysii (On the discrimination of complex stimulation with increasing amount of information by the auditory analyzer in man). *Fiziol. Zh. SSSR*, 1957, **43**, 1086–1097.

Goldiamond, I., and W. F. Hawkins. Vexierversuch: The log relationship between word-frequency and recognition obtained in the absence of stimulus words. *J. exp. Psychol.*, 1958, **56**, 457–463.

Goldman, S. *Information theory*. Englewood Cliffs, N. J.: Prentice-Hall, 1953.

Goldman-Eisler, F. Speech production and the predictability of words in context. *Quart. J. exp. Psychol.*, 1958a, **10**, 96–106.

Goldman-Eisler, F. The predictability of words in context and the length of pauses in speech. *Language and Speech*, 1958b, **1**, 226–231.

Grant, D. A. The discrimination of sequences in stimulus events and the transmission of information. *Amer. Psychologist*, 1954a, **9**, 62–68.

Grant, D. A. Information theory and the discrimination of sequences in stimulus events. In *Current Trends in Information Theory*. Pittsburgh: University of Pittsburgh Press, 1954b.

Grant, D. A., H. W. Hake, and J. P. Hornseth. Acquisition and extinction of a verbal conditioned response with differing percentages of reinforcement. *J. exp. Psychol.*, 1951, **42**, 1–5.

Green, B. F., and L. K. Anderson. Color coding in a visual search task. *J. exp. Psychol.*, 1956, **51**, 19–24.

Green, B. F., and L. K. Anderson. Size coding in a visual search task. M.I.T. unpublished research. 1955.

Gregg, L. W. The effect of stimulus complexity on discriminative responses. *J. exp. Psychol.*, 1954, **48**, 289–297.

Hake, H. W. The perception of frequency of occurrence and the development of "expectancy" in human experimental subjects. In H. Quastler (Ed.), *Information theory in psychology*. Glencoe, Ill.: Free Press, 1955.

Hake, H. W. Contributions of psychology to the study of pattern vision. *USAF WADC Tech. Rep.*, 1957, No. 57-621.

Hake, H. W., and C. W. Eriksen. Role of response variables in recognition and identification of complex visual forms. *J. exp. Psychol.*, 1956, **52**, 235–243.

Hake, H. W., and W. R. Garner. The effect of presenting various numbers of discrete steps on scale reading accuracy. *J. exp. Psychol.*, 1951, **42**, 358–366.

Hake, H. W., and R. Hyman. Perception of the statistical structure of a random series of binary symbols. *J. exp. Psychol.*, 1953, **45**, 64–74.

Halle, M. The strategy of phonemics. *Word*, 1954, **10**, 197–209.

Halsey, R. M., and A. Chapanis. On the number of absolutely identifiable spectral hues. *J. opt. Soc. Amer.*, 1951, **41**, 1057–1058.

Hanes, R. M., and M. V. Rhoades. Color identification as a function of extended practice. *J. opt. Soc. Amer.*, 1959, **49**, 1060–1064.

Harris, Z. S. From phoneme to morpheme. *Language*, 1955, **31**, 190–222.

Hartley, R. V. L. Transmission of information. *Bell Syst. tech. J.*, 1928, **7**, 535–563.

Hartman, E. B. The influence of practice and pitch-distance between tones on the absolute identification of pitch. *Amer. J. Psychol.*, 1954, **67**, 1–14.

Haslerud, G. M., and R. E. Clark. On the redintegrative perception of words. *Amer. J. Psychol.*, 1957, **70**, 97–101.

Hick, W. E. Information theory and intelligence tests. *Brit. J. Psychol.*, 1951, **4**, 157–164.

Hick, W. E. On the rate of gain of information. *Quart. J. exp. Psychol.*, 1952, **4**, 11–26.

Hochberg, J., and V. Brooks. The psychophysics of form: Reversible-perspective drawings of spatial objects. *Amer. J. Psychol.*, 1960, **73**, 337–354.

Hochberg, J. E., and E. McAlister. A quantitative approach to figural "goodness." *J. exp. Psychol.*, 1953, **46**, 361–364.

Hodge, H. M. The influence of irrelevant information upon complex visual discrimination. *J. exp. Psychol.*, 1959, **57**, 1–5.

Horowitz, L. M. Free recall and ordering of trigrams. *J. exp. Psychol.*, 1961, **62**, 51–57.

Hovland, C. I. A "communication analysis" of concept learning. *Psychol. Rev.*, 1952, **59**, 461–472.

Hovland, C. I., and W. Weiss. Transmission of information concerning concepts through positive and negative instances. *J. exp. Psychol.*, 1953, **45**, 175–182.

Howes, D. H. On the relation between the intelligibility and frequency of occurrence of English words. *J. acoust. Soc. Amer.*, 1957, **29**, 296–305.

Howes, D. H., and C. E. Osgood. On the combination of associative probabilities in linguistic contexts. *Amer. J. Psychol.*, 1954, **67**, 241–258.

Howes, D. H., and R. L. Solomon. Visual duration threshold as a function of word-probability. *J. exp. Psychol.*, 1951, **41**, 401–410.

Hyman, R. Stimulus information as a determinant of reaction time. *J. exp. Psychol.*, 1953, **45**, 188–196.

Hyman, R., and H. W. Hake. Form recognition as a function of the number of forms which can be presented for recognition. *USAF WADC Tech. Rep.*, 1954, No. 54-164.

IRE Standards on Information Theory: Definitions of Terms, 1958. *58 IRE 11.S1.*

Jacobson, H. The informational capacity of the human ear. *Science*, 1950, **112**, 143–144.

Jacobson, H. The informational capacity of the human eye. *Science*, 1951, **113**, 292–293.

Jakobson, R. Observations sur le classement phonologique des consonnes. *Proc. 3rd int. Congr. Phonet. Sci.*, 1939, 34–41.

Jakobson, R., C. G. M. Fant, and M. Halle. Preliminaries to speech analysis: The distinctive features and their correlates. Acoustics Laboratory, *M.I.T. Tech. Rep. No. 13*, 1952.

Jones, A., H. J. Wilkinson, and I. Braden. Information deprivation as a motivational variable. J. exp. Psychol., 1961, **62**, 126–137.

King-Ellison, P., and J. J. Jenkins. The durational threshold of visual recognition as a function of word-frequency. *Amer. J. Psychol.*, 1954, **67**, 700–703.

Klemmer, E. T. Discrete tracking in one and two dimensions. *AFCRC-TN-56-2*, Operational Applications Laboratory, USAF, 1956.

Klemmer, E. T. Simple reaction time as a function of time uncertainty. *J. exp. Psychol.*, 1957a, **54**, 195–200.

Klemmer, E. T. A further study of information transmission with matrix patterns. *AFCRC-TN-57-1*, Operational Applications Laboratory, USAF, 1957b.

Klemmer, E. T., and F. C. Frick. Assimilation of information from dot and matrix patterns. *J. exp. Psychol.*, 1953, **45**, 15–19.

Klemmer, E. T., and J. P. Loftus. Numerals, nonsense forms, and information. *AFCRC-TR-57-2*, Operational Applications Laboratory, USAF, 1958.

Klemmer, E. T., and P. F. Muller, Jr. The rate of handling information—keypressing responses to light patterns. *Human Factors Oper. Res. Lab. Memo Report 34*, March 1953.

Krulee, G. K. Information theory and man-machine systems. *J. oper. Res. Soc. Amer.*, 1954, **2**, 320–328.

Krulee, G. K. Some informational aspects of form discrimination. *J. exp. Psychol.*, 1958, **55**, 143–149.

Krulee, G. K., J. E. Podell, and P. G. Ronco. Effect of number of alternatives and set on the visual discrimination of numerals. *J. exp. Psychol.*, 1954, **48**, 75–80.

Krulee, G. K., and A. Weisz. Studies in visual discrimination of multiple-unit displays. *J. exp. Psychol.*, 1955, **50**, 316–324.

Kuethe, J. L., and C. W. Eriksen. Personality, anxiety, and muscle tension as determinants of response stereotypy. *J. abnorm. soc. Psychol.*, 1957, **54**, 400–404.

Lawrence, D. H., and G. R. Coles. Accuracy of recognition with alternatives before and after the stimulus. *J. exp. Psychol.*, 1954, **47**, 208–214.

Lawrence, D. H., and D. L. LaBerge. Relationship between recognition accuracy and order of reporting stimulus dimensions. *J. exp. Psychol.*, 1956, **51**, 12–18.

Leonard, J. A. An experiment with occasional false information. *Quart. J. exp. Psychol.*, 1954, **6**, 79–85.

Leonard, J. A. Partial advance information in a choice reaction task. *Brit. J. Psychol.*, 1958a, **49**, 89–96.

Leonard, J. A. The effects of "machine" lag on a serial choice task with balance and biased input frequencies. *Ergonomics*, 1958b, **2**, 44–51.

Leonard, J. A. Tactual choice reactions: I. *Quart. J. exp. Psychol.*, 1959, **11**, 76–83.

Lincoln, R. S., and L. T. Alexander. Preferred patterns of motor and verbal responses. *J. exp. Psychol.*, 1955, **50**, 106–112.

Long, E. R., R. H. Henneman, and W. D. Garvey. An experimental analysis of set: The role of sense-modality. *Amer. J. Psychol.*, 1960, **73**, 563–567.

Long, E. R., L. S. Reid, and R. H. Henneman. An experimental analysis of set: Variables influencing the identification of ambiguous, visual stimulus-objects. *Amer. J. Psychol.*, 1960, **73**, 553–562.

Lotz, J. Speech and language. *J. acoust. Soc. Amer.*, 1950, **22**, 712–717.

Luce, R. D. *Developments in mathematical psychology.* Glencoe, Ill.: Free Press, 1960.

MacKay, D. M. Quantal aspects of scientific information. *Phil. Mag.*, 1950, **41**, 289–311.

MacKay, D. M. Towards an information-flow model of human behavior. *Brit. J. Psychol.*, 1956, **47**, 30–43.

Mackworth, J. F. Paced memorizing in a continuous task. *J. exp. Psychol.*, 1959, **58**, 206–211.

Marks M. R., and O. Jack. Verbal context and memory span for meaningful material. *Amer. J. Psychol.*, 1952, **65**, 298–300.

McGill, W. J. Multivariate information transmission. *Psychometrika*, 1954, **19**, 97–116.

McGill, W. J. Isomorphism in statistical analysis. In H. Quastler (Ed.), *Information theory in psychology.* Glencoe, Ill.: Free Press, 1955.

McGill, W. J. Applications of information theory in experimental psychology. *Trans. N. Y. Acad. Sci., Ser. II*, 1957a, **19**, 343–351.

McGill, W. J. Serial effects in auditory threshold judgments. *J. exp. Psychol.*, 1957b, **53**, 297–303.

Meyer, L. B. *Emotion and meaning in music.* Chicago: Univ. of Chicago Press, 1956.

Meyer, L. B. Meaning in music and information theory. *J. Aesthet.*, 1957, **15**, 412–424.

Miller, E. E. Context in the perception of sentences. *Amer. J. Psychol.*, 1956, **69**, 653–654.

Miller, G. A. *Language and communication.* New York: McGraw-Hill, 1951.

Miller, G. A. What is information measurement? *Amer. Psychologist*, 1953, **8**, 3–11.

Miller, G. A. Communication. *Annual Rev. of Psychol.*, 1954, **5**, 401–420.

Miller, G. A. Note on the bias of information estimates. In H. Quastler (Ed.), *Information theory in psychology.* Glencoe, Ill.: Free Press, 1955.

Miller, G. A. The magical number seven, plus or minus two. *Psychol. Rev.*, 1956, **63**, 81–97.

Miller, G. A. Free recall of redundant strings of letters. *J. exp. Psychol.,* 1958, **56,** 485–491.

Miller, G. A., J. S. Bruner, and L. Postman. Familiarity of letter sequences and tachistoscopic identification. *J. gen. Psychol.,* 1954, **50,** 129–139.

Miller, G. A., and F. C. Frick. Statistical behavioristics and sequences of responses. *Psychol. Rev.,* 1949, **56,** 311–324.

Miller, G. A., and E. A. Friedman. The reconstruction of mutilated English texts. *Information and Control,* 1957, **1,** 38–55.

Miller, G. A., G. A. Heise, and W. Lichten. The intelligibility of speech as a function of the context of the test materials. *J. exp. Psychol.,* 1951, **41,** 329–335.

Miller, G. A., and P. A. Nicely. An analysis of perceptual confusions among some English consonants. *J. acoust. Soc. Amer.,* 1955, **27,** 338–352.

Miller, G. A., and J. A. Selfridge. Verbal context and the recall of meaningful material. *Amer. J. Psychol.,* 1950, **63,** 176–185.

Miller, I. Perception of nonsense passages in relation to amount of information and speech-to-noise ratio. *J. exp. Psychol.,* 1957, **53,** 388–393.

Moray, N. and A. Taylor. The effect of redundancy in shadowing one of two dichotic messages. *Language and Speech,* 1958, **1,** 102–109.

Morrison, H. M., and J. W. Black. Prediction of missing words in sentences. *J. Speech Dis.,* 1957, **22,** 236–240.

Mowbray, G. H., and M. V. Rhoades. On the reduction of choice reaction times with practice. *Quart. J. exp. Psychol.,* 1959, **11,** 16–23.

Muller, P. F., Jr., R. C. Sidorsky, A. J. Slivinske, E. A. Alluisi, and P. M. Fitts. The symbolic coding of information on cathode ray tubes and similar displays. *USAF WADC Tech. Rep.,* 1955, No. 55–375.

Munson, W. A., and J. E. Karlin. The measurement of human channel transmission characteristics. *J. acoust. Soc. Amer.,* 1954, **26,** 542–553.

Newbrough, J. R. Interaction between total stimulus information and specific stimulus information in visual recognition. *J. exp. Psychol.,* 1958, **55,** 297–301.

Newman, E. B. The pattern of vowels and consonants in various languages. *Amer. J. Psychol.,* 1951, **64,** 369–379.

Newman, E. B. Men and information: A psychologist's view. *Nuovo Cimento,* 1959, **13,** 539–559.

Newman, E. B., and L. S. Gerstman. A new method for analyzing printed English. *J. exp. Psychol.,* 1952, **44,** 114–125.

Newman, E. B., and N. C. Waugh. The redundancy of texts in three languages. *Information and Control,* 1960, **3,** 141–153.

Noble, M., P. M. Fitts, and C. E. Warren. The frequency response of skilled subjects in a pursuit tracking task. *J. exp. Psychol.,* 1955, **49,** 249–256.

Nyquist, H. Certain factors affecting telegraph speed. *Bell Syst. tech. J.,* 1924, **3,** 324–346.

Osborne, J. W., H. Quastler, and K. S. Tweedell. Flash recognition—scale reading. *Control Systems Lab.,* University of Illinois. No. R-78, October 1955.

Pierce, J. R., and J. E. Karlin. Reading rates and the information rate of a human channel. *Bell Syst. tech. J.,* 1957, **36,** 497–516.

Pinkerton, R. C. Information theory and melody. *Sci. Amer.*, 1956, **194**(2), 77–86.

Pollack, I. The information of elementary auditory displays. *J. acoust. Soc. Amer.*, 1952, **24**, 745–749.

Pollack, I. The information of elementary auditory displays, II. *J. acoust. Soc. Amer.*, 1953a, **25**, 765–769.

Pollack, I. Assimilation of sequentially encoded information. *Amer. J. Psychol.*, 1953b, **66**, 421–435.

Pollack, I. Method of reproduction and the identification of elementary auditory displays. *J. acoust. Soc. Amer.*, 1954, **26**, 1060–1063.

Pollack, I. Message procedures for unfavorable communication conditions. *J. acoust. Soc. Amer.*, 1958, **30**, 196–201.

Pollack, I. Message uncertainty and message reception. *J. acoust. Soc. Amer.*, 1959a, **31**, 1500–1508.

Pollack, I. Message repetition and message reception. *J. acoust. Soc. Amer.*, 1959b, **31**, 1509–1515.

Pollack, I., and L. Ficks. Information of elementary multidimensional auditory displays. *J. acoust. Soc. Amer.*, 1954, **26**, 155–158.

Pollack, I., and L. B. Johnson. Reproduction and identification of elements of auditory displays. *J. acoust. Soc. Amer.*, 1959, **31**, 7–8.

Pollack, I., L. B. Johnson, and P. R. Knaff. Running memory span. *J. exp. Psychol.*, 1959, **57**, 137–146.

Pollack, I., and E. T. Klemmer. Visual noise filtering by the human operator. II. Linear dot patterns in noise. *AFCRC-TR-54-15*, Operational Applications Laboratory, USAF, 1954a.

Pollack, I., and E. T. Klemmer. The assimilation of visual information from linear dot patterns. *AFCRC-TR-54-16*, Operational Applications Laboratory, USAF, 1954b.

Pollack, I., H. Rubenstein, and L. Decker. Intelligibility of known and unknown message sets. *J. acoust. Soc. Amer.*, 1959, **31**, 273–279.

Postman, L. Choice behavior and the process of recognition. *Amer. J. Psychol.*, 1950, **63**, 576–583.

Postman, L., and M. R. Rosenzweig. Perceptual recognition of words. *J. Speech Dis.*, 1957, **22**, 245–253.

Poulton, E. C. Perceptual anticipation in tracking with two-pointer and one-pointer displays. *Brit. J. Psychol.*, 1952a, **43**, 222–229.

Poulton, E. C. The basis of perceptual anticipation in tracking. *Brit. J. Psychol.*, 1952b, **43**, 295–302.

Poulton, E. C. The precision of choice reactions. *J. exp. Psychol.*, 1956, **51**, 98–102.

Poulton, E. C. On the stimulus and response in pursuit tracking. *J. exp. Psychol.*, 1957a, **53**, 189–194.

Poulton, E. C. Learning the statistical properties of the input in pursuit tracking. *J. exp. Psychol.*, 1957b, **54**, 28–32.

Poulton, E. C. On prediction in skilled movements. *Psychol. Bull.*, 1957c, **54**, 467–478.

Poulton, E. C. Copying behind during dictation. *Quart. J. exp. Psychol.*, 1958, **10**, 48–55.

Prokhovnik, S. J. Pattern variants on a square field. *Psychometrika*, 1959, **24**, 329–341.

Quastler, H. (Ed.) *Information theory in psychology: problems and methods.* Glencoe, Ill.: Free Press, 1955.

Quastler, H., and B. Brabb. Human performance in information transmission. V. The force of habit. *Control Systems Lab.*, University of Illinois. No. R-70, January 1956.

Quastler, H., and V. J. Wulff. Human performance in information transmission. *Control Systems Lab.*, University of Illinois. No. R-62, March 1955.

Rappaport, M. The role of redundancy in the discrimination of visual forms. *J. exp. Psychol.*, 1957, **53**, 3–10.

Reid, L. S., R. H. Henneman, and E. R. Long. An experimental analysis of set: The effect of categorical restriction. *Amer. J. Psychol.*, 1960, **73**, 568–572.

Riley, D. A. Rote learning as a function of distribution of practice and the complexity of the situation. *J. exp. Psychol.*, 1952, **43**, 88–95.

Royce, J. R. The search for meaning. *Amer. Sci.*, 1959, **47**, 515–535.

Rubenstein, H., and M. Aborn. Immediate recall as a function of degree of organization and the length of study period. *J. exp. Psychol.*, 1954, **48**, 146–152.

Rubenstein, H., and M. Aborn. Learning, prediction, and readability. *J. appl. Psychol.*, 1958, **42**, 28–32.

Samson, E. W. Fundamental natural concepts of information theory. *Etc. Rev. gen. Semant.*, 1953, **10**, 283–297.

Senders, V. L. Further analysis of response sequences in the setting of a psychophysical experiment. *Amer. J. Psychol.*, 1953, **66**, 215–228.

Senders, V. L., and J. Cohen. Effects of sequential dependencies on instrument-reading performance. *J. exp. Psychol.*, 1955, **50**, 66–74.

Senders, V. L., and A. Sowards. Analysis of response sequences in the setting of a psychophysical experiment. *Amer. J. Psychol.*, 1952, **65**, 358–374.

Shannon, C. E. A mathematical theory of communication. *Bell Syst. tech. J.*, 1948, **27**, 379–423, 623–656.

Shannon, C. E. Prediction and entropy of printed English. *Bell Syst. tech. J.*, 1951, **30**, 50–64.

Shannon, C. E., and W. Weaver. *The mathematical theory of communication.* Urbana: Univ. of Illinois Press, 1949.

Sharp, H. C. Effect of contextual constraint upon recall of verbal passages. *Amer. J. Psychol.*, 1958, **71**, 568–572.

Shelly, M. W., II. The effects of response contingent probabilities which favor response change. *J. exp. Psychol.*, 1958, **56**, 239–245.

Shepard, R. N. Production of constrained associates and the informational uncertainty of the constraint. *Amer. J. Psychol.*, 1962, in press.

Shepard, R. N., C. I. Hovland, and H. M. Jenkins. Learning and memorization of classifications. *Psychol. Monogr.*, 1961, **75**, No. 13.

Siegel, S. Theoretical models of choice and strategy behavior: Stable state behavior in the two-choice uncertain outcome situation. *Psychometrika*, 1959, **24**, 303–316.

Solley, C. M., and F. W. Snyder. Information processing and problem solving. *J. exp. Psychol.*, 1958, **55**, 384–387.

Solomon, R. L., and D. H. Howes. Word-probability, personal values, and visual duration thresholds. *Psychol. Rev.*, 1951, **58**, 256–270.

Solomon, R. L., and L. Postman. Frequency of usage as a determinant of recognition thresholds for words. *J. exp. Psychol.*, 1952, **43**, 195–201.

Sumby, W. H., D. Chambliss, and I. Pollack. Information transmission with elementary auditory displays. *J. acoust. Soc. Amer.*, 1958, **30**, 425–429.

Toda, M. Information-receiving behavior of man. *Pyschol. Rev.*, 1956, **63**, 204–212.

Watanabe, S. A study of ergodicity and redundancy based on intersymbol correlation of finite range. *Trans. 1954 Symposium on Information Theory.* Cambridge, Mass.: M.I.T., 85–92.

Watanabe, S. Correlation indices. *Nuovo Cimento,* 1959, **13**, 576–582.

Watanabe, S. Information theoretical analysis of multivariate correlation. *IBM J. Res. Dev.,* 1960, **4**, 66–82.

Wiener, N. *Cybernetics.* New York: Wiley, 1948. (Out of print.)

Name Index

Subject Index